SCIENCE *Meets* *Vedanta*

LOOKING FOR THE SAME REALITY

Essays by

Jayant Kapatker

"Really great and brilliant explanation. Keep up the good work. Thanks for the clarity."

Napa Khan-Williams

"Brilliant! Explained in such a simple manner."

Sudhir Goyal

"Very clearly drafted and explained essays. They are helpful. Please accept my sincere gratitude."

HP

"You have really done us all a favor by sharing this. This is a beautiful work. Everything has been explained so well and so systematically! Thanks a lot."

Indu

"Very much logical and scientific."

Anita Kulkarni

"I thoroughly enjoyed the clarity of the explanation of self-awareness."

Krishna Priya

"You have explained well in simple language."

Seema

"Well written, Jayant ji. I appreciate your efforts in bringing science and Vedanta together."

Ramesh

"Namaste. This is the clearest description. I feel blessed in reading this."

Guru

"Mind-bending concept and beautifully written. I enjoyed reading all the essays."

Vishwanath

"Superb explanation. Many of my personal experiences also align with your essays. Thanks a lot!"

Sam

"Your essays are excellent, Jayant ji. I am so happy to have chanced upon them."

Gayatri

Comments Received at Our Website

Dedicated to ॐ

Inspired by ॐ

Knowledge of ॐ

Love for ॐ

ॐ (OM) is a symbol deeply rooted in the Indian scriptures. OM represents the divinity within us and the divinity within all the objects in the universe. It is the short form for the underlying reality of the universe.

Science Meets Vedanta

Website: https://vedantaandscience.com/

ISBN: 978-0-578-26340-3

Cover design and illustrations by: Manoj Vijayan, Bengaluru, India

Typeset by: Khurram Kazmi, Lucknow, India

Table of Essays

My Journey

Growing up in India and living mostly in hostels, my awareness of religion or spiritual matters was limited. My first exposure to these happened while studying at the Indian Institute of Technology, Kanpur. As part of the curriculum, we had a course on Indian philosophy. In those days, the focus was to study and get a decent grade, and I really did not retain much knowledge. However, living in India, you are always exposed to the underlying truths of Vedanta and the scriptures, albeit with little understanding. That was my status regarding the Indian scriptures.

Everything changed in 2004. For this I must thank my wife, Maya. She was a keen follower of Vedanta and persuaded me to join her studies. We were then living in Princeton Junction, New Jersey. I started attending the Vedanta class at Arsha Bodha Center in Somerset, NJ. Arsha Bodha Center is a traditional ashram founded by Swami Tadatmananda, to teach the wisdom (bodha) of the sages of ancient India (arsha). Swami Tadatmananda, an engineer by training, is a teacher par excellence with in-depth knowledge of Vedanta and complete mastery over Sanskrit. Swami Tadatmananda is a disciple of Swami Dayananda who, in turn, was a disciple of Swami Chinmayananda–a strong lineage with a focus on teaching only Advaita Vedanta. There were no religious overtones and no hidden agenda. This was important to me. If one traces back this lineage, the starting source will be Sri Shankaracharya. Imagine a lineage which is over 1400 years old! What a great saint and inspiration is Sri Shankaracharya! What precision, what clarity, and what directness in the teachings of Sri Shankaracharya! This methodology and tradition were followed at the Arsha Bodha Center.

While attending classes at this center, I was introduced to a wide variety of texts. On Saturdays, Swamiji taught the Bhagavad Gita. A detailed explanation was given for each verse. Studying the 700 verses of the Gita took over four years, and we completed two rounds of the text. In between the two rounds, Swamiji picked other relevant spiritual teachings from different parts of the Mahabharata. On Tuesdays, I attended an advanced class on Vedanta. Every year Swamiji taught a new text. Over the years, I have had the opportunity to gain an understanding of many different Upanishads and related scriptures–the Vivekachudamani, and the Isa, Kaivalya, Mandukya, Katha, Kena, and Brihadaranyaka Upanishads, to name a few. What an amazing learning experience this was. I never thought I would have the opportunity to be exposed to such a wide array of Indian scriptures, that too in the USA. I was blessed.

During these years, my focus in life changed completely. I was always a consistent reader of both fiction and nonfiction for entertainment. All that stopped. The only thing I wanted to do was study, understand, and assimilate the teachings of Vedanta. During my walks, I would listen to Swamiji's lectures repeatedly. I only read books which were related to the teachings of Vedanta. During this study, with Maya's help, I learned about Sri Ramana Maharshi–a true saint and a self-realized person. Evaluating a self-realized person is not easy, but given the way he answered questions, there can be no doubt that Sri Ramana Maharshi was a self-realized soul. His teachings had a great impact on me. They helped me lay a solid foundation to assimilate the knowledge being taught in the scriptures. Questions arose and were resolved with contemplation and investigation. Slowly but surely, I have built a strong foundation for the knowledge in the scriptures.

At the Indian Institute of Technology, we had a course on quantum physics. At that time, I really did not understand the true implications of this subject. In the early days of attending classes on Vedanta, I had the opportunity to read an introductory book on quantum physics by Jim Al-Khalili. This book had a tremendous impact on me–all that weirdness in the quantum world, sometimes an object being a particle and sometimes a wave! What about entangled particles which can be light-years apart but still communicate instantaneously! All this fascinated and intrigued me. I started reading many books on the subject. One of the best books is *The Dancing Wu Li Masters* by Gary Zukav. In this book, many connections have been made between physics and Vedanta. If you look around, there are many other books which also make this connection between science and Vedanta. Most of these books are written by scientists who do not have a full understanding of Vedanta.

I have concluded that science does not understand the importance of the teachings of Vedanta. If the teachings are applied with logic, reasoning, and scientific rigor, they can add a new dimension to an understanding of this universe as we see it. This new dimension could resolve many of the stumbling blocks being faced within science.

With my understanding of Vedanta and my growing knowledge about quantum physics and other related subjects, I thought I had something to contribute.

Based on the new knowledge I had gained, sometime in 2014 I decided to give writing a try. Before this, I had never written anything except college assignments. Wow, I have found writing to be one of the most rewarding experiences! The grounding of my knowledge has become much stronger. When you are writing, you are forced to encounter unresolved questions and doubts, and you must find a solution to these to be a convincing writer. This is what happened during my writing process. Something within me provided the solutions. It was an amazing feeling when a solution popped up from within. This learning process was stronger and deeper than all the listening and reading I had done. I felt this was my knowledge now and not something external. I knew this knowledge would never leave me; it was part of me.

With this focus. I started writing regularly. After finishing an essay, I always felt I knew more about the subject than I had before I started writing. I had new knowledge and new insights. Based on this, I felt I could tackle new issues and subjects. This meant I had new subject matter for a new essay. When I completed that essay, new ideas, new knowledge, and new subject matter popped up. In this way, slowly but surely, I built a good collection of essays. You can see from the table of contents that I have covered a wide range of subjects. In fact, many of the subjects are unique; you will not see them anywhere else. All this has been possible with the inspiration from within. I will always be indebted to this inspiration, which is nothing but SatChitAnanda, our innermost core–the source of all the possible knowledge in this universe.

One of the goals of writing this book is to share this inspiration and knowledge with the world. This book is suitable for anyone with a curious mind who wants to learn more about Vedanta and discover how these teachings impact science. My only request is that the reader keep an open mind and try and understand the subject matter without any prejudice. This is especially true for the science community all over the world who are dealing with unresolved issues in their respective fields–be it trying to find the Theory of Everything, or trying to hunt down missing graviton particles, or trying to find the structure of space–how and why it is expanding the way it is–or trying to find the source of time and energy.

The scientific community needs help; they have many unresolved issues. As I have shown in these essays, most of the issues can be resolved with a basic understanding of the tenets of Vedanta and with the proper interpretation of quantum physics and Einstein's Theory of Relativity. It is my hope that these essays will start a proper debate within the scientific community and maybe bring about the required change in their approach. This may sound ambitious, but someone must make a start. Without this change, the roadblocks within science will continue and be never-ending.

This has been my journey so far. I look forward to the next phase when my readers send back their feedback and comments.

Jayant Kapatker

About the Book

Vedanta is the spiritual teaching from India. These ancient texts help in understanding and discovering our innermost core. If you understand the nature of this inner core, you will understand the universe.

If you apply these teachings of Vedanta to science, it can radically change many aspects of the way we think about the universe. Yes, this is true. The focus of the various essays in this book is to show some of the dramatic changes which can take place within science. This does not mean that the teachings of Vedanta have been applied blindly. You will see that, in this book, we have used scientific facts, logic, and reasoning to suggest these changes. The changes must be correct because they resolve and remove the different stumbling blocks currently being faced by science.

If you think about it, both Vedanta and science are looking for the same underlying reality, though they approach the issue differently. Science is trying to understand and discover the universe "out there," and Vedanta is trying to explain the universe "inside you" or "in here." Everyone will agree that there is only one universe. Both "out there" and "in here" must be part of the same universe. If this is true, both must have the same underlying reality. If you are part of the universe then your underlying reality must be the same as the underlying reality of the universe "out there." There cannot be two independent realities for the same universe. So, it seems that both science and Vedanta are looking for the same underlying reality.

Rishis in ancient India took a direct approach. They closed their eyes and looked inward; they meditated, they contemplated, and they discovered much on a wide variety of subjects. They revealed their findings and insights in the different Upanishads and scriptures. They discovered and understood that the inner core of each living being is the same. They taught that we all have a common inner core. This inner core is SatChitAnanda or Self-Awareness. This inner core is the source of the universe. It is the substratum for everything in the universe. Each living being, each object in this universe, all the laws of nature are part of the inner core. This inner core is the only reality. This inner core is the reality of both Vedanta and science.

Science is trying its best to find this underlying reality in the objects "out there." Scientists are trying to find a common Singularity for all objects. They are trying to discover the Theory of Everything. This theory will be the source equation, the source law that will explain everything in this universe. Over the centuries, scientists have made a great deal of progress in understanding these objects. Galileo, Isaac Newton, and other great scientists showed to the West how the macro-objects in the world functioned. In modern days, Albert Einstein and other scientists have made great strides in understanding subatomic particles. Despite all this effort, they are still nowhere near discovering the underlying reality of the universe. As I show in this book, science will never discover the truth by studying objects "out there" unless and until it first understands the truth within ourselves. Scientists need to understand the inner core. Everything "out there" is dependent on the inner core. Therefore, knowledge of the inner core is a must.

For science to succeed, it must understand the inner core, it must understand the core teachings of Vedanta. If properly understood and applied correctly, these teachings can change how we think and how we approach science. A new dimension will be added to science. This added knowledge will remove many stumbling blocks and resolve many of the unanswered questions that exist in science.

Just to illustrate this point, let us look at some examples.

1. Quantum physics is clear about the wave/particle duality. Every object in the universe has a particle and wave property, right from subatomic particles to planets and galaxies. The focus of science has been on the particle aspect of this duality. What about the wave aspect of these objects? Where are the wave aspects of living beings? Where are the wave aspects of the stars? Where is your wave aspect and where is my wave aspect? The wave aspect must exist. This is a known fact. Unfortunately, it appears that there is no curiosity within science to search for the wave

aspect of different objects. This lack of investigation is a stumbling block. If we apply the teachings of Vedanta, this issue can be resolved. In many different essays, I have given a detailed analysis of the wave aspect of all micro- and macro-objects. Understanding and resolving this issue will help science in many ways.

2. Quantum physics posits that the wave aspect of the wave/particle duality collapses in the presence of an observer. Scientists usually interpret the measuring device as the observer. The question is, how does a measuring device have the power to collapse a wave? From where does the measuring device gain this power? Besides, the measuring device itself has the wave/particle duality. Can some other observer collapse the wave function of the measuring device? This process can go on. You must find the ultimate observer who collapses all the possible wave functions. Who is this ultimate observer? Think correctly and you will conclude that the observer within you is the ultimate observer. This observer is part of the inner core. See the connection between the observer as stated by quantum physics with the inner core as stated by Vedanta. Both are talking the same language. Understanding the inner core can help resolve the observer issue raised by quantum physics.

3. Science must be fully aware of this, but it never acknowledges that all objects in the universe are "memory objects"; they are "recorded objects" and not "live objects." What does this mean? Light takes a certain amount of time to travel from objects to the observer within us. Because of the time taken, these objects in the universe are not "now objects" or "live objects"; they are always dated objects. If this is true, the question must be answered–where are the "now objects" or "live objects"? How do we investigate this? Science has neither raised nor ever addressed this question. This is where we can use the perspective of Vedanta. Unpacking this information can help change our perspective on a wide range of subjects. This can have a dramatic effect on science.

4. Einstein's Theory of Relativity makes a clear connection between motion, time, and space. This theory states that wherever there is motion, time slows down and there is a contraction in space. Yes, time slows down and space contracts with any motion. This is a proven fact. The problem is that this fact is not applied to our daily experiences. Since we move around all the time, this motion must affect how we perceive time and

space. If we move around at different speeds, then the clock for each person will tick at a different rate. Yes, each one's clock will tick at a different rate and the size of space will also be different. Agreed, the changes will be so small that they are not noticeable, but they are there. This would mean that each person has a different size of space and their clocks have different rates of ticking. The implication of this is profound. It would mean that each person projects their own separate space and the objects therein. This implication is present in Einstein's Theory of Relativity, but science does not apply this knowledge. If we do apply this knowledge, a lot of things change–our perception changes, and we will understand the structure of space in the universe.

Relevant concepts from Vedanta must be welcomed by science. Especially if these concepts are rooted in science, logic, and reasoning. When science meets Vedanta, it appears that magical things can happen. Science gets a new dimension; it gets a new perspective. Combining the knowledge of Vedanta with science can help science immensely.

This is the goal of the essays in this book. Use the knowledge of Vedanta to give science a new perspective, a new direction.

Structure of the Book

As the table of contents indicates, this book consists of a series of essays covering a wide range of topics. The essays are grouped as follows:

Concepts: This is essential reading. The key concepts from Vedanta and science are covered here. These essays must be read and understood properly. They are important because these concepts are the foundation of most of the essays.

Vedanta: The more you learn about and understand Vedanta, the better you can appreciate how the teachings can help science. The essays in this section cover a good cross-section of key topics in Vedanta.

Science: In these essays, science "meets" Vedanta. I have taken a range of topics and shown the influence Vedanta can have on science. With the help of Vedanta, a new dimension is added, a new perspective is given to science. Vedanta helps remove many roadblocks faced by science.

Cosmos: In these essays, the cosmos meets Vedanta. There is so much misunderstanding and confusion in understanding space and the universe "out there." Based on the logic of the teachings of Vedanta, we have resolved many of the issues in these essays.

I have tried to make each essay self-contained, so that it can stand on its own. This means that many of the key concepts have been repeated in different essays. I feel this is important as these key concepts must be properly understood for a true appreciation of these essays.

I enjoyed writing these essays. Many of the insights I gained came to me as I was writing them! It is an amazing feeling when you get a new thought which finds a solution to the problem you are tackling. It felt like divine intervention–my inner core was guiding me in my writing process.

Concepts

This is essential reading. The key concepts from Vedanta and science are covered here. Understanding our inner core as taught by Vedanta is important. The nature and power of the inner core are the substratum of everything in the universe, including all the physical laws. As we will see in different essays, the best way to connect Vedanta with science is through a proper understanding of Einstein's Theory of Relativity and of quantum physics.

It is therefore important that these essays be read and understood properly. They are the foundation for most of the essays.

1 | Understanding Our Underlying Reality

Who am I? Many people may not ponder this question because they are very sure—they are the body-mind complex. They are born with this body and they have grown up with this body, so the association with the body is deep-rooted. A simple question to ask is: which part of the body are you? Are you the hands, or legs, or the eyes? There is no clear-cut answer, but they may reply: we are the cumulative total of all the body parts. If so, what happens to the person if they lose a hand, a leg, or their vision in an accident? Do they feel incomplete? Do they feel only a fraction of the total?

If you were to ask a disabled person, they would answer that despite losing a body part, they still feel complete. Their Self is not a fraction; it is always full. This goes to show that they are not the body but something else. But what is that something else?

Another way to look at it is to ask yourself the question, are you the tree outside the window? You will look shocked and reply—of course not! Why aren't you the tree? Because you can perceive the tree; it is outside—you know it is a tree; you are aware of the tree. Since you are the knower, the tree is known to you. Anything known to you cannot be you. It is something external. For this reason, you are not the tree. This logic and reasoning will apply to all external objects in the world. It is quite simple and straightforward when you talk about objects external to yourself.

What about your body? Do you know or are you aware of your hands, legs, and all the body parts? Of course you are. So, we can apply the same logic as used for external objects. Applying the same reasoning, you will realize that your body and body parts are external to you. You are aware of your body and body parts; therefore, you cannot be the body.

Then you may say you are the mind. The mind is full of thoughts made up of perceptions, feelings, and emotions. Once again, you are aware of what is happening in your mind. You are the witness to your thoughts. There is no thought which you do not know about or of which you are not aware. This means that you are also not the mind.

As a next step, you may say you are the ego. This may be close but the ego is only a thought, like any other thought masquerading as the Self. Below are some of the typical statements made by the ego:

- I am a father / mother.
- I am a son / daughter.
- I am a husband / wife.
- I am a writer.
- I am a meditator.
- I am a player (of golf).

All the above are different roles played by the ego. You are aware of each one of these roles. You know you are a son or a daughter, father or mother, husband or wife, and so on. If you are aware of these roles of the ego, then you are a witness of them, so you cannot be your ego.

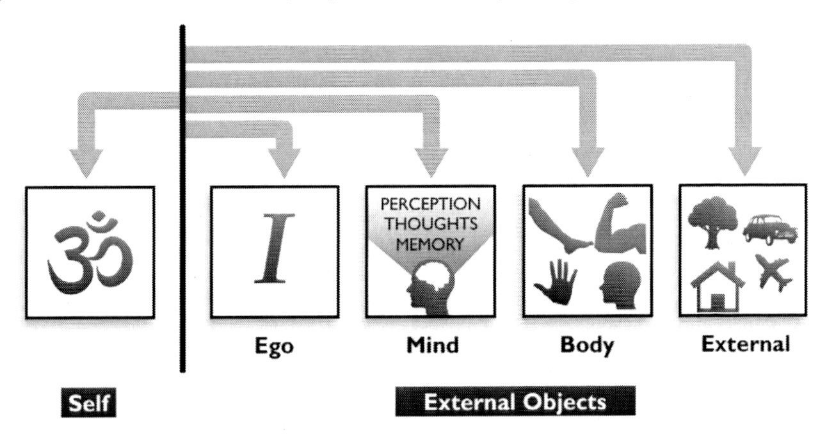

So, what are you or who am I? As Vedanta teaches, there are only two things in this universe: the Self and all the external objects. The universe is that simple. This is entirely logical and not complicated. We are obviously not external objects–not the body, not the mind, nor any of the objects of the world. Vedanta states that we are the Self who is aware of all the external objects.

Who is the Self? What is the nature of the Self? The Self is our innermost core; it is beyond our body, mind, and ego. Vedanta teaches us that our true self is SatChitAnanda.

- Sat = Real
- Chit = Awareness
- Ananda = Bliss

Sat: Sat means Real. If you look up any dictionary, you will get a wide variety of meanings for "real." These dictionary meanings are not good for understanding Sat. According to Vedanta, for anything to be Sat, it must exist and be present in all the three tenses–past, present, and future. If you investigate Nature, you will not find anything which is Sat.

- This universe was born 13.7 billion years ago, and therefore it did not exist before that, so it cannot be Sat. We also know that if anything is born, it must die. So Sat must be unborn. And anything which is unborn must be uncreated (to make it existent forever).
- Everything which is born must have a cause. You were born because of your parents, and they were born because of their parents. Since Sat is unborn, it is also uncaused. No cause created it. It was and it will be always present.
- If anything changes in any way, small (e.g., atoms have been displaced) or big (e.g., planetary positions are different), it is not the same as it was before. Therefore, it cannot be Sat, because Sat is unchanging.

Atma or "I" is Sat and it is uncreated, uncaused, and unchanging.

Chit: Chit means Awareness. Many books will also translate this as Consciousness, but I feel this is not fully accurate. When the mind comes into contact with Chit or Awareness, that mind becomes Conscious. The essential nature of Atma is Awareness. This Awareness has no edge or boundary; it is limitless. Basically, it is everywhere, and everything in the universe is Awareness or full of Awareness. There cannot be a single spot or area where Awareness is not present. To visualize this, look at the sun's rays, which are everywhere in the solar system.

If you look at Awareness more closely, you will realize that Awareness must always have two elements.

1. If you are Aware, then there should be someone who is Aware. Awareness needs a subject.
2. To be Aware, there must be some type of object of which you are Aware. Awareness needs an object.

Subject and object are needed to complete the Awareness process. Usually subject and object are separate, but in Chit there is no separate subject and object. Chit is always Self-Aware; it is Aware of its Awareness (it is witnessing its Awareness). It is both the subject and object rolled in one. Chit is therefore self-sufficient and complete. Due to ignorance, the subject and object become separate.

Here is an appropriate quote from Sri Nisargadatta Maharaj, an Indian sage who explains the difference between Awareness and Consciousness:

> Awareness is primordial: it is the original state, beginningless, endless, uncaused, unsupported, without parts, without change. Consciousness is on contact, a reflection against a surface, a state of duality. There can be no consciousness without awareness, but there can be awareness without consciousness, as in deep sleep. Awareness is absolute, but consciousness is relative to its content–consciousness is always of something. Consciousness is partial and changeful; awareness is total, changeless, calm, and silent–it is the common matrix of every experience.[1]

Like the sun which glows, the Chit or Awareness also glows and is present everywhere. Anything which comes in touch with Chit becomes Conscious. Only when the objects become Conscious can Atma or "I" witness these objects. Anything you witness in this world is because those objects became Conscious–because of the light of Atma or your true nature.

Ananda: Your essential nature is Ananda or Bliss. This term can be confusing because we do get momentary bliss in our day-to-day lives, but

---

[1] Sudhakar S. Dikshit, ed., *I Am That: Talks with Sri Nisargadatta Maharaj* (Durham: Acorn, 2012:28).

this is not the Ananda we are talking about. Basically, there are two types of Ananda or Bliss.

- **Vishesha Ananda:** This is the bliss or happiness we get from objects. We know and experience this bliss. It is momentary; it comes and goes. Vedanta has a complete explanation of how this process works, but this is not the place to discuss it.
- **Swarupa Ananda:** Swarupa Ananda means your essential nature is Ananda or Bliss. We saw earlier that the Chit is both the subject and object. This means "I" is complete and full; it is self-sufficient and does not need anything else. This condition of completeness and fullness gives "I" continuous and unbroken Ananda or Bliss. The reason we do not experience this type of bliss on a continuous basis is because we have forgotten who we are, due to our ignorance. This ignorance creates a separation between subject and object. This duality is the source of our unhappiness.

Vedanta does teach us that our innermost core is SatChitAnanda. Unfortunately, it is not easy to assimilate this knowledge. This is because our understanding is deep-rooted that we are the ego. From the time we are born, we are closely associated with this body-mind complex. It is not easy to overcome this. Serious effort is required to assimilate this knowledge.

2 | Understanding Self-Awareness

Self-Awareness is our innermost core. To understand Self-Awareness, you need to break down what is meant by Awareness. To learn about Awareness, you need to first understand and analyze your experiences. All our perceptions, feelings, thoughts, and current thinking are nothing but the experiences we have. When we are awake, there is hardly any moment when we do not have some sort of experience. We have experiences continuously; sometimes they are structured and willful while at other times they are random, jumping from one thought to another.

Experiences can happen only in the mind and nowhere else. The world is "out there," but we experience it only in our minds. Science also states the same thing. Light is reflected from an external object, and this light travels to the retina in our eye. The retina converts the incoming light into an optical signal. This optical signal is transmitted to the visual cortex in the human brain. Science still does not tell us how the optical signal is converted to an actual image, but somehow the visual image is created, and we experience this visual image in the mind. This is true for all the five senses–sight, hearing, touch, taste, and smell. Even the internal thoughts and emotions which we experience happen only in the mind.

Everyone has a unique and private experience. Even if two people see the same object, the experience each of them has will be different. For example, I am color-blind. To most people, red roses appear red; to me, red roses appear green when viewed against the green bushes. In this way, I have a different experience of the world compared to other people.

If you think about it, experience is the only connection we have with the external world. There is no other way to learn and understand the universe. If we do not experience a thing, then the question can be asked: does that thing even exist? Experience is the only way to validate the existence of the universe. We understand and learn from experience—there is no other way to get to know the external world.

Experiences Decoded

The only way forward is to analyze our own experiences. The following simple equation is a perfect analysis of an experience.

Experience = Awareness + Form

We are always aware of our experience. We can never say we had an experience but are not aware of it. This is simply not possible because awareness is a critical prerequisite and ingredient of an experience. You are having an experience because you are aware of it. If there is no awareness, there can be no experience. We are aware that we have a non stop flow of experience.

No two experiences are the same. The form part of the experience is always different and keeps changing. Sometimes it is visual, sometimes it is auditory, and sometimes it is based on memories. The form keeps changing, the experience keeps changing, but does the underlying awareness also keep changing? Our experience confirms that awareness will always remain the same. It would seem that the form is superimposed on the unchanging Awareness to complete the experience.

If you expand this logic and apply it to the entire human race, each person will have their own experience in their own mind. This experience equation is valid for everyone. Everyone has different forms superimposed on Awareness to complete the experience. Everyone will have their own unique form to create their own unique experience.

The common factor in everyone's experience is Awareness. This Awareness seems to be present in everyone's mind. Can there be so many different Awarenesses? Is the same Awareness present in everyone's mind? Is your Awareness different from mine and everyone else's? These questions will answer themselves once we get a better understanding of what we really mean by Awareness.

Understanding Awareness

Awareness is the most powerful force in the universe, and it is the underlying reality of this universe. It has the power to connect with a form present in the mind and create an experience of which you are aware. As an analogy, think of the sun. When there is no light from the sun you cannot see anything, but in the presence of sunlight everything becomes visible. In the same way, when any form enters the presence of the light of Awareness, the experience bulb lights up in your mind and you are aware of the form. If you think about it, even the light of the sun is a form in the presence of the light of Awareness.

If you carefully study Awareness, you will conclude that it is made of Subject, Object, and Intelligence, and has the following functions:

1. There must be a subject, who is aware of the experience. This subject is the knower part of Awareness.
2. There must be an object, which must be experienced. This object is the known part of Awareness.
3. There must be intelligence, by which the subject gets to know the object. This is the knowing part of Awareness.

Knower, Known, and Knowing are the three powers of Awareness. It must be clear that:

- Awareness = Subject + Object + Intelligence
- Power of Awareness = Power of Knower + Power of Known + Power of Knowing

Awareness is made of Subject, Object, and Intelligence, and it has three different powers–Knower, Known, and Knowing. It must be understood that Subject, Object, Intelligence, and the three powers are not something outside in the world–they are within Awareness and make up Awareness. If any one of them is missing, Awareness will not work and will be incomplete.

- If there is an object to be observed but there is no subject, there will be no Awareness as there is no one to see the object.
- If there is a subject but no object to see, there will be no Awareness as the subject has no objects to observe.

- If there is an object but the subject has no way of knowing what this object is, no Awareness will take place. This knowing must have intelligence.

Wherever there is Awareness, there must be present Subject, Object, and Intelligence with all the three powers. Let us try and understand this in a little more detail.

1. Power of Knowing or Intelligence

The Knowing or Intelligence component of Awareness is extremely powerful. In fact, language and words may not be enough to describe its awesome power. Here are some examples that indicate its strength and power.

Example 1: I am seeing a tree. A Vedantic way to put it will be "I am the seer seeing a tree."

This is a simple experience that we have every moment, but it shows the extraordinary power of Awareness. Let us break up this experience into the different components of Awareness.

Ego = I am

Subject = Seer

Object = Tree

Intelligence = Seeing is the power of Awareness, which makes it possible for "I" to know the tree. Without the power of Seeing, none of us will see any object. Someone may argue that the eye provides this power. The eye does nothing other than converting the image into an optical signal and bringing that signal to the mind. What is the ability that decodes this optical signal into the understanding that this object is a tree? It is the power of Seeing, which is within Awareness, which allows us to know that there is a tree. This Intelligence in Awareness knows that the optical signal is a tree.

Awareness = Seer + Seeing + Seen

Example 2: You are reading a book or "You are the reader reading a book." This power of Intelligence is within Awareness and is available to everyone. Let us decode the experience of reading.

Ego = You

Subject = Reader

Object = Book

Intelligence = Reading is a power within Awareness which allows the Subject or Reader to connect with the contents of the book. It is within Awareness because you are aware that you are reading–first, to know the words and sentences, and then to know what is being read. We are so used to reading that we do not think of this ability as anything special. If there was no power of reading within Awareness, there would be no way you could read anything. With this power of reading, we are aware we are reading, and this awareness completes the reading experience.

Awareness = Reader + Reading + Read

Example 3: You are visiting a friend or "You are the visitor visiting a friend."

Subject = Visitor

Object = Friend

Intelligence = You are aware that you are visiting a friend. This power of knowing that you are visiting is part of the Intelligence within Awareness and of knowing that this person is a friend. If you did not have this power within you, you would never know that this person is your friend and that you have specifically gone to visit him.

Awareness = Visitor + Visiting + Visited

We can continue to give any number of examples to highlight the power of Awareness. We can take any verb in the English language and add "ing" to this verb. This word, when connected with a subject and object, will have the power of creating an Aware experience within the mind. Some more examples:

- Awareness = Eater + Eating + Eaten
- Awareness = Sleeper + Sleeping + Slept

- Awareness = Fighter + Fighting + Fought (an Object)
- Awareness = Player + Playing + Played (an Object)
- Awareness = Learner + Learning + Learned

The Intelligence within Awareness has an unlimited range of power that is impossible to comprehend. We can comprehend only the experiences that our mind can handle. Our minds are limited and therefore can handle only a limited range of experiences.

Awareness is not limited by the capacity of our mind. It is much more and has an infinite amount of Intelligence, an infinite amount of knowledge about everything that is possible. What is amazing is that this unlimited Intelligence, this pure Intelligence, this Awareness, is available within everyone's mind.

2. Power of Knower or Subject

In the earlier section, we saw the power of knowing, the intelligence of knowing. There must be a Knower to see an object and perceive how it looks. This is done by the Subject within Awareness. The Subject is the Knower of the experience. This Subject is not only the Knower of seeing, but is also the Knower of hearing, the Knower of reading, the Knower of sleeping, and so on.

- When it is the Knower of seeing, the Subject is a seer.
- When it is the Knower of hearing, the Subject is a hearer.
- When it is the Knower of reading, the Subject is a reader.
- When it is the Knower of running, the Subject is a runner.

There is only one Subject, and it is the Knower of so many things. In fact, it is the Knower of everything. All this is within Awareness. The Subject with Power of Knowing is available within the mind of each one of us. It is the only way we can know what our experiences are.

Our minds are limited and therefore the power and range of the Knower is limited. Awareness is beyond the mind and this Subject within Awareness is the Knower of everything that is possible. There is nothing that Awareness does not know.

We should never confuse this Subject with the ego. This Subject is part of Awareness and this Subject does NOT have an ego. If I say "I am the

Knower" or "I am the Subject," the "I am" is the ego. The Knower or the Subject is not part of the ego, it is part of Awareness. In Awareness there is no attachment and no ego, it is simply aware. The ego attaches itself to the Subject and thinks it is the Subject.

3. Power of Known or Object

The Object component of Awareness is also extremely powerful, and it has the ability to take any form that we experience in the mind.

If you see a circle, then Awareness cannot take the shape of a square. If it does, you will never experience the (round) circle. Awareness must also be a round circle with exactly the same dimensions. If you see a tree, then Awareness must also take the shape of the tree. This tree must be filled with Awareness. If the tree is half-filled with Awareness or if Awareness does not have the same shape as the tree, you will not be Aware of the tree.

If you want to observe any object:

- The form must be filled with Awareness and nothing but Awareness. If the form does not have Awareness, then the observer or subject will not be able to experience the object with that form.
- The Awareness must take the exact shape of the form.

Awareness has the potential to take any form. If you look into a powerful microscope, Awareness can take the shape of a molecule, or if you look at the universe through a telescope, Awareness can take the shape of the stars and galaxies. Big or small, Awareness can take the shape of anything. Awareness has the potential to take any form.

It is therefore correct to conclude that the content of the object must be Awareness. Awareness by itself is formless, but it has the potential to become any object. The object it will become depends on the input received from the five senses. A good metaphor to explain this is that Awareness is like a lump of Play-Doh, which is formless, but you can manipulate the Play-Doh into any shape. Whatever shape you create, the content is always Play-Doh. In the same way, the content of all the objects in the universe is only Awareness. It can take any shape or form, but the content is always Awareness.

Understanding Self-Awareness

Awareness is the underlying force in the mind. It is the Knower of everything happening in the mind. It can take the form of all possible objects and has infinite Intelligence to give meaning and understanding to the experience.

Awareness = Subject + Intelligence + Object

There must be a Self, who is Aware—someone who can say, "I am Aware." So, who are we? We are the Self, the "I." No one can deny this fact.

Vedanta teaches that we are Self-Aware. What does this mean? It means that the Self IS Awareness and nothing but Awareness. Also, Awareness IS Self. They are the same. When you say Self, it automatically means Awareness, and when you say Awareness, it automatically means Self. There is no separation between them. This also means that the Self is the Subject and the Self is also the Object.

How do we understand this with our experience? What does Self-Aware mean? It means the Self is Aware that it is the Self. Let us put this in the Awareness statements we have used before.

- Self is Knowing it is the Self.

Here Self is the Subject, and the Self knows Self, therefore Self is also the Object. Knowing is the Intelligence connecting the Subject and Object. If Self is Self-Aware, then the Self is both Subject and Object. The Self being both Subject and Object is the only way Self can be Self-Aware. Further, the Intelligence connecting the two is also the Self.

Self = Subject = Intelligence = Object

- The experience the self (small s) has in the mind has duality; it experiences the separation between the subject and object. The subject is "over here" and the object is "over there." In Self-Awareness, there is no duality—the Self is both the subject and object. It is non-dual, it is one, and there is unity.
- We saw earlier that to have an experience you need a subject, object, and intelligence. Self-Awareness has all three components to complete an experience. It is thus self-sufficient and self-contained. It does not need anything else for its existence.
- It must be understood that in Self-Awareness, the subject and object are not different components or parts. They are completely

homogenous, undifferentiated, undivided, and part-less. It is not easy to grasp or visualize this, but this is the nature of Self-Awareness.

- Self-Awareness is like a bulb of Awareness. This bulb is shining with Awareness. It does nothing except radiate Awareness. If any form meets with Awareness, it creates the experience of which you are Aware.
- Self-Awareness is beyond the mind. The mind is limited and has duality. Self-Awareness is pure, non-dual, and complete. It has all the infinite powers we have described earlier. It Knows everything and it has infinite Intelligence. It has the ability and potential to create all the required forms. What more does Self-Awareness need? Nothing.

Vedanta teaches that you are the Self, and this Self is not the mind but SatChitAnanda. SatChitAnanda is your true nature, your underlying reality. Based on all that we have discussed so far, we can conclude the following:

Self is Self-Aware = Self is SatChitAnanda

Self-Awareness is Sat: Sat means Real. According to Vedanta, for anything to be Sat, it must exist and be present in all the three tenses–past, present, and future. Self-Awareness meets this requirement. Self-Awareness is therefore unborn, uncaused, unchanging, and uncreated. It has always been there and will always be there.

Self-Awareness is Chit: Chit means Awareness. It means it is the Subject and Object with all the creative powers and Intelligence we have discussed earlier.

Self-Awareness is Ananda: Ananda means Bliss. This term can be confusing because we do get momentary bliss in our day-to-day lives, but this is not the Ananda we are talking about. We are talking about the Ananda of Self-Awareness. Self-Awareness is full and complete; it has the Subject, Object, and Intelligence. It does not need anything extra, and it is not dependent on anything external. This fullness and completeness lead to full-time (not partial) Bliss or Ananda, and this is the essential nature of Self-Awareness.

3 | Einstein's Theory of Relativity

lbert Einstein is the best-known scientist in the modern era. His contribution to science is immense. He is famous for presenting the following two theories:

1. Theory of Special Relativity
2. Theory of General Relativity

It is importanl to understand both thesc theories properly. If the implications are properly understood, they can change our world view radically. We will be discussing the implication of these theories in many essays.

Fun fact: In 1921, Einstein was awarded a Nobel Prize for his discovery of the "photoelectric effect" phenomenon, which showed that light is a particle. It is surprising that he was awarded the Nobel Prize for this discovery and not for the Theory of Relativity, for which he is better known.

1. Theory of Special Relativity

The Theory of Special Relativity was introduced in 1905. This theory covers objects moving at constant speed in straight lines. Without being too technical, let us examine this theory. It makes the following connections:

- Motion and space
- Motion and time
- Space and time

Motion and Space: There is a connection between motion and space. Whenever there is motion, space contracts. Yes, motion influences space. This is not an easy concept to grasp. We are so used to seeing space that we think it is unchanging. All this happens because the speed of light is fixed at 186,000 miles per second, irrespective of the frame of reference.

Let us understand the basics of this theory. We all experience relative speed. Going in a car at 60 mph, we look into another car traveling in the same direction at 55 mph, and we see things inside the other car because the relative speed is only 5 mph.

We do not have this experience with reference to the speed of light. Light travels at 186,000 miles per second. Suppose that you are traveling in a car at 60% of the speed of light. Sitting in the car, you would logically expect the light to travel at only 40% of its usual speed. However, if you take measurements sitting in your car, you will find to your amazement that light is still traveling at 186,000 miles per second.

What has happened is that space has contracted and shrunk so that light still covers 186,000 miles in one second. If you increase the speed of the car to 80% of the speed of light, space will contract further. If you slow down to 30% of the speed of light, space will expand. Whether you increase or decrease the speed of the car, the speed of light will remain constant at 186,000 miles per second. The speed of light is fixed; it never changes.

This expansion and contraction of space also happens even when walking or running. However, the speed at which you walk or run is so slow when compared to the speed of light that you are unable to notice the difference–but changes to the space framework are occurring.

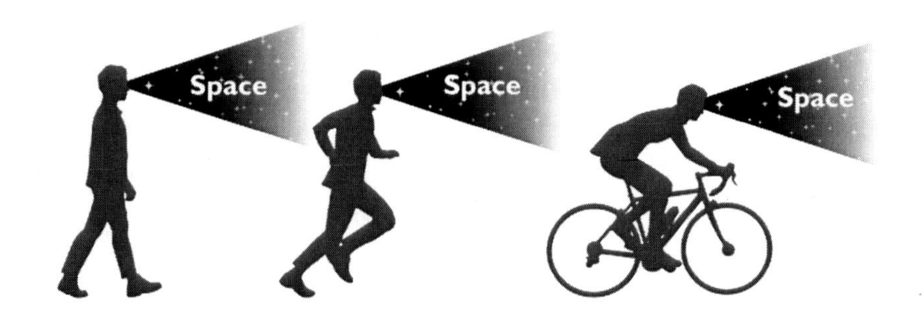

The important takeaway point from this discussion is that each person creates their own space framework. Person A is sitting in a chair, Person B is walking, Person C is running, Person D is cycling, and Person E is driving a car; all of them are moving at different speeds.

Since the motion speed is different, the space contraction is different for each person. The space framework is different for each person. It is counterintuitive. It shows that each of them will have their own separate and independent space framework. Each living being in the universe has their own framework of space.

This entire universe is based on relative motion as we just cannot find anything which is fixed. We are walking on Earth; Earth is moving around the sun; the sun is moving in the Milky Way; the Milky Way is moving farther away from other galaxies. The relative motion keeps changing. This means that the framework of space will constantly change with motion.

The speed of light is always fixed, but the framework of space is never fixed. It is different for each living being and keeps changing with the speed of motion.

Motion and Time: To explain the connection between motion and time, Einstein provided a thought experiment.

You are on Earth and your twin brother goes into space in a rocket. Both of you have top-of-the-range atomic clocks. Your twin brother's rocket is traveling at the speed of 0.8 c. You, on Earth, measure the speed of light, and you find it to be c. Your twin brother also measures the speed of light; he also finds that it is c. How come? The clock in the rocket slows down, and the space gets compressed so that the speed of light is still c. The speed of light does not change, but space and time do change. His time oscillation is slower, but the speed of light is still c.

Your twin brother returns to Earth. Your clock shows that he traveled for 10 years, while his clock shows that he traveled for six years. Amazing but true–the clocks are ticking at different rates for you and your twin brother. In fact, you are aging differently. All this is because of motion and speed.

Your twin brother goes on another trip, and now he increases his speed to 0.9999 c. He measures the speed of light and he still finds it to be c, the same as you will find on Earth. His clock will be running very slowly as compared to your clock on Earth. He returns after 50 days, according to his clock. Your clock on Earth will show he has traveled for 10 years. His time is extremely slow and compressed. His clock is ticking much slower compared to your clock on Earth.

This clock ticking at different rates also happens even when walking or running. However, the speed at which you walk or run is so slow when compared to the speed of light that you are unable to notice the difference, but changes to the rate of time are happening. The smallest time unit is 10^{-44} seconds. It is impossible for any living being to notice this small unit of time. Even for the smallest change in speed, the rate of time does change. Motion has an influence on time.

Space and Time: We have just seen that motion influences both space and time. Does that mean that space and time are connected? Yes, they are. Einstein made this connection by coining the term "spacetime." Space and time are two sides of the same coin. When you look at space in terms of distances, it is space. However, when you look at the same space in terms of time, that space is spacetime.

This spacetime is a fabric made of time. In space you measure distances. The sun is 93 million miles away, the tree is 500 feet away. In spacetime you measure everything in time–the amount of time light takes to reach us. The sun is eight minutes away. Different objects are so many seconds away from you. The distant star is five million light-years away.

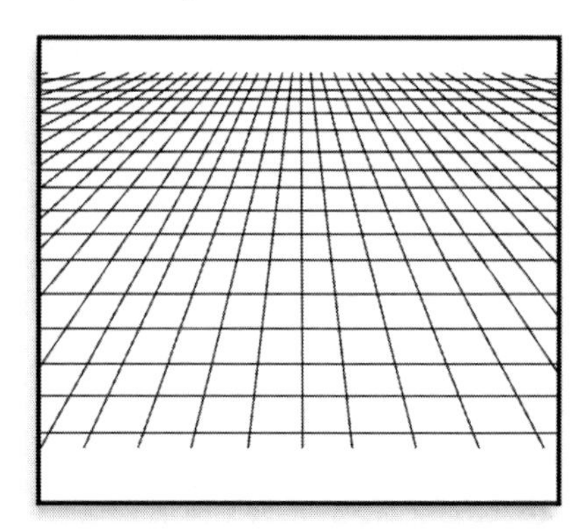

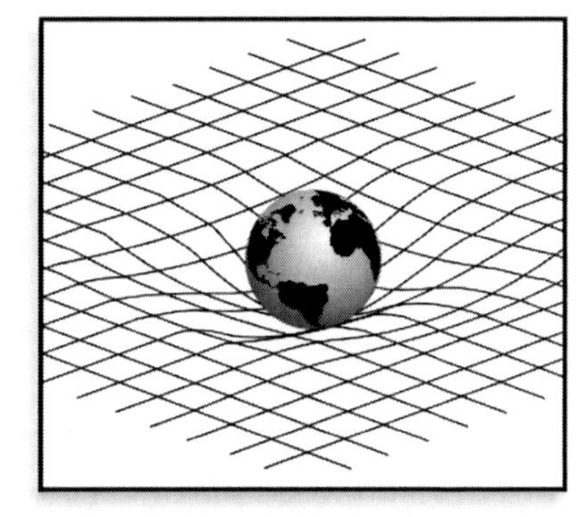

2. Theory of General Relativity

The Theory of Special Relativity is about objects with constant speed. What about acceleration or gravity? This is missing–the Theory of Special Relativity did not cover this. Einstein introduced the Theory of General Relativity in 1915 to cover acceleration. It must be noted that gravity is a type of acceleration.

Acceleration is a type of motion, but the speed keeps doubling every second. How does this affect space and time? We have seen earlier that increasing speed slows down time and contracts space. With acceleration, the speed doubles every second; this means time is slowing down at double the rate. Even space is contracting at double the rate. Based on this scenario, mathematical calculation will show that the spacetime fabric will curve whenever there is acceleration. See the images below. The greater the acceleration, the greater the dip in the curvature.

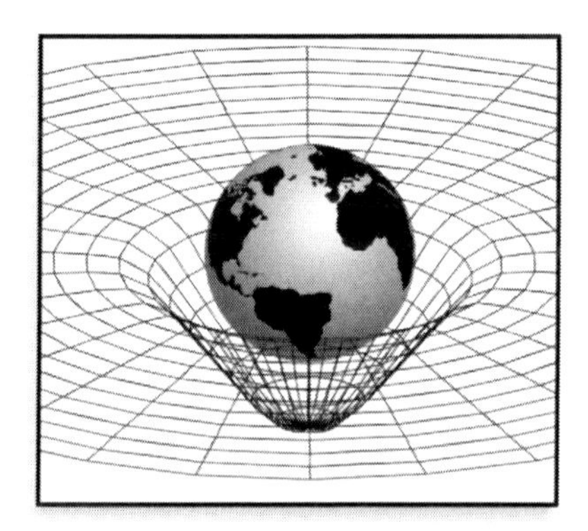

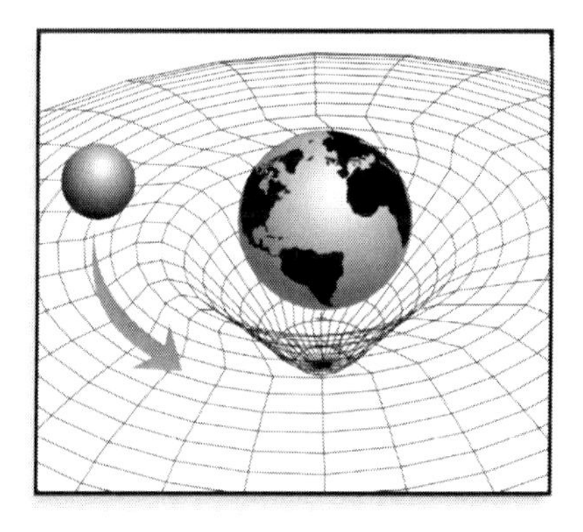

Another outcome of this theory is that in the presence of matter, time slows down. The slowing down of time is represented by the spacetime fabric bending or curving around an object. The heavier the mass, the greater the curvature. Not only planets and stars, but matter with any mass will slow down time and curve the spacetime fabric. For objects with a small mass, the curve will not be noticeable.

Based on the discussion in this essay, we can conclude as follows. We will be using these conclusions in different essays.

1. Space contracts with motion. The faster the motion, the greater the contraction.
2. Time also slows down with motion. The faster the motion, the slower the time.
3. Time slows down in the presence of energy. The greater the energy, the slower the ticking of time.

4 | Quantum Physics—Overview

Physics can be divided into two distinct divisions or phases:

- Classical Physics
- Quantum Physics

Classical physics started with Isaac Newton, who made many discoveries and formulated many laws which are relevant even today. Newton's laws did not focus on atomic-level objects but on macro-objects that we can see around us. Based on these laws, people believed that the universe was a giant machine, and one could easily predict the motion of the planets and the objects therein. In this way, they could know exactly what was happening in the universe and in some way could even predict all the future movements of celestial bodies. Physicists thought they knew everything in the universe and that there was nothing new to discover.

In the early 20th century, things took a dramatic turn. As physicists started exploring atomic-level particles, they found that none of the classical laws were applicable to these particles. Classical physics became outdated at the atomic and subatomic levels. To understand and explain the happenings in the realm of the subatomic, quantum physics was born.

What Is Quantum Physics?

Quantum physics is the study of the behavior of matter and energy at the molecular, atomic, nuclear, and even smaller, microscopic levels. We will give a quick overview of quantum physics by highlighting some of the key developments. In the coming essays, this will help us make connections to Vedanta.

Light Is a Wave

In 1805, Thomas Young demonstrated that light is a wave. He used the famous double-slit experiment. There was a light source and in front of it there was a barrier, and this barrier had two slits. On the other side of the barrier was a photographic plate to study the light's propagation

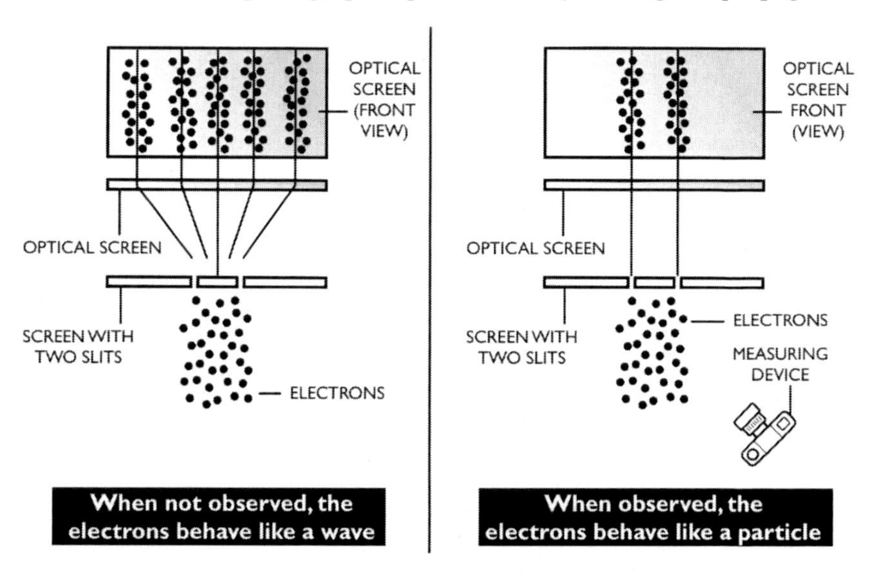

through the slits. The result on the photographic plate clearly showed that light was not a particle but a wave. If it was a particle, there would be only two bands on the plate, but the plate showed multiple bands, proving that light was a wave which passed through the two slits and then combined to form all the different bands. If you search for "double-slit experiment" on YouTube, you will see many videos explaining this concept.

Light Is a Particle

In 1905, Einstein published a paper on the "photoelectric effect" phenomenon, which showed that light is a particle. In 1921, he was awarded a Nobel Prize for this discovery. In this experiment, you shine light (which is a wave) on a photoconductive metal, and you get light reflected on the other side. On studying or observing this reflected light, Einstein found that the reflected light was not a wave–it was made up of packets of energy. Each packet is a unit of fixed energy, and this packet is known as a photon and has all the characteristics of a particle.

The double-slit experiment explained earlier was updated slightly–instead of two slits, there was only one slit. Light was passed through a single slit and then onto a photographic plate. In the two-slit experiment, scientists found a series of bands on the photographic plate, which suggested that light was a wave. When a single slit was used, they found only a single band on the photographic plate, suggesting that light was a particle and not a wave. The curious part of this experiment is, what made light behave as a wave when there were two slits and behave as a particle when there was only one slit? This experiment was repeated again and again and the result was always the same. There was something which was telling light when to behave as a wave and when to behave as a particle. This dilemma was the birth of quantum physics.

Matter Is Both Wave and Particle

So, light exhibits properties of both a wave and a particle. In 1923, Louis de Broglie, a French doctoral student, made a bold assertion that not only light but all matter must have both wave and particle properties. Here, matter means matter including you, me, planets, cars–in fact, any living or nonliving object in this universe. The tree in front of you is a particle and, using the de Broglie formula, you can also calculate the wavelength of the tree based on its energy content. In 1927, the de Broglie hypothesis was proven experimentally; thus, all matter is both a wave and a particle. In 1929, de Broglie was awarded the Nobel Prize for his theory. He is the only person to ever receive a Nobel Prize based on a doctoral thesis.

How can we comprehend that everything that exists is both particle (matter) and wave (non-matter)? Is this possible? The tree outside my window looks like a particle, so the question is: when is the tree a wave? Is it ever a wave? It must be a wave otherwise the de Broglie theory would be wrong. Let us try to understand this.

If I turn my back to the tree, is the tree still a particle? Is the tree even there? You really cannot be sure because you do not see the tree. Maybe the tree is now a wave. This type of logic can be applied to all objects in the universe, including any living being. For example, you are talking to your friend sitting in front of you. You are sure he is a particle because he is right in front of you and you can see him. You now move to the next room and you cannot see your friend anymore. Is it now possible that your friend has become a wave? When you come back to the room, your friend is once again a particle. All this may sound strange, but this is what happens when you try and understand quantum physics.

You now ask your friend, “Were you a wave a short time ago?” He may think you have gone mad, but out of politeness he will confirm that he has always been a particle. The friend may want to play the same game with

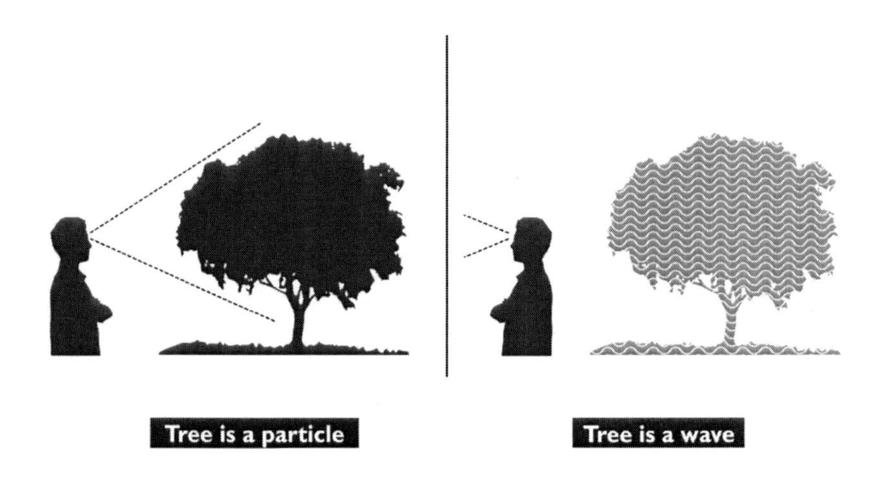

you. He may say to you, “I did not see you when you went to the next room. Were you a wave till you came back to this room and till I saw you once again?” He has a valid point. When you moved to the next room, you may have thought your friend was a wave, and your friend might also have thought you were a wave.

Looking at the example of the tree and your friend, it would suggest that anything in your presence would always be a particle, but if something is not in your presence it could mean that it is a wave. Your presence is necessary for anything to be a particle. This is the implication of the de Broglie theory.

Can something be a wave and a particle at the same time, or must it be either a wave or a particle at any given time? If the tree is a particle, then it just cannot be a wave at the same time, and vice versa. Science has no answer yet to this question. Here is some food for thought–if an object is a particle, then where is the wave residing? Is the wave also part of this spacetime framework or does the wave reside in another dimension?

There are so many questions which the de Broglie theory generates about matter being wave or particle. Unfortunately, science has not been able to answer them so far. In the coming essays we will try and understand these questions using the teachings of Vedanta.

Schrodinger's Wave Function

Like Newton's Laws of Motion are the heart of classical physics, Erwin Schrodinger's wave function is the heart of quantum physics. To understand the wave part of the de Broglie theory, Schrodinger formulated a complex equation for the wave function. Without being too technical, let us examine Schrodinger's wave equation. This can be represented by the following:

1. Schrodinger's equation represents a physical system, and this physical system always consists of an observing system and an observed system. The observed system is a wave function, and this wave function is the wave component of the wave/matter duality as postulated by de Broglie. The de Broglie theory says that every object in this universe is both a particle and a wave. The wave part can be represented by Schrodinger's wave equation, and this wave is being observed by the observing system.

2. Schrodinger's wave equation represents only "standing" waves and not "traveling" waves. We see traveling waves when we throw a stone in a pond and see the waves traveling outward, or when we see waves in the ocean. Standing waves, on the other hand, are waves which propagate in an enclosed environment; they keep bouncing off the enclosing walls. Electrons, as waves, are standing waves because they are enclosed within

an atom. For the observing system to observe a standing wave, it must be enclosed in some type of environment.

3. Schrodinger's wave equation is a generic equation which represents all the possible standing wave functions in the universe. The main variables of Schrodinger's wave equation are time and energy. If you input the correct variables for a particular observed system, Schrodinger's wave equation will represent that wave function. If you input the energy variables of the electron wave, Schrodinger's equation will represent the electron wave function over time. Understanding the energy structure of electrons, photons, molecules, and other micro-objects is simpler. Macro-objects have more complex wave functions and are much more difficult to understand. In conclusion, we may say that Schrodinger's wave equation is applicable in every wave function, both simple and complex. The only limitation is that science still does not understand the input variables needed for the complex waves representing macro-objects like you and me, or cars and planets.

4. You can convert Schrodinger's wave function into a probability wave function by squaring the wave function. The probability wave function contains all the possible outcomes. There could be infinite possibilities. To explain this, the famous "Schrodinger's cat" example is given. A cat is enclosed in a box which contains a vial of poison attached to an atomic trigger. The atomic trigger can randomly trigger the poison vial. One is never sure if the cat is dead or alive at any given time. As per the probability function yielded by Schrodinger's equation, the cat could be dead or alive, and it could also be half dead or half alive, one-third dead or two-thirds alive, and all the other different possible mixes of ratios between dead and alive. It has infinite possibilities, but only a few logical possibilities. You cannot have anything one-quarter alive and three-quarters dead.

5. Another important aspect of the physical system for Schrodinger's wave equation is the observing system. When this observing system interacts with the observed system at any given time, the wave function of the observed system collapses to only one of the logical possibilities at that given time. In the example of Schrodinger's cat, if you open the trapdoor to see the cat, the cat will be alive or dead. If it is found alive, all the other possibilities become zero. In other words, when the observing system

interacts with the observed system, the wave collapses to one of the possibilities for that given time, and then all the other possibilities have a zero chance of occurring. Till the trapdoor is opened, the cat is in a waveform with infinite possibilities. When the door is opened by the observing system, the cat wave collapses into being alive, and then all the other possibilities become zero.

Here is a direct hint that the wave function only collapses in the presence of an observing system. If there is no observing system, the observed system will continue to be a wave function. Before interacting with an observing system, the observed system is a wave, and the moment after interacting with the observing system, the observed wave function collapses to become a particle.

If you take the broader viewpoint, you will realize that the photographic plate in the double-slit experiment itself is matter, and therefore it also has a wave function. So, what observing system collapses the wave function of the photographic plate? The logical answer would be your eyes. But the eye is also matter and therefore it also has a wave function. So, what observing system collapses the wave function of the eye? The answer would be your brain. But the brain is also matter and therefore it also has a wave function. So, what observing system collapses the wave function of the brain? I think that at this point, science has come to the end of the road; it cannot explain what or which observing system collapses the wave function of the brain.

If we understand Vedanta properly, most of these questions can be answered. In the coming essays, we will try to explain some of the key teachings of Vedanta that help answer these questions.

Vedanta

The underlying truth as taught by Vedanta is the foundation of everything in this universe. The more you learn about Vedanta, the better you can appreciate how the teachings can help science. Since the teachings of Vedanta may be new to many readers, some of the key concepts are repeated in different essays.

The essays in this section cover a good cross-section of key topics in Vedanta.

5 | Understanding the Mind

The mind indeed is mysterious. Nobody has seen it, but we know it exists. We have thoughts, perceptions, and emotions, and we know all this happens in the mind. So, it does exist, but where does it exist, how does it function, and how and why was it created? These are indeed key questions, and if you investigate you will not find many good answers.

Fortunately, sages and rishis in ancient India showed us the correct path. They closed their eyes, looked inward, and analyzed their experiences and thoughts. They meditated on and contemplated these issues. They used their minds to understand the Mind! They learned a lot, they understood a lot, and they documented their findings in the ancient scriptures.

This essay is based on the understanding and analysis of the Mind as taught in the ancient scriptures. It will cover the following different aspects of the Mind:

- Source of the Mind
- Evolution of the Mind
- Structure of the Mind
- Functioning of the Mind
- States of the Mind
- Qualities (Gunas) of the Mind
- Control of the Mind

Source of the Mind

To learn about the source of the Mind, it is important to know your innermost core–your Real Self. Vedanta teaches us that our inner core is SatChitAnanda or Self-Awareness.

Self-Awareness is like a bulb within us, shining Awareness. It does nothing except radiate Awareness. For a detailed analysis of Self-Awareness, please read the essay "Understanding Self-Awareness." Here we will give a quick overview.

As we have discussed in the earlier essay mentioned above, Awareness is the most powerful force in the universe, and it is the underlying reality of the universe. It has the power to connect with a form present in the mind and create an experience of which we are aware. Awareness is made of three things: Subject, Object, and Intelligence. If any one of them is missing, there will be no Awareness.

- There must be a subject, who is aware of the experience. The Subject is the knower part of Awareness.
- There must be an object, which must be experienced. This Object is the known part of Awareness.
- There must be Intelligence, by which the Subject gets to know the Object. This is the knowing part of Awareness.

Awareness = Subject + Object + Intelligence

Power of Awareness = Power of Knower + Power of Known + Power of Knowing

Awareness is made of Subject, Object, and Intelligence, and it has three different powers–Knower, Known, and Knowing. Subject has the Power of the Knower, Object has the Power of the Known, and Intelligence has the Power of Knowing.

It must be understood that Subject, Object, Intelligence, and the three powers are not something outside in the world–they are within Awareness and make up Awareness. Wherever there is awareness, Subject, Object, and Intelligence are present with all the three powers. Right now, you are aware of reading this essay, therefore Subject, Object, and Intelligence are present within your awareness of this essay.

What is Self-Awareness?

There must be a Self who is Aware. The nature of Self is Awareness. Self is our inner core, which is full, complete, and self-sufficient. Self-Awareness means that "Awareness is aware of Awareness." It is like saying "I am reading this essay." Here, "I am" is the subject and the essay is the object. Reading is the intelligence connecting the object with the subject.

Applying this to Self-Awareness, you will notice that the subject is Awareness, the object is Awareness, and the intelligence is Awareness. The Self in Awareness is the Subject, Object, and Intelligence. Self is the Subject, Self is the Object, and Self is the Intelligence. This is not easy to grasp. This complete, independent Self is our inner core. It is both Subject and Object. Self-Awareness is non-dual and homogenous. It is Self-Shining.

- Awareness = Subject + Object + Intelligence
- In Self-Awareness, Self = Subject = Object = Intelligence
- Power of Self = Power of Knower = Power of Known = Power of Knowing

This Self shines Awareness. It is like a bulb radiating Awareness. This is our inner core. It is not dependent on anything else, and it generates its own light of Awareness.

Evolution of the Mind

If Self-Awareness is our reality, why don't we know it, why don't we feel it? The simple answer is that we are Ignorant, we are not aware of our true nature. This Ignorance has a tremendous impact on our true nature of Self-Awareness. Due to Ignorance, we no longer know that we are both the Subject and Object. If we have forgotten this fact, it means that the subject and object are no longer a single entity but separate and independent entities.

This separation of Subject and Object is the basis of the Mind. Mind has duality with the separation of Subject and Object. Self-Awareness is the source, and the mind is created due to the ignorance of our true nature. With the separation of subject and object, the three powers of Awareness–power of the knower, power of the known, and power of knowing–also become active in the Mind.

Mind = Awareness + Ignorance

Mind = Subject + Object + Intelligence + Ignorance

The mind has duality, therefore has a feeling of the subject being "in here" and the object being "out there." This is the experience for most of us.

It must be understood that Self-Awareness does NOT undergo any change. Self-Awareness is pure and it has NO Ignorance. Ignorance gives the impression that it is changing non-dual Self-Awareness to a mind with duality. Self-Awareness does not change at all, it only gives an "impression," "as though" it has changed. How do we understand this "as though" change? Vedanta gives the following two examples.

Example 1—Rope/Snake: In the evening, we are walking on the road, and we confuse a rope for a snake. We see the snake and think it is real. When we shine a torch on it, we realize it is a rope. Only because of ignorance do we mistake the rope for a snake. The rope has never undergone any change; it has always been a rope. In the presence of ignorance, it is "as though" the rope has become a snake.

Example 2—Red Water: Put a clear glass pitcher of water in front of a red wall. What will we see? We will see red water. Is the water red? No, water is never red; it is always colorless. In the presence of the red wall, the water appears "as though" it is red.

In the same way, in the presence of Ignorance, non-dual Self-Awareness "appears" as Mind with duality. Self-Awareness does not undergo any change; it is only an "as though" change, and this is because of Ignorance. If there was no Ignorance, the Self would never experience the Mind; the Self would only experience Self-Awareness.

Structure of the Mind

We have seen that Ignorance creates the Mind. Earlier, we saw that the Self in Self-Awareness is the Subject, the Object, and the Intelligence. We can summarize as follows:

- Awareness = Subject + Object + Intelligence
- In Self-Awareness, Self = Subject = Object = Intelligence

Due to ignorance, these four parts of Self-Awareness separate to become independent functions in the Mind. Just like a prism refracts lights and breaks it into seven different colors, in the presence of ignorance Self-

Awareness breaks into four parts. The Subject becomes the Sakshi (witness) in the mind, the Intelligence becomes the Buddhi, the power of the objects becomes the Manas, and the Self becomes the ego. As discussed earlier, these changes are "as though" changes. If there was no Ignorance, these parts would be one in Self-Awareness.

1. Sakshi–the home of the Subject
2. Manas–the home of the Object
3. Buddhi–the home of the Intelligence
4. Ahamkara–the home of the Ego (self)
5. Chitta–the home of the Memory

All the activity in the Mind is in the form of mental waveforms, which are called vrittis. Buddhi, Manas, and even Ahamkara are nothing but vrittis. They are just mental waveforms.

Let us try and understand this structure of the mind.

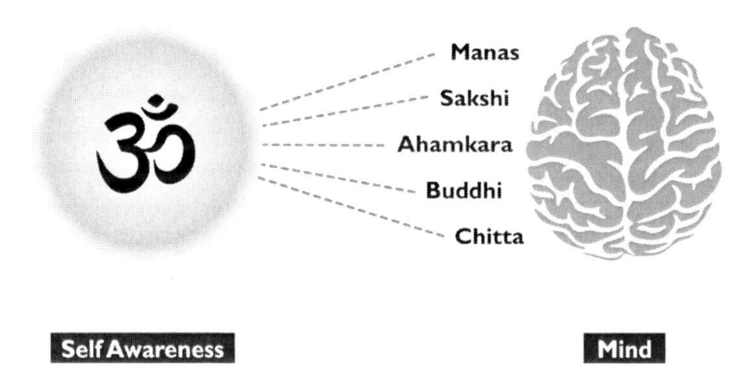

Sakshi–The Home of the Subject

Sakshi means "witness." Power of the Knower, which is within Awareness, now resides in the mind as the Subject or Sakshi. This Sakshi witnesses everything which goes on in the mind. It is the seer, hearer, feeler, taster, and the witness of all other activities in the mind. If there is any activity in the mind, Sakshi is the one who witnesses it. It is important not to confuse ego with Sakshi. Sakshi has no ego; its only function is to witness what is going on in the mind. There are no desires, no "I-ness" or feelings within Sakshi.

If you see a tree outside, it is Sakshi within your mind which perceives this tree. Power of the Knower within the mind allows the perception of the tree. This power is like a gift which has been given to the mind by Awareness. If this Power of the Knower was unavailable, you would not be able to perceive anything.

Manas–The Home of the Object

Manas is the home of the Object. Power of the Known resides within Manas. Power of the Known is a power within Awareness. It is the power which deals with objects, the power to become any object. This power does not create any objects but becomes the object which is superimposed on it. A good metaphor to explain this is that it is like a lump of Play-Doh. You can manipulate the Play-Doh into any shape. You can make a tree, car, house, or a person with the Play-Doh. In the same way, Power of the Known can be manipulated to become any object in this universe. Manas is connected to the following organs:

- **Five Sense Organs:** The five sense organs bring the input to Manas from the external world. Eyes, ears, nose, tongue, and skin are the five sense organs. Input signals from the external world pass through the sense organs to Manas.
- **Five Organs of Action:** These are the output organs. Hands, feet, mouth, reproductive organs, and excretory organs are the five organs of action.
- **Antahkarana or Internal Organs:** These are organs which operate at the subconscious level. Organs like heart, liver, stomach, muscles, etc. There is no direct control over these organs, but they function at the subconscious level.

1. We know the sense organs and organs of action at the gross or physical level. Vedanta teaches us that every gross organ must have a subtle organ. If there is a physical eye, then there is also a subtle eye. This subtle eye is connected to Manas. In the same way, if you have physical hands, then you also have subtle hands. The subtle version of the sense organs and of the organs of action are connected to Manas.

2. The sense organs in Manas interact with the objects available in the outside world in the subtle form. The subtle eyes interact with the visual world outside. They receive the subtle version of what is happening "out there" on a continuous basis. In the same way, the subtle version of the ear, nose, tongue, skin is in constant interaction with the subtle world of sound, smell, taste, and touch. The subtle world operates in the waveform. In Vedanta, these waveforms are called vrittis.

3. Each of these organs is smart, intelligent, conscious, and an independent power center. Manas passes on the power of Awareness to each organ. These organs also become conscious and intelligent. Each of them has a function to perform: the eyes to see, legs to walk and stand, the heart to pump blood, and so on. Each of these organs is a power center, with its own likes and dislikes. For example, the taste buds in the tongue like a sweet taste, and when there are chocolates or ice cream available, they can push the ego to order the feet to walk to the fridge and eat chocolates or ice cream to satisfy the craving. This type of power is present in all the sense organs. Logically, the ego must control the sense organs and direct their activity. However, if we are not vigilant, these sense organs can overpower the ego and take control of our day-to-day activity.

Buddhi–The Home of the Intelligence

Buddhi means "intelligence." Power of Knowing resides within Buddhi. It provides the intelligence to the mind. Buddhi has many different powers and capabilities. Let us discuss some of the key powers.

Power of Cognition or Sensation: This is the Power of Knowing that is available in the sense organs. This is the power which we have described earlier of changing the object waveform of ignorance to the object waveform of knowledge.

Power of Imagination: Daydreaming or creative/positive thinking are good examples. We are involved in this on a regular basis, where we can construct an imaginary vision for ourselves. This power is present in Buddhi.

Power of Logic: The power of comparing, drawing inferences, discussion, etc. So, we can say that the power of logic is within Buddhi. If you see smoke on the hill, you conclude there is fire. A wide range of logic "circuitry" is available in Buddhi, which we use daily.

Power of Will: This is the power to execute desires, wishes, and ideals, and is available within Buddhi and within Ahamkara. It is originally within Ahamkara, but Buddhi also learns this skill over time.

Power of Memory: This is where all the things learned and experienced are stored. This storage is Chitta. The next time a similar vritti is presented, Memory knows what the vritti represents.

Ahamkara–The Home of the Ego

Aham means "I" and kara means "maker," so Ahamkara means "I-Maker." This is what we usually refer to as ego. The Self in Self-Awareness, in the presence of Ignorance, becomes the Ahamkara or ego in the individual mind. We have discussed earlier that Self is full and complete and does not undergo any change. In the presence of Ignorance, the Self "as though" changes to become the ego. Ego is not the Self but is a mental waveform or vritti and behaves as if it is the Self. Ego adds the "I-ness" and "My-ness" to the mind. Ego is part of the mind, and anything in the mind is part of the Subtle Body.

In Self-Awareness, the Self is both the Subject and Object. In the same way, the ego thinks it is both Sakshi and Manas. The ego attaches and identifies itself with Sakshi and Manas.

Chitta–The Home of the Memory

The literal meaning of Chitta is "mind stuff." In Vedanta, the subconscious mind is termed Chitta. Much of the subconscious mind consists of submerged experiences which are stored in Chitta. Chitta is like a calm mind lake with vrittis or thought waves on the surface and stored experiences below the surface.

Whenever Sakshi (home of Subject) encounters Manas (home of Object), an experience or thought wave is created on the surface of Chitta. The technical word for this experience in Vedanta is samskara or impression. When this thought wave, experience, or samskara completes its presence on the surface, it sinks below the surface into Chitta and creates an impression of that experience. A specific experience creates a specific impression. This impression is stored in Chitta. No experiences are lost in

Chitta. Even the smallest experiences are available in the subconscious mind as impressions in Chitta.

When you perceive an orange and taste it for the first time, you get an experience of the orange. You know the taste and you know the object orange. The samskara of this knowledge is stored in Chitta. The next time you think of an orange, this knowledge will instantly move from the subconscious mind to the surface of your mind to complete the experience.

When an impression or experience is triggered by an external or internal event, the impression bubbles up to the surface as a vritti or thought wave, and this thought wave is termed "memory." Impressions are stored in Chitta and when they come up to the surface it is called a memory.

The profile of the experiences stored in Chitta can create tendencies or personality traits. If you have a whole bunch of positive experiences, your personality traits will be different from a person who has had only negative experiences. So, when you are born again your personality traits and tendencies are carried over.

Functioning of the Mind

Due to Ignorance, these four components (ego, subject, object, and intelligence) are sitting in different departments in the mind. Intelligence is sitting in Buddhi, the Object part is sitting in Manas, the Subject part is sitting in Sakshi, and the Self or "I-ness" is sitting in Ahamkara. These four parts are separated, but there is a natural tendency for them to combine to create Self-Awareness. There is a mutual attraction to come together so that they can achieve the original status of being Self-Aware. When the Subject, Object, and Intelligence are separated, the self feels incomplete; it feels inadequate and it wants to feel full and complete. The only way the self can feel complete is when the Subject, Object and Intelligence combine into one entity.

In the mind this can happen only when the subject (in Sakshi), object (in Manas) and intelligence (in Buddhi) combine to create Awareness. Only when these three parts combine is Awareness generated. Ahamkara then links with this Awareness to complete the feeling of Self-Awareness, which is the original state of fullness and non-duality which we have discussed earlier. This happens every time we experience something; for example, when we look at a tree all the components combine to create an experience of "completeness" and we are Aware of the tree. When this is achieved, the feeling of completeness and fullness (Ananda) is felt, but the problem is that it does not last long. It is momentary. It lasts for a single thought. When the second thought pops up, the full process must be repeated. We know we have countless thoughts every day; the same cycle is repeated with every thought.

We will now undertake a step-by-step analysis of a how a typical

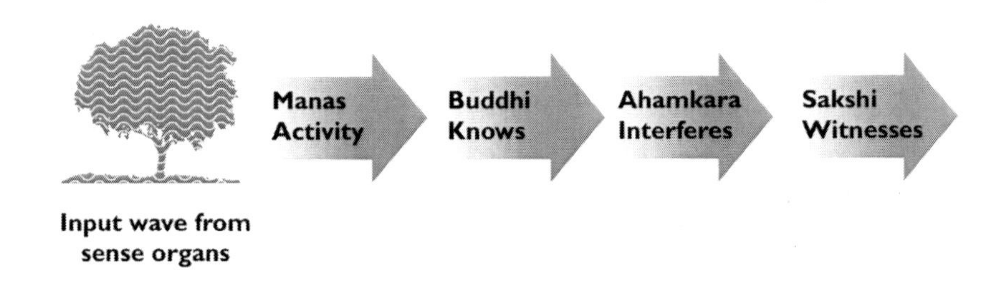

experience is created in the mind.

- Step 1: Activity in Manas
- Step 2: Buddhi Knows
- Step 3: Ahamkara Interferes
- Step 4: Sakshi Witnesses

Step 1: Activity in Manas

Manas is the home of Objects, and it has Power of the Known (Objects). This power allows it to become any object superimposed on it.

This power has unlimited capacity, but it is limited by the human mind. The human mind is limited by the capacity of the five sense organs–eyes, ears, tongue, nose, and skin. The sense organs have their own limitation. For example, the human ear can hear sounds up to only 20 kHz frequency. This is limited. We know other animals can manage a much wider spectrum. Our eyes can only see the "light part" of the electromagnetic (EM) spectrum. There are species which handle other parts of the EM spectrum. In other words, there is a much bigger universe than we can experience with our five senses.

There is a lot of activity taking place in Manas. All the sense organs and internal organs are continuously sending information into Manas. Manas is a busy place. The objects coming from the external world through the sense organs have a waveform representation. When these object waveforms contact Power of the Known in Manas, this power adds building blocks to the object. It adds the required code for the object. It is like adding the software code for the object. With this addition of the code, the object waveform has the infrastructure to become that object.

It could be vision, sound, touch, smell, and taste–the perception of these objects takes place in Manas. For example, when the input signal is for a tree, Manas adds the code which makes up the tree. This code is in the form of mental waveforms or vrittis. These mental waveforms have the required ingredients to become a tree. If the input is music, it creates the code which makes up the sound for the music. In this way, it handles all the input signals coming from the outside world.

The perception does take place in Manas, but Manas has no clue what these objects are. It creates the code, but it is clueless about what it is. It has no knowledge about the object. Manas needs help, and it therefore passes on the input signals to Buddhi for decoding.

Step 2: Buddhi Knows

Buddhi is the intelligent part of the mind, and it has Power of Knowing. It can know anything and everything in this universe and beyond. It has that decoding power. Power of Knowing is within Buddhi. If any object waveform comes in the presence of Buddhi, Buddhi will know what that object waveform represents.

Buddhi is like the Central Processing Unit (CPU) of the human being. The input signal comes to the CPU to be processed. In the same way, the input signal from Manas comes to Buddhi to be processed. We saw that the input waveforms coming from Manas are lacking the object knowledge. Buddhi adds the object knowledge to the waveform. With this knowledge, the mental waveform knows its identity. The mental waveform knows the object it represents. It knows it is a tree. It knows it is music. The object waveform is now made of knowledge. Knowledge is the substratum of the waveform. Not easy to grasp, but this is true.

We can say that Buddhi is the most powerful CPU with parallel processing capability. It can handle so many different input stimuli from the five sense organs and from the internal organs simultaneously. It adds knowledge for every waveform forwarded by Manas.

It awaits further action from Ahamkara on some of the object vrittis (not all) which have come from the five sense organs. In many of the routine vrittis from sense organs and all the vrittis from the internal organs, Buddhi knows what action to take. Over time, it has learned what action is to be taken, so it can undertake these actions automatically. These actions can also be described as subconscious–the actions of which you are not aware, but which continue to happen almost automatically.

Buddhi is a self-learning CPU, which learns and knows how to handle different actions. Like the CPU which is connected to output devices in a computer, Buddhi is also connected to output devices like the five organs of action–hand, feet, mouth, etc., and all the internal organs.

Step 3: Ahamkara Interferes

After Buddhi processes the object waveform from Manas to a known mental waveform (called vritti), this object vritti is now presented to Ahamkara.

Ahamkara means "I-Maker"; it is the sense of "I-ness" within you. It is not the Self in Self-Awareness, but it is a vritti and thinks it is the "self." It masquerades as the Self and Ahamkara is just a mental waveform, "I" or "self."

The vrittis–from the five senses and also from Chitta, the memory bank of past events–are presented to Ahamkara. You have object vrittis coming in from your senses. Ahamkara now must interact with these vrittis. We saw that Buddhi could handle parallel processing by handling multiple inputs at the same time. The interaction between Ahamkara and this wide range of object vrittis happens only one at a time. You can only have one experience at a time. So, Ahamkara interacts with only one vritti at a time and it gives "my-ness" to the vritti.

How does Ahamkara choose between the different vrittis which are available? There are two ways this can happen.

1. Ahamkara chooses a vritti.
2. A vritti chooses Ahamkara.

1. Ahamkara Chooses a Vritti: This is a willful action, where Ahamkara deliberately chooses one of the object vrittis for further action. It is a noisy street, but you stop to admire a beautiful flower. Your Ahamkara did not focus on all the noise; it deliberately chose the flower vritti to admire. This is a complicated process, and many factors can make Ahamkara choose one of the vrittis available.

There are many instances where Ahamkara does not choose any of the available vrittis but instructs Buddhi to locate another vritti which will meet its current requirements and desires. For example, you have a desire to eat ice cream but there is no ice cream in the house. Buddhi then instructs Manas to go to the car and drive to an ice cream shop to satisfy this desire.

2. A Vritti Chooses Ahamkara: It must be understood that each of the vrittis is conscious and has a life of its own. We have seen that most of these object vrittis are provided by the sense organs. These sense organs have their own likes and dislikes. The eyes want to see beautiful things, the tongue to taste delicious food, and so on. We have all had experiences where our sense organs have "hijacked" Ahamkara, as though forcing it to take a particular action against its will. The doctor has told us that any sweets can be harmful to our health. We are fully aware of this, but when we see a delicious sweet our hands reach out against our will, and we put it into our mouths. In such instances the vritti dominates and manipulates Ahamkara to undertake an action.

Vritti Modification: It is important to understand that whenever Ahamkara interacts with an object vritti, it will modify the object vritti according to its likes and dislikes. In Vedanta this is called raga (like) and dvesha (dislike). We have seen earlier that Ahamkara is also a mental waveform, and when it interacts with or is superimposed on the object vritti, the resultant vritti is a vritti modified by raga and dvesha. If you like something, you will modify the vritti differently than when you dislike something.

The bottom line is that Ahamkara modifies the incoming vritti according to its own disposition. If Ahamkara is feeling angry, it will react to the vritti differently than it will if it is feeling happy and peaceful. Ahamkara or ego adds a personal touch to the interacting object vritti. In fact, it also adds the "I-ness" to the vritti. Ahamkara can become attached or addicted to certain vrittis because they give it momentary happiness, and it wants to repeat these moments of happiness.

Step 4: Sakshi Witnesses

This is the last step in the process. We have seen that Self-Awareness has Self, Subject, Object, and Intelligence.

We have seen in this step-by-step process that the object waveform in Manas combines with the Intelligence in Buddhi, and the modification of this object vritti by Ahamkara or ego. To have awareness, the only missing element is the Subject with Power of the Knower.

When the modified object vritti from Ahamkara combines with the Sakshi, you have something "magical"–you have awareness of the experience. You have awareness of the experience because all the elements of awareness are now present. Till we reached Step 4, the object viewed was a waveform or vritti. When the last missing element of the subject encounters the object vritti, the waveform collapses to create the experience of gross objects around you. The Sakshi or Subject is the one which witnesses this experience.

The current experience of reading this essay, or any other experience, must go through this step-by-step process to create Awareness of any experience.

This four-step process is how the mind functions for all experiences. Let us discuss some examples to reinforce this concept.

Example 1–Scientist at Work: A scientist is working hard to prove a hypothesis. His current level of knowledge is far from the goal. The object vrittis of the current level of knowledge pass through Manas and Buddhi. The scientist's Ahamkara interacts with these object vrittis and modifies the vrittis according to what the scientist thinks is the best way to solve the problem. When the Subject or Sakshi collapses this updated waveform, the scientist will find that he has gained more knowledge, but the goal is not yet in sight. The scientist keeps repeating this cycle till, one day, Ahamkara modifies the object vritti to match the vritti for proving the hypothesis. When this object vritti collapses, the scientist has gained the knowledge to solve this hypothesis.

Every object, concept, idea in this universe has a pre-defined vritti. Ahamkara in every person keeps trying to modify the incoming object vritti. When the modified vritti matches any of the pre-defined vrittis, then this wave collapses and the person gains knowledge for that object, concept, or idea. This is how our minds work while gaining knowledge.

Example 2–Subconscious Driving: When we are driving, many times our mind is engrossed in some thought, but when the traffic light changes to red, we automatically stop the car. We sometimes wonder how this happens. The red-light vritti from Manas is presented to Buddhi. Over years of driving, Buddhi has learned that one stops at the red light. So even without the involvement of Ahamkara, Buddhi on its own instructs the output device (the feet) to stop the car. Buddhi is always self-learning and can manage the day-to-day activity at a subconscious level while the ego is not involved.

States of the Mind

All experiences happen only in the mind. The following are the three states for having experiences:

- Waking State
- Dream State
- Deep Sleep State

It is not possible to have any experience outside these three states. Let us discuss each one of them in a little detail.

Waking State Experiences

In the waking state, we experience the external world through the five sense organs. The four-step process explained earlier is very much applicable in the waking state. The vrittis from the five sense organs pass through Manas to Buddhi. They are modified by Ahamkara and, when combined with Sakshi, the vrittis collapse to give you all the experiences of your waking state. These experiences are nothing but Awareness with forms superimposed on it.

In the waking state, the experience of objects is made up of the external world perceived through the five sense organs. In Vedanta, the entity (Atma) which is experiencing the waking state is called Vishva. Vishva in Sanskrit means “the world.”

Waking State Atma = Vishva

In the waking state, all the three bodies are available to generate experiences:

- Causal Body
- Subtle Body
- Gross Body

Waking State = Atma (Vishva) + Causal Body + Subtle Body + Gross Body

Dream State Experiences

Vedanta teaches us that **all** the experiences and impressions we have during the waking state are stored in Chitta. As discussed earlier, Chitta is the storage device of the mind.

In the dream state, the five sense organs are no longer active because we don’t experience the external world in the dream state. Manas with Power of the Known (objects), Buddhi with Power of Knowing, and Ahamkara, Sakshi with Power of the Knower, however, are all available in the dream state. The same four-step process is applicable in the dream state.

1. Manas, instead of getting the input waveforms from the five sense organs, gets them from Chitta. The experiences we have during the waking state play out during the dream state.
2. These input waveforms move on to Buddhi, so that the knowledge of the waveforms can be gained. Some of the logical circuitry of Buddhi is inactive in the dream state. We can infer this because the dreams we have can be quite illogical and unreasonable; they do not reflect the reality of the waking state.
3. Object vrittis from Buddhi are presented to Ahamkara, which will modify them based on its likes and dislikes.
4. Finally, with the interaction of the vrittis with Sakshi, the object vrittis collapse, so that we can experience a dream while sleeping.

The experiences in the dream state are quite different from the experiences in the waking state. There are no inputs from the sense organs. For this reason, the profile of Atma in the waking state is different from the profile in the dreaming state. Vedanta teaches that Atma in the dream state is called Taijasa. Taijasa in Sanskrit means "light" or "illumination"–the illumination of the dreams.

Dream state Atma = Taijasa

Dream State = Atma (Taijasa) + Subtle Body + Causal Body

The Gross Body is missing in the dream state; it is not available to the dreamer. The dreamer has no clue about the Gross Body.

Deep Sleep State Experiences

In deep sleep, dreams are not available to the experiencer. In the deep sleep state, the four components of the mind–Manas, Buddhi, Ahamkara, and Sakshi–are still available. Also, the four steps still take place in the deep sleep state.

Both the five sense organs and the bank of experiences stored in Chitta are inactive in deep sleep. They do not operate in deep sleep. We saw earlier that ignorance is the cause of the Mind. Manas is filled with ignorance. In deep sleep there are no waveforms as the five sense organs and Chitta are inactive. What is left is only ignorance. This ignorance alone is present in Manas in deep sleep.

1. This ignorance moves into Buddhi. Buddhi knows this is ignorance.
2. This ignorance is presented to Ahamkara. Ahamkara normally adds raga (like) or dvesha (dislike) to the object vritti. But in this instance, it cannot do anything because it is dealing with ignorance. You have no likes or dislikes because this is ignorance, so you have no clue what it is!
3. When Sakshi encounters ignorance, it collapses ignorance to create an experience of ignorance.

Experience of ignorance means you do not experience anything. In the waking and dream states, the experience or thoughts keep changing, and the bliss is momentary–it lasts for the duration of the experience. In deep sleep there are no changing thoughts, there is only one continuous experience of ignorance. This means that during deep sleep we have one continuous experience of bliss. When we wake up or return to the dream state, this continuous bliss is gone. Vedanta teaches us that this bliss in deep sleep is like the bliss experienced by SatChitAnanda, except that in deep sleep we are ignorant of this fact, while SatChitAnanda is fully aware of this bliss. That is the only difference.

Deep Sleep Atma = Prajna

The Atma which experiences ignorance in deep sleep is called Prajna. Deep sleep is a mass of ignorance.

Deep Sleep State = Atma (Prajna) + Causal Body

In the deep sleep state, there is no Subtle body nor Gross Body nor physical body. There exists only the Causal Body which is made up of ignorance.

Gunas (Qualities) of the Mind

Guna means "quality" or "characteristic" of the mind. Vedanta teaches that the mind has three types of gunas:

- Rajas Guna–Passion, Motion
- Tamas Guna–Inertia, Darkness
- Sattva Guna–Bliss, Goodness

The mind is a combination of these three gunas. Sometimes one of the gunas dominates, while at other times another guna will take over. Whenever we act, one of the gunas is used to complete the action. It is not wrong to say that the gunas are the driving force for action.

If you review the four-step process in the functioning of the mind, the guna comes into play when Ahamkara interacts with the object vrittis. We saw that Ahamkara either likes or dislikes the object vritti. This like and dislike by Ahamkara will depend on the disposition of Ahamkara at that moment. If Ahamkara is filled with tamas guna at that moment, it will show signs of laziness and lethargy. If Ahamkara has rajas guna, it will show activity by wanting new and a variety of sensations. This will drive action or inaction.

All the three gunas are there for everyone, but the amount of each guna varies. The rajas guna will be dominant for an extrovert or go-getter. The tamas guna will be stronger for a depressed person. The sattva guna will be stronger for a spiritual person. These personality traits will be applicable to Ahamkara of a person.

Let us briefly examine how the gunas apply when Ahamkara interacts with the object vrittis.

Rajas Guna: The rajas guna will not allow Ahamkara to sit still; it always wants action; it wants new objects with which to interact. It is restless; when one action is complete, it will choose another action to complete. This person will not sit idle. A person with rajas guna has many desires and wants to satisfy all the desires which come up. This requires Ahamkara to interact with object vrittis on a continuous basis. When rajas guna is dominant, a lot of activity takes place in the mind. There is nothing wrong with having the trait of rajas, but the question is that all this continuous action does not guarantee happiness and peace. If this is the case, then many actions would be a waste of time and effort.

Tamas Guna: This is the other side of the scale as compared to rajas guna. Here Ahamkara is inactive; it does not undertake action. A range of object vrittis are presented to Ahamkara by Buddhi, but Ahamkara does not want to interact with any of them. Ahamkara is lazy and lethargic. This leads to inactivity, which is a characteristic of tamas.

In such situations, it is possible that some of the dominant object vrittis can force Ahamkara to undertake an action to satisfy the object vrittis' own agenda. This action could be wrong and against Dharma. Over time, this Ahamkara would be at the complete mercy of these dominant object vrittis.

Ahamkara in tamas guna is very weak and is prone to inactivity and wrong actions.

Sattva Guna: In rajas we saw that the focus of Ahamkara is on the object vrittis. Instead, if you focus Ahamkara on SatChitAnanda within you, this approach can bring about a radical change. Compassion, goodness, forgiveness, and other positive qualities will come forward. Interaction with the object vrittis will continue, but you will follow Dharma or do the right thing in any action you take. Everyone has this sattva guna within them, but the question is, how dominant is this in our day-to-day activity? The profile of the sattva guna can be improved if you can train your mind adequately. This is our next topic for discussion.

Control of the Mind

Controlling the mind is comparable to trying to control the wind. It is not easy. Just try to focus and hold onto a single thought. You will find this quite difficult, for within no time the mind will have drifted to another series of thoughts. You may apply your will to control your thoughts in your mind, but success is only momentary.

In the functioning of the mind, as we have discussed on many occasions, the object vrittis, which have their own agenda, take over Ahamkara. This way, Ahamkara is unable to apply itself in controlling these thoughts. Desires which pop up in the mind can also take over the mind. Desire for wealth, desire for happiness, desire for pleasure are powerful forces which can drive the mind to action. Ahamkara is trapped and is unable to control these desires. If you do not satisfy these desires, you have anger, frustration, jealousy. This is an unending circle we face in our lives.

So, we see that it is not easy to control the mind. It is a major problem. The mind is the problem. What is the solution? Vedanta teaches that the solution is also the mind. The only tool we have is the mind. Basically, we must purify our minds, so that the knowledge of Self as SatChitAnanda starts to sink in. This purification of the mind is important and is the only way to control the mind. Sri Shankaracharya taught the following steps, which will help us in this purification process.

1. Viveka–Discrimination
2. Vairagya–Dispassion
3. Sama–Quietude
4. Dama–Self-control
5. Titiksha–Tolerance
6. Samadhana–A mind that understands correctly
7. Mumuksutva–Desire for freedom

Let us discuss how these steps can help us in purifying and controlling our minds.

1. Viveka–Discrimination

Viveka means "discrimination," but in Vedanta it means the discrimination between the Real and Unreal. We think the world is real, but Vedanta teaches us that this is wrong, and this misconception is the root cause of our suffering.

The definition of Real, according to Vedanta, is that it must pass the test of the three time periods–past, present, and future. It should be unchanging in all three time periods. If an object undergoes any change in any one of the three time periods, then that object is not Real, it is Unreal. Our body was born a few decades ago and will perish in the future, so it does not meet the requirement of Real. This applies to any object in the universe; it was not always available in the past and will perish in the future. Even this universe was born 13.7 billion years ago; it was not available before that, and we know it will come to an end in the future.

So, nothing in this universe is Real, everything is Unreal. Everything we perceive and experience is Unreal. So, the question is–where is the Real stuff? This must be discovered. We have to find out and realize what is Real. As we have discussed, Awareness is the underlying reality of any experience. It is the substratum of any experience. This Awareness is the only Real stuff, everything else is Unreal. This Awareness has been there in the past and will be there in the future. This Awareness is unborn, unchanging, uncreated, and is the only Real thing and provides continuous bliss and happiness.

We have also discussed earlier that Self is nothing but Awareness, and Awareness is nothing but Self. The "I" within you is the only Real thing in this universe, everything else is Unreal.

This understanding can come only by applying viveka or discrimination on a continuous basis to all our experiences.

2. Vairagya–Dispassion

Vairagya translates as "dispassion" or "detachment." Vairagya is born out of viveka. Once you understand what is Real and what is Unreal, your approach to the unreal objects and experiences in this universe will undergo a change. You need dispassion and detachment toward objects and experiences of the world. The question is how to develop this dispassion and detachment.

The best way to start is to understand the value and function of all the objects and experiences with which we interact. We like ice cream, and we think this ice cream gives us happiness. If you look at the ingredients of ice cream, you will not find happiness listed there. So, from where does the happiness come? We think the ice cream provides us with happiness. What if we have a bad throat? The ice cream will not give us any happiness then–it will make us sicker! The happiness is within us, but we think the happiness comes from the ice cream. This wrong conclusion is the source of the problem. By applying vairagya, we can reach the proper understanding that ice cream is not the source of happiness.

People have a strong conviction that money and wealth provide happiness. There is no doubt that if you want to survive in this world, you need money. You cannot do without money. Money has an inherent value which will allow you to buy and sell goods, but happiness is not a quality of money. Money can be a source of unhappiness too. When you spend money, you feel sad. If money is lost in the stock market, it creates unhappiness and anger. Money is money; happiness, unhappiness, or sadness are our superimposition on money.

The same logic can be applied for all objects and experiences. We must learn to understand the actual value of any object or experience, and not add our own superimposition or commentary.

Vairagya does not mean that we give up objects we like or, conversely, run away from our responsibilities. Vairagya means understanding that the world and its objects are incapable of providing permanent peace and happiness. We must interact with objects with that attitude and approach. You should see this limitation again and again, every time you encounter any object or experience. This constant practice is important to help develop vairagya in our daily lifestyle.

3. Sama–Quietude

Sama means "a quiet mind." Sama is born out of vairagya. When you have understood vairagya and can implement it whenever you interact with an object, this will mean these objects do not trouble you anymore.

If you want a certain thing in life and you do not obtain it, you might be frustrated and irritated. With the attitude of vairagya, it does not matter if the desire is fulfilled or not. It is okay either way. This does not mean inaction but the acceptance of the outcome. This approach gives a peace of mind, which is called sama. With this quiet mind, it is possible to interact with anything in the world and not be affected by the outcome. You take all objects and experiences at their face value.

4. Dama–Self-control

Dama means "self-control." You need to control the five sense organs and the five organs of action. If these organs are drawn toward objects of the world, it means you are drawn away from your true nature of Awareness. You would need to apply your willpower to willfully restrain the sense organs from moving toward sense objects. If you truly want to avoid eating harmful sweets, then, when walking in front of a sweet shop, restrain your eyes by not looking at the sweets, restrain your hands and feet by not walking into the shop.

Sama is effortless and is born out of understanding. Dama requires willpower and willful restraint. If you do not have sama and are unable to cultivate vairagya, then you require dama or self-control.

5. Titiksha–Tolerance

Titiksha means "tolerance," enduring any pain or hardship without complaining about it. This does not mean you do not try to change the situation. You must. If it is not possible to change the situation, you should accept the pain with tolerance. On a cold winter day, if the window has been kept open, it does not mean you accept this by suffering the cold–you should go and shut the window. However, if you continue feeling cold even after you shut the window, you just tolerate it and accept the situation with equanimity. This attitude of equanimity in both good and bad situations is titiksha.

6. Samadhana– A mind that understands correctly

Samadhana could mean meditation, but the correct interpretation would be–a mind which is always "well placed" under all circumstances. The idea is to keep directing Ahamkara toward our true nature of Awareness–SatChitAnanda. This is not easy but requires constant practice. For example, your boss makes some nasty remarks. In such a situation, instead of getting angry, you try and think that you are SatChitAnanda, you are full and complete. If you have this feeling, then you will be able to forgive your boss for making those nasty remarks and understand that maybe he is having a rough day. This attitude keeps the mind in the right place. The more you practice, the better the chance of achieving this goal of purification of your mind.

7. Mumuksutva–Desire for freedom

Mumuksutva means the desire for Moksha, to be free from bondage or suffering. There is no denying that the goal for everyone in life is to have continuous happiness. We want to be free from suffering in our day-to-day life. Vedanta teaches us that when Ahamkara identifies with the body, mind, and external world, we are bound to go through cycles of happiness and suffering. We have seen that none of the objects of the world are a source of permanent happiness. We think they are and this wrong identification only leads to bondage and unhappiness. We need to train our mind to identify with Self-Awareness or SatChitAnanda. We can do this if we have a desire to achieve this goal. Instead of having the desire for external objects, you have to have the desire for SatChitAnanda. Focusing on this goal will take us a long way in controlling the mind.

The achievement of this lofty goal is that you could be on the path of enlightenment or Moksha. You fully realize and discover your true nature of Self-Awareness. Once you achieve this, you will treat the body and mind as any other external object and watch the body and mind like another character in a movie of life. You will know that the pain belongs to the body and not you; you will realize that sadness belongs to the mind and not you. Nothing will affect you. This is the state of enlightenment. Vedanta teaches us that if you can achieve this state of mind, you will not be born again. The cycle of bondage will be over. The first step in this direction is to have the desire to achieve this goal. In fact, this should be the only goal. This attitude is called mumuksutva.

6 | Three Forms of Reality

If you are a student of Vedanta, you are taught that SatChitAnanda or Brahman is the only Reality. It is explained that SatChitAnanda is our innermost core, and Brahman is the underlying reality of the universe. With the powerful mahavakya ("major sentence") "Tat Tvam Asi" ("That You Are"), Vedanta makes a connection between our inner core SatChitAnanda and Brahman. That (Brahman) You (SatChitAnanda) Are. In this way, Vedanta explains that Brahman and SatChitAnanda are the same. There exists no dichotomy between the two and they are identical. Your innermost core and the underlying reality of the universe is the same. There is only One Reality.

Both SatChitAnanda and Self-Awareness are identical. Awareness is a much easier way to understand our inner core. Please read the essay "SatChitAnanda vs. Self-Awareness" for a detailed explanation.

Vedanta teaches us that SatChitAnanda or Brahman is the only Reality. This essay shows that SatChitAnanda and Brahman are part of Awareness. It is therefore correct to conclude that Awareness is really the only Reality. Awareness is our innermost core and Awareness is also the underlying Reality of the universe. Does that mean that Awareness of the inner core is different from the Awareness of the universe "out there"? No, they are identical, but they are different forms of the same Awareness. Awareness is One, but there are different forms. Can there be different forms of the same single Reality?

Yes, the best example is H_2O. H_2O is one, but it comes in three different forms–liquid, vapor, and solid. In liquid form it is called water, in vapor form it is called steam, and in solid form it is called ice. H_2O remains the same in all the three different forms. In the same way, Awareness is the only Reality, but it comes in the following three different forms:

1. Self-Awareness
2. Reflected Awareness
3. Refracted Awareness

The Bible touches upon these three forms with the famous Trinity quote, “the Father, the Son, and the Holy Spirit.” These are three forms of the same reality. An equivalent statement from Vedanta could be “Brahman, Ishvara, and Guru.” Not any type of guru, but a pure self-realized Guru. These three types can be co-related with the three forms mentioned. SatChitAnanda is Self-Awareness. Ishvara is another name for Reflected Awareness, and Guru and Refracted Awareness are identical.

The focus of this essay is to explain these connections and the three forms of Reality in more detail.

Self-Awareness and SatChitAnanda

A simple question: are you aware of reading this essay? Are you aware of your surroundings? Are you aware of any background noise? If your answer is no, then you will not experience anything. You will not know you are reading this essay; you will not be aware of your surroundings; you will not be aware of the background noise. In fact, without Awareness, you will not be aware of anything of the external universe.

When this Awareness interacts with this essay, you have the experience of reading this essay. Awareness has intelligence and the power of reading within itself. When Awareness interacts with the background noise, you have the experience of hearing the background noise. That is because the power of hearing is part of Awareness. Without Awareness, we would not know any objects which are perceived by all the five sense organs–eyes, ears, nose, tongue, and skin. Objects from the sensory organs must encounter Awareness, and only then can we experience the object in its concrete and viable form.

As an analogy, let us think of the sun. If there is no light emanating from the sun, the entire world will be dark; things become visible only when there is light. In the same way, when any form encounters the light of Awareness, we become aware of it. If there is no light of Awareness, you will perceive nothing, not even the sun.

Awareness has the intelligence to connect with a form present in the mind and fill the object with Awareness. As we have discussed in earlier essays,

Awareness is made of Subject, Object, Intelligence, and the three powers–Knower, Known, and Knowing.

- Awareness = Subject + Object + Intelligence
- Power of Awareness = Power of Knower + Power of Known + Power of Knowing

Subject, Object, Intelligence, and the three powers are not something outside in the world–they are within Awareness and they alone make up Awareness. Wherever there is Awareness, there must be present Subject, Object, and Intelligence with all the three powers.

What Is Self-Awareness?

Our inner core is full, complete, and it stands alone. For Awareness to be full and complete, it must be Self-Aware. Self-Awareness means that "Awareness is aware of Awareness."

In Self-Awareness, the subject is Awareness and the object is Awareness. Awareness plays the role of subject and object. In other words, both the subject and object are the same. There is only one entity, which is non-dual. This complete, self-standing Self-Awareness is our inner core. There is no separation between the subject and object. Even Power of the Knower (subject/witness) is the same as Power of the Known (object-making ability). Self-Awareness is one–non-dual and homogenous. It is Self-Shining.

This Self-Shining Awareness is like a bulb of Awareness, and it is our inner core. It is not dependent on anything else, and it generates its own light of Awareness.

Self-Awareness is non-dual, homogenous, and it has many inherent characteristics.

- It is Formless.
- It is Unchanging.
- It is Unborn.
- It has the three powers of Awareness–the power of knower, known, and knowing.

SatChitAnanda is the name given to this inner core of Self-Awareness. This inner core is present in every living being. So, it is present within you, me, and everyone. This Self-Awareness just shines like a bulb of

Awareness, and it does not do anything except radiate Awareness. Nothing affects Self-Awareness; it is independent of everything. It is always at peace. Peace is its inherent nature. Because Self-Awareness does not do anything, all the characteristics mentioned are lying dormant within Self-Awareness.

Reflected Awareness and Ishvara

If our nature and inner core is Self-Awareness, why don't we know it, why don't we feel it? The simple answer is that we are ignorant of our inner core. Ignorance has the power to cover Self-Awareness. When we forget who we really are, ignorance pops up and covers our inner core. Ignorance is like a veil covering Awareness.

Self-Awareness does not do anything; it just keeps shining. When this Self-Awareness is covered by ignorance, it gets reflected in this ignorance.

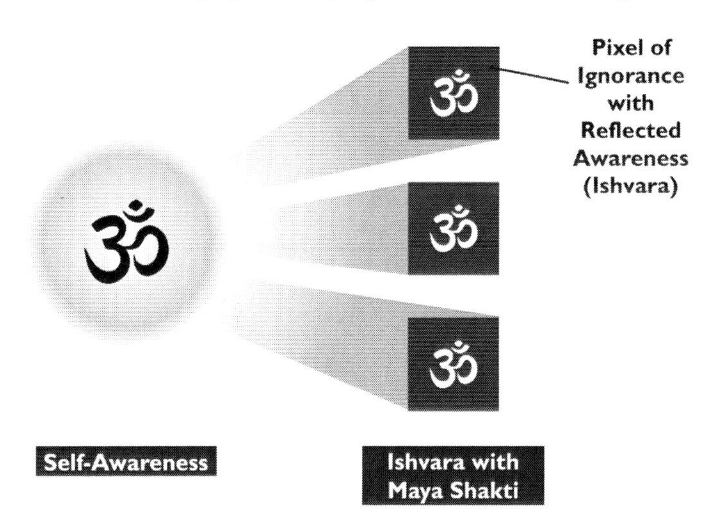

Ignorance is like a mirror in which reflection takes place. What you get then is Reflected Awareness. When the Sun is reflected in a mirror, you still have the Sun, and you also have a reflected Sun. This is exactly what happens here. You have SatChitAnanda, the non-dual Self-Awareness, and the Reflected Awareness. This Reflected Awareness is called Ishvara.

- It is quite strange to know that our ignorance is the cause of Ishvara, which is Reflected Awareness. If there was no ignorance, there would be no Reflected Awareness, and then there would be no Ishvara either. If there was no ignorance, the only thing present would be Brahman, the Self-Shining Self-Awareness. So, **our** ignorance is the cause of Ishvara.
- Even if there is Reflected Awareness, nothing happens to the non-dual Self-Awareness or SatChitAnanda. It will continue to shine, irrespective of whether there is ignorance or there is no ignorance. This is like the sun, which will shine even if it is cloudy or night. Nothing can stop the sun from shining. Similarly, Self-Awareness will continue to shine in both situations–ignorance and no ignorance.
- It must be understood that in the presence of ignorance, there is no effect on Reflected Awareness. Reflected Awareness remains pure and unaffected. This does seem counterintuitive. It would be reasonable to assume that ignorance would rub off a little on Reflected Awareness or Ishvara. Then again, we know Ishvara is pure, limitless, and just cannot have any ignorance. How should we understand this? The classic example that can be narrated here is, suppose you pour water in a red glass bottle. The water will appear to be red. It seems that the redness of the bottle has affected the water. Our ignorance can lead to this conclusion. If you have proper knowledge, you will know that the water in the bottle is always colorless, and the red color of the bottle has no effect on the water. With this logic we can understand that Ignorance has no effect on Reflected Awareness, and Ishvara is pure and limitless.
- Ignorance has two sides–an input side and an output side. Reflected Awareness appears on the input side of ignorance. We will discuss the output side of ignorance in the next section.

We have seen that Self-Awareness is non-dual, in which Self is both Subject and Object. Unfortunately, because of our ignorance, we have forgotten that our inner core is non-dual and we are both the subject and the object. Since we no longer know that we are both the subject and the object, it simply means that there is a separation of the subject being "in here" and the object being "out there." Ignorance converts the non-duality into the duality of the subject "in here" and the object "out there." Ignorance has that power.

In the non-dual Self-Awareness, the power behind the subject is Power of the Knower, and the power behind the object is Power of the Known. In non-duality, the subject and object are the same. Therefore, logically, Power of the Knower is the same as Power of the Known. They are homogenous with no separation. This is what happens in non-dual Self-Awareness or Brahman. We have just seen that because of ignorance, the subject and object separate, creating duality. With this separation, even Power of the Knower and Power of the Known get separated. They are no longer one entity; Power of the Knower and Power of the Known appear as two separate entities in Reflected Awareness. Even the third power, Power of Knowing, is available in Reflected Awareness. Each of these three powers of Awareness is very much active in Ishvara.

Vedanta teaches us that Maya Shakti is the power or force behind the creation and intelligence of the universe. Power of the Knower, Power of the Known, and Power of Knowing are now available in Reflected Awareness. These three powers are nothing but Maya Shakti as mentioned in Vedanta.

Maya Shakti = Power of Knower + Power of Known + Power of Knowing

Maya Shakti is within Reflected Awareness, and Ishvara wields this Maya Shakti to operate and control this universe. Maya Shakti lies dormant within Self-Awareness, within the Self-Shining bulb of Awareness. Due to ignorance, this Maya Shakti becomes active within Reflected Awareness. The nature of Awareness remains the same; Reflected Awareness or Ishvara is a different form of Awareness. In this form, Reflected Awareness wields the power of Maya Shakti to create, control, and manage the universe. In Reflected Awareness, Self-Awareness becomes Ishvara.

Refracted Awareness and Guru

In the earlier section, we saw that Ishvara as Reflected Awareness is on the input side of ignorance. In this section, we will discuss the output side of ignorance. This is the side where the Guru functions. In the essay "Ignorance Decoded," we have given a detailed analysis of Ignorance. Here are a few highlights.

Pixel of Ignorance

It is important to understand the process of Knowledge. The lack of Knowledge (Ignorance) shows that there are different degrees of ignorance. These play a central role in our existence.

There is a knowledge-ignorance profile of objects. This depends on the knowledge/ignorance we have of the different objects. To this you must also add the knowledge profile of the Self. This spectrum can be broken down into countless parts, and each part has a different amount of Ignorance. An enlightened person will have 100% knowledge of the Self, while a completely ignorant person will have 0% knowledge or 100% ignorance.

In this complicated knowledge-ignorance profile, there are a countless number of "pixels of ignorance." Each pixel of ignorance has its own unique mix of ignorance and knowledge. Each pixel of ignorance represents a single living being with his/her own knowledge-ignorance profile. There are countless living beings and each living being has

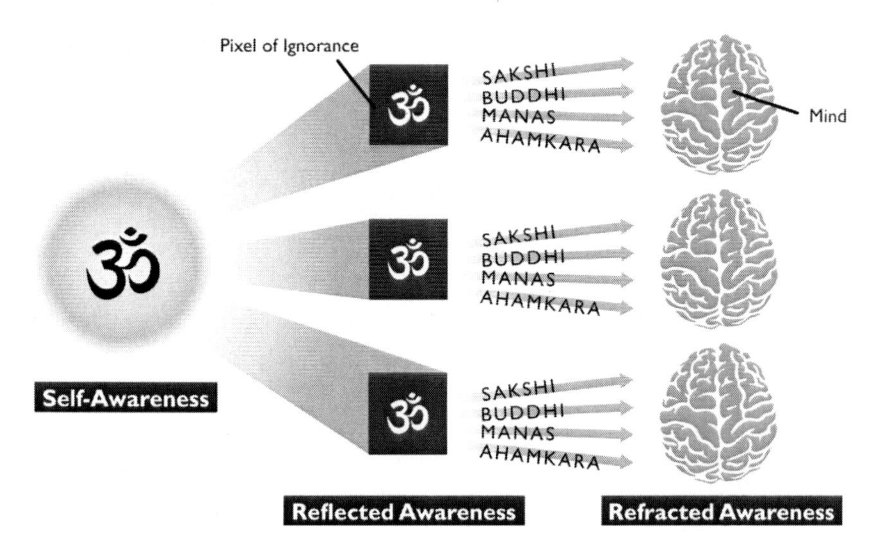

his/her own pixel of ignorance. You have a pixel of ignorance and I have a pixel of ignorance and, in the same way, every living being has their own unique pixel of ignorance.

We have seen that on the input side of ignorance, Reflected Awareness is present with duality, with separate subject, object, and intelligence. This Reflected Awareness or Ishvara makes the pixel conscious and sentient. When this pixel of ignorance interacts with Reflected Awareness, it breaks up Self-Awareness into four parts.

In Self-Awareness, Self = Subject = Object = Intelligence

It is like refraction. Place a prism in front of a ray of light and we can see the seven different colors on the other side. In the same way, the ignorance of the Self within the pixel refracts Reflected Awareness into the following four different components.

- Manas–the home of the Object
- Buddhi–the home of the Intelligence
- Sakshi–the home of the Subject
- Ahamkara–the home of the self

These four components make up the mind. The creation of the mind is the output side of the pixel of ignorance. The mind is part of the Subtle Body. So, the ignorance of the Self has that power to create the mind.

Mind = Refracted Awareness + Ignorance

There are countless pixels of ignorance–one for each individual living being. This refraction takes place in each pixel, and thereby countless minds are created. Each mind thus created will be different; it will depend on the knowledge–ignorance profile for each pixel. The simple calculation is this: the greater the ignorance, the less efficient the mind.

A sattvic mind will have no ignorance. In Sanskrit, sattvic means “pure.” This means a pure mind with no Ignorance. This is the mind of a true guru. These days the term guru is overused, and it can mean a teacher or expert. In Vedanta, the term Guru is much more specific, it means a self-realized spiritual person with no Ignorance.

Guru’s Mind = Refracted Awareness (no Ignorance)

The Guru's mind with no Ignorance is no different from SatChitAnanda. Guru is SatChitAnanda in human form.

The Guru's mind has no Ignorance. What does this mean? It means that the Guru knows that his innermost core is Self-Awareness. He knows that it is his inherent nature. He knows he is full and complete, and he displays a higher quality of mind, knowledge, reflection, and freedom from materialistic desires. He is at peace with everything, good and bad. This state is permanent; it is not a fluctuating state. His mind is always immersed in Awareness. In fact, it is correct to say that the Guru has no mind; he has only Self-Awareness. The Guru abides in the source and has no need of the mind.

Almost every living being experiences duality–the subject "in here" and the object "out there." This is our daily experience. We have seen the ignorance of our non-dual nature of Self-Awareness leading to duality with the separation of the subject and the object. Since the Guru does not experience duality, does that mean that the Guru does not perceive the universe "out there"? That is incorrect; he perceives the world "out there," but experiences non-duality. The Guru perceives the world and knows it is part of the Self, which is his nature.

The Guru is not Ignorant; the Guru operates on the side of Refracted Awareness. He knows that his true nature is Self-Awareness. He has no confusion regarding this. Since the content of all the objects is Awareness, the Guru who is Self-Aware sees his true nature of Awareness in all the objects of the universe. He sees no difference between his own Self and all the objects "out there." He therefore sees non-duality everywhere in the universe. He sees all the forms of the objects, but he sees them as Awareness, as his own Self.

7 | Doctrine of Karma

Karma means action. The doctrine of Karma deals with the results of these actions. The technical word for the results of action is karma phala–fruit of our actions. Whenever we act, there can be any one of the four possible phalas (results):

- The result is as expected.
- The result is worse than expected.
- The result is better than expected.
- The result is totally different.

To explain this, my Guruji always gave the following example. You have to cross the road to catch your office bus. You cross the road and catch the bus–the result is as expected. You cross the road but miss the bus–the result is worse than expected. You cross the road but meet a friend who gives you a ride–the result is better than expected. While crossing the road you are hit by the bus, and you go to the hospital instead–the result is totally different.

These four options apply to all the actions we take. For every action we take, one of the four results will happen. Which one? Unfortunately, we have no clue which one of the four results will fructify. It is impossible to guess till the results of the action are known. It would seem there is a hidden variable which manages the results. There is something unknown which drives the karma phalas. What is that hidden variable which gives the fruit of our actions? Chapter 2, Verse 47 of the Bhagavad Gita explains this concept brilliantly. This is one of its most quoted verses.

karmaṇy-evādhikāras te mā phaleṣhu kadāchana
mā karma-phala-hetur bhūr mā te saṅgo 'stvakarmaṇi

You have authority or control over the action you do, but you have no authority or control over the results of the action.

This is a profound and universal truth. It is applicable to everyone and to every action we undertake. We can only act; we have no choice or control over the result. This sounds like an obvious statement to make. But how often do we undertake an action without any expectation of what the result will be?

The question is who decides or controls these results. The Bhagavad Gita teaches us that it is Ishvara or Bhagavan (God) who decides the results. Does that mean Ishvara is judgmental and uses His own likes and dislikes to pass judgment? The answer is No. Ishvara has a Will but it is unlike the human will; it has no ragas (likes) and dveshas (dislikes). Ishvara's Will is the Laws of Nature. Ishvara controls the universe through the Laws of Nature. Once these laws are set in motion, Ishvara does not do anything. The doctrine of Karma is part of these Laws. You are the karma karta (doer or agent of action), while Ishvara is the Karma Phala Daata (the giver of the results of action).

With this background, let us discuss the different aspects of the doctrine of Karma in the following four sections.

1. Understanding Karmas
2. Understanding Karma Phalas
3. Understanding Pending Karma Phalas
4. Exhausting the Sanchita Karmas

Understanding Karmas

It is obvious that "I am" or ego is the doer of all the karma/actions. It is important to understand how "I am" or ego performs karma and what we really mean by karma. It must be understood that **all** karmas happen in the Mind itself. This seems contradictory. It does appear that we perform action in the world "out there." As we have discussed in other essays, everything happens first in the subtle world. This subtle world is then manifested as the gross world.

To perform any karma we need a subject who does the action, and we also need an object on whom or which the action is performed. We have the "I am" or ego, the subject, and all the vrittis or mental waveforms representing different objects in Manas.

It is part of nature that when ego encounters the object vritti, the ego **MUST** make a response. All living beings are pre-programmed and compelled to make this response. It is part of their genetic makeup. This applies even to a single cell body. Put a drop of vinegar close to a cell, and the cell will be repulsed, and it will move away. Put a drop of liquid sugar, the single cell body will be attracted to the sweetness and move toward it. Basically, the ego of the cell is reacting to the object vritti. The ego of the cell either likes the situation or dislikes the situation.

This duality of like/dislike, attraction/repulsion, positive/ negative, good/bad is the underlying force that compels the "I am" or ego to do karmas. This logic applies to every living being, irrespective of what type of creature it is. Even human beings must react in the same manner to every situation. We cannot remain still.

Whenever the ego comes in touch with an object vritti, it cannot remain still, it must act. The response is either raga (like) or dvesha (dislike). This response by the ego is karma. **The interaction between ego and object is NOT karma; the response of "like" or "dislike" is karma**. Let us discuss some examples so that this point becomes clear.

- People think that when we talk it is karma. This is incorrect. Talking is natural and is a standard feature which comes with the body. The human body is meant to talk. However, it is only when you talk negatively or positively about anyone that you have done a bad or good karma.
- Walking is a natural action. There is no karma when you walk. However, while walking you see an insect and with purpose you squash it with your foot. The intentional squashing of the insect is karma. However, if without your knowing an insect comes under your foot, this is not karma because the ego is not involved.
- If you have ears, you are going to listen to things. For example, if you listen indifferently to all the chattering around you in the airport lounge, that is not karma; it is natural. However, if you get irritated by all the noise around you, that is karma.
- Watching the physical world outside is natural. If you are standing in front of a few people, you cannot say you do not want to see them. Seeing is natural, you have no power to stop this. However, if you make a judgment–what a horrible shirt someone

is wearing, or how nice this person is looking–these judgment calls are karmas.

The ego must be involved while doing a karma. We know we are doing karma on a continuous basis. It is only logical that anyone who does karma also owns that karma. We know that the ego is the doer of karmas, therefore "I am" is the owner of all the karmas. These karmas go into the "bank balance" of that person. As we shall see in the next section, the doer of the action which is ego should also face the consequence of the karma committed.

Understanding Karma Phalas

Any karma you perform, good or bad, must have a result. In Vedanta, this result is called karma phala (fruit). In science, an equivalent scenario would be Newton's Third Law of Motion, which says: *For every action, there is an equal and opposite reaction.* If you do any karma, it must have a reaction; this is the basic law of nature. If you rub your hand against the bark of a tree, the tree will rub back with equal intensity. If you do good actions or deeds, the reaction or results will be positive (punya karmas) and if you do bad karmas, the results will be negative (paapa karmas).

Good actions = Good results = Punya karmas

Bad actions = Bad results = Paapa karmas

The question can be asked, how do you define good and bad actions? This can be arbitrary. A surgeon with a knife can heal people by operating on them. A criminal with the knife can kill people. The surgeon uses a knife for a good action while a criminal uses a knife for a bad action. So, how do you decide between a good and bad action? Vedanta uses the following phrase, which is the gold standard to distinguish between good and bad actions.

Ahimsa Paramo Dharma–Non-violence is the highest moral virtue.

Non-violence does not mean only physical action. Even bad thoughts–thinking bad things about people and other objects–is part of ahimsa. Both physical and mental actions are part of this moral virtue. If you think about it, it is impossible to live without causing harm. You may give up eating meat, but even as a vegetarian you are causing harm to plants. The ideal goal is complete non-violence. Since this is impossible, the goal should be to minimize harm by all your actions. If any action has multiple choices, the best choice is the one which causes the least harm. Minimizing harm should be the driving force of all actions.

The doctrine of Karma as taught by Vedanta states that every karma must yield two types of results:

- **Seen Result (Drishta Phala):** Every karma has a Seen Result. If you do any karma, it will have an immediate result which can be seen or felt immediately.
- **Unseen Result (Adrishta Phala):** The same karma will also have a result which will be felt in the future. The result of the karma could be felt in a few seconds, 20 minutes later, next year, 20 years later, in this lifetime, or in a future lifetime. When this karma ripens, it will yield its fruit. When this will happen no one knows, but it will happen. You must reap what you sow. This concept is only logical and correct.

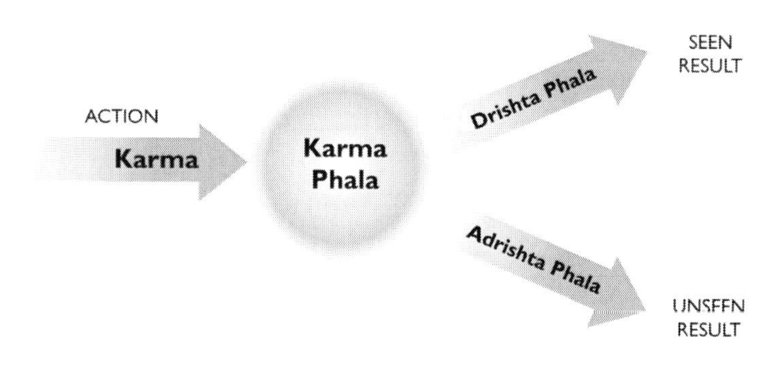

How should we understand this? When the ego interacts with the object vrittis in the mind, it modifies the object vrittis. This modification of the object vrittis is the Seen Result. It must be understood that the object vrittis are part of the cosmic waveform. This cosmic waveform is the total of all the possible object vrittis in the world.

When the ego modifies the object vrittis, the modification has a ripple effect within the cosmic waveform. This ripple circulates within the cosmic waveform, making changes. Some actions may make minor ripples, while other actions could cause major ripples. Squash an insect intentionally, it will cause a minor ripple in the cosmic waveform. But if a president or king starts an unprovoked war, this can cause a major ripple in the cosmic waveform. People dying, livelihoods destroyed. The ripples can last multiple years or decades. The unseen results of this action will take a much longer time to fructify.

The ripple could have a positive effect (punya) or negative effect (paapa) on the cosmic waveform. The cosmic waveform stores all these modifications. In the end, this ripple will come back to interact with the ego. When, no one knows. This is the Unseen Result.

Some Examples

- Let us say you give $100 to charity. The immediate Seen Result is that you are poorer by $100, but the Unseen Result is that you accumulated a punya karma and this will result in some type of favorable situation in the future.
- You get angry and insult your close friend. The Seen Result is that your friend starts to cry, and the Unseen Result is that you have accumulated a paapa karma and this will result in some type of negative situation in the future.
- You drop your reading glasses from 10 feet. The Seen Result is that the glasses start falling downward as per the Laws of Nature. The Unseen Result will be evident when the glasses hit the ground; they may or may not break. You are not sure until they hit the ground; the Unseen Result is delayed by a few seconds.

These pending unseen results are like your bank balance. Your bank balance will have all the pending results of good karmas and bad karmas which were done earlier. The bank balance includes pending karma phalas from this life and all your previous lives. Everyone has a balance of pending karmas which still must yield their fruit.

Good actions will result in punya karma phalas and bad actions will result in paapa karma phalas. This doctrine of Karma is the instrument which Ishvara uses to provide the results or fruit of your actions. The results you are getting now are based on the pending phalas of your past actions. They are not arbitrary. This is a Vedantic explanation of why bad things happen to good people and good things to bad people. It is because they are receiving the fruit of their past actions.

Understanding Pending Karma Phalas

Why are we reborn? The simple reason is that we have pending karmas. These karmas need their phala or results. These karmas cannot be left unfinished. The loop must be completed. All good or bad actions must face their consequences. If you do not receive the result in this life, the pending karma is carried over to a future life. The result to your action is a must. All action must achieve its unseen or adrishta phala. We are born again and again to face the good and bad results of actions done in the past.

You would think that the goal is to exhaust all the pending karmas. Is this possible? Impossible. We do exhaust karmas on a continuous basis, but then we are also creating new karmas awaiting results. In this way, the bank balance of pending karmas hardly changes. In fact, Vedanta teaches us that each one of us has an infinite number of karmas–an infinite number of punya and paapa karmas. This is because we have an infinite number of rebirths. Infinite rebirths is not an easy concept to understand. We will not discuss this subject now, as it is not the focus of this essay.

To exhaust the infinite karmas, you must live for infinite years. This is impossible. We all live only for a finite number of years. Therefore, we exhaust a finite number of karmas in one lifetime. The doctrine of Karma explains this concept by dividing the karmas into the following three groups:

1. **Sanchita Karmas**–Sanchita means "accumulated." This is the total of all the pending karmas collected over all the past lives. It is the storage for all the pending karmas. This storage is a mix of paapa and punya karmas. All these karmas are still awaiting their results.

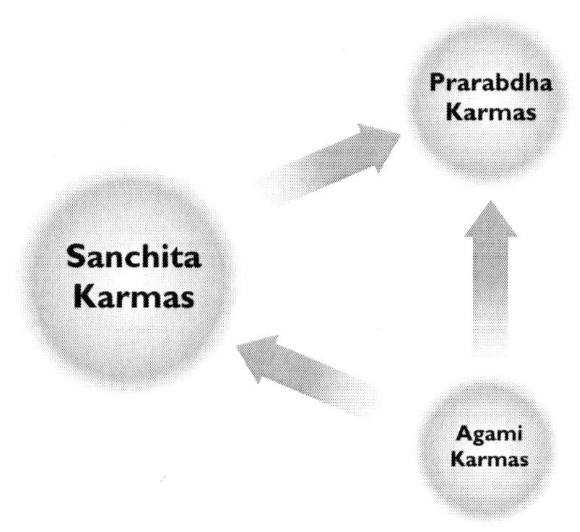

2. **Prarabdha Karmas**–Prarabdha means "that which has already begun." These karmas fructify in this lifetime. From the sanchita karmas a certain number of paapa and punya karmas are chosen. These karmas will be exhausted in the current lifetime. You will face the results of these karmas in this life. The selected karmas are placed in your Seed Body. As the Seed Body germinates and blossoms, these karmas will slowly but surely fructify. Our daily life is responding to these karmas. The happy times we enjoy are due to the past punya karmas, and the unhappiness and difficulties we face are because of the past paapa karmas.
   The ratio between the paapa and punya will vary from life to life. The greater the punya karmas, the easier and happier will be life. If the paapa karmas are dominant, life will be one big struggle. We can see that the prarabdha karmas are the driving force for the duration of one's life. Once the prarabdha karmas are exhausted, the person will die. After we die, there is still an infinite number of pending sanchita karmas. We are reborn with a new body to exhaust a new batch of karmas. When we exhaust this lot, we take up another body. This cycle is unending; the pending karmas will never be exhausted. We will continue this cycle of rebirths. The picture does look bleak and depressing.

3. **Agami Karmas**—While we are exhausting karmas continuously, we are also creating new karmas. The ego is acting every day, some good actions and some bad actions. The unseen results of these actions must happen. When, we do not know. Some of the unseen results will be felt in this lifetime itself. Other karmas will be added to your bank balance. They will be added to the pending sanchita karmas.

Exhausting the Sanchita Karmas

It is impossible to exhaust sanchita karmas. Even an infinite lifetime will not do the job. Does that mean we are doomed, with no possible solution to break this unending cycle? Fortunately, there is a solution. The teachings of Vedanta.

The ego is the doer of all the actions; it is the karma karta. Therefore, the results must be faced by the ego. The ego is the owner of the sanchita karmas. The ego cannot escape this fact. It must face the consequences of all its past karmas. What is the solution? How do we break this cycle? To explain this, my Guruji liked to give the example of Bill Gates, who has hundreds of billions of dollars. He writes a check for $10 every day, hoping to exhaust his account. With his vast bank balance, it is impossible to empty his bank balance with a check for $10 every day. The only solution is to disown the bank account and the bank balance. This way, the bank account does not belong to Bill Gates.

How does the ego disown the sanchita karmas? If you are a student of Vedanta, you will learn that there is the Real Self and ego. The Self is your innermost core; it is SatChitAnanda or Self-Awareness. It is non-dual, in which the Self is Subject and the Self is Object.

When we forget our true nature of being full and complete, the ego pops up. In the presence of ignorance, the Self appears to become the ego. This ego masquerades as the Real Self and lives with the world of forms and objects. This is the ego which accumulates the sanchita karmas. If you follow the teachings of Vedanta, you can remove the ignorance of your Real Self. By gaining knowledge, you become your Real Self. You become

Self-Realized. When you discover your true Self, the ego will disappear–like the snake which disappears when you discover that it is a rope.

The ego owns the sanchita karmas. If the ego is no longer there, the connection with the sanchita karmas is broken. If you are Self-Realized, there is no ego who must face the results of these pending karmas. The Real Self is full and complete. It does not act. It is like a witness to all the actions. It is impossible for the sanchita karmas to be passed on to the Real Self. Once the ego disappears, the bank account for the sanchita karmas is closed. There is no owner for the sanchita karmas.

What about the prarabdha karmas? Does the Self-Realized person face the prarabdha karmas, which are already fructifying in this lifetime? Yes, the body-mind complex will face the results, but the Self-Realized person has nothing to do with the body-mind complex. Yes, to an outsider it does seem as though the Self-Realized person is acting, but from the point of view of the Self-Realized person, he is not performing any action. He is just a witness to all the action.

8 | Ignorance Decoded

If you are a student of Vedanta, you will hear the word "ignorance" very often. The word used in Vedanta is "avidya." Vidya means knowledge and avidya means the lack of knowledge, or ignorance. Ignorance or avidya is one of the most common words used in Vedanta. This is because ignorance is the cause of all suffering and unhappiness in our daily life, and Vedanta provides a solution to overcome this. Ignorance is the cause of this birth and all future rebirths. Ignorance traps us in this recycle of rebirths because of our attachment to worldly objects.

If you go deeper, Vedanta teaches that ignorance is the cause of the duality in this world–the separation of the subject and object. This separation of the subject and object is the underlying cause of the creation of the mind and the suffering thereafter. Also, the form of all the objects in the world is made of ignorance. Trees, stars, living beings, and everything in this universe is made only of ignorance. In the famous snake/rope example, ignorance has the power to create a snake when there is no snake but only a rope. In the same way, all the objects in the world are created by ignorance. Ignorance is powerful. It is deep-rooted, and it has the capacity and capability to do all these things and more. Ignorance or avidya may seem like a simple English or Sanskrit word respectively, but it has the power to afflict us in so many ways.

Ignorance is the opposite of knowledge–it is the lack of knowledge. Lack of knowledge of what? In general, ignorance could be a lack of knowledge of anything and everything. Knowledge is all-encompassing. Knowledge of the Chinese language, knowledge of rocket science, knowledge of golf, knowledge of the mind. We can go on and on, adding topics to this list–we will find that this list is limitless.

All this is the knowledge or ignorance of worldly objects. Vedanta does not talk about this type of knowledge or ignorance. Vedanta talks about the knowledge of our true nature, who we really are. What is our underlying reality? This knowledge is more critical and important than any knowledge about objects.

So, how do we gain this knowledge? To effectively gain knowledge, we need to understand the role of ignorance. This is important because ignorance obscures and hides the knowledge of our true nature. To peel off ignorance, we need a better understanding of the functioning of ignorance. If we understand the functioning of ignorance and the role it plays, it will help us reach the goal of understanding and assimilating the "ultimate knowledge."

Ignorance and Awareness

Self-Awareness is our innermost core. It is non-dual, full, complete, and self-contained. If Self-Awareness is our reality, why don't we know it, why don't we feel it? The simple answer is that we are ignorant, we are not aware of our true nature. This ignorance has a tremendous impact on Self-Awareness.

With ignorance, we no longer know that we are both the subject and object; we do not know that both subject and object are one and non-dual. If we do not know that we are both the subject and object, it means that the subject and object are no longer a single entity but are separate and independent entities. The Mind is created due to the ignorance of our true nature of being Self-Aware.

With ignorance, the Self is no longer the Self. It forgets it is full and complete. The Self is replaced with a self (small s), and this is the ego we feel and have.

Mind = Awareness + Ignorance

Mind = Subject + Object + Intelligence + Ignorance

self (ego) = Self + Ignorance

This ignorance is the underlying force which creates the mind with duality from the non-dual Self, and it also creates the ordinary ego. It is difficult to comprehend, but ignorance has the force to create this separation between subject and object. The unity between subject and object is lost. The mind has duality, therefore it has a feeling of the subject being "in here" and of the object being "out there." This is the experience for most of us.

It must be clearly understood that Self-Awareness does NOT undergo any change. It is unchanging, full, and complete. Self-Awareness is pure, and it has NO ignorance. Ignorance gives the impression that it is a changing Self-Awareness. Self or Self-Awareness does not change at all, it only gives an "impression," "as though" it has changed.

Powers of Ignorance

Ignorance is extremely powerful, and it comes with three shaktis or powers:

- A "Veiling" Power
- A "Projecting" Power
- A Power of "Mutual Superimposition"

To explain these powers, the classic example given in Vedanta is the rope/snake example. On a dark night with limited visibility, there is a rope in our path but, instead of seeing the rope, we see a snake. We have

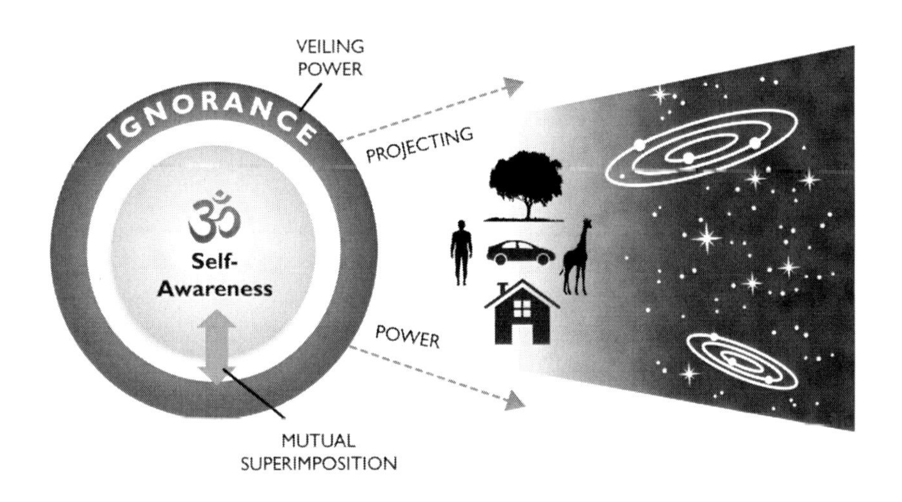

all experienced this at one time or another. If there was no ignorance, we would never see the snake; we would know straightaway that there is a rope "out there." So, the snake has been created by our ignorance. How does ignorance create the snake?

First, the veiling power of ignorance covers up the rope completely so that the rope is not visible. As a second step, the projection power of ignorance projects the snake onto the rope. Finally, the power of mutual superimposition, which superimposes the rope's qualities on the snake and the snake's qualities on the rope. The shape and size of the rope are transferred to the "snake," and the awesome and fearful qualities of the "snake" are superimposed on the rope. So, by looking at this superimposed snake in the shape of the rope you get frightened.

We will now focus on the veiling and superimposition aspects of ignorance.

The same veiling power of ignorance covers up Self-Awareness, your essential nature; you don't know you are Self-Aware. You don't know you are SatChitAnanda; you don't know you are Uncreated, Unchanging, Limitless, Blissful, and Self-Aware. With mutual superimposition, the qualities of the Self and ignorance are mutually interchanged. The new entity created is the ego (small self). The Awareness part of the Self is superimposed on ignorance to make it conscious and sentient. The nature of ignorance, which is always limited and incomplete, is superimposed on the Self to create the ego. This limited ego is the root and foundation of the mind.

Ignorance Is Beginningless

There is no start time for ignorance. Ignorance is beginningless; it has always been there. There cannot be a beginning for ignorance, for this will imply that before the beginning there was no ignorance, and if there was no ignorance it would mean there was only knowledge. This is not possible because once you have knowledge, you cannot have ignorance after that. Once you have knowledge of 2 + 2 = 4, you cannot have ignorance of this fact. Ignorance does not exist once you have knowledge, but it does exist before you have knowledge. Since we still do not have the knowledge that we are Self-Aware, therefore we always have been ignorant. This only implies that ignorance is beginningless and it has always been there. However, ignorance does have an end. Once you gain knowledge, then ignorance is gone. This applies to any type of knowledge. So, ignorance is beginningless, but it does have an end.

Types of Ignorance

Vedanta teaches us that there are only two things in this universe. The witnessing Self and all external object forms. The universe is that simple. So, there can be two types of ignorance.

1. Ignorance of Objects
2. Ignorance of the Self (our true nature)

Ignorance of objects is the lack of knowledge of all the possible topics and objects in the universe. With our limited minds, we have a limited knowledge of a limited number of objects and topics. The ignorance of objects only has the veiling power, it does not have the projection power. The veiling power covers the required knowledge of the object or topic and, because of this covering, we lack knowledge of this object. Therefore, we are ignorant about this object or topic.

Ignorance of the Self is the lack of knowledge about our true Self. Our true nature is Self-Awareness but, unfortunately, we are mostly ignorant about this fact. We think we are the ego and this body-mind complex. This ignorance underlies all suffering and unhappiness. This ignorance is much more powerful. It has all the three powers–it has the veiling power, projection power, and the power of mutual superimposition.

Cumulative Ignorance = Ignorance of Objects + Ignorance of Self

Degrees of Ignorance

Knowledge and lack of knowledge (ignorance) have a complex profile. It is important to understand this profile. It will show that there are different degrees of ignorance.

Let us start by taking the example of knowledge of the Chinese language. If someone has a complete knowledge of the Chinese language, he knows everything that is possible; this person will have 100% knowledge of the Chinese language. On the other end of the scale, there are people who are completely ignorant of the language; they are 100% ignorant of this language. Every living being in the universe will fall between this scale of 100% knowledge to 100% ignorance. So, there is a knowledge-ignorance profile about the Chinese language.

Take another subject, say mathematics. Here again, there will be a scale of 100% knowledge to 100% ignorance. People will fall somewhere on the scale of 100% knowledge to 100% ignorance. So, there is a knowledge-ignorance profile for mathematics.

In the same way, there must be a knowledge-ignorance profile for every possible topic or object in the universe. If we combine this scale of 100% knowledge to 100% ignorance for every topic, we will get a cumulative knowledge-ignorance profile for all possible topics and objects. Within this cumulative knowledge-ignorance scale, each person will know their own knowledge or ignorance profile. Each living being has more knowledge of some topics and less or no knowledge of other topics. Each living being will have a spot in the complex knowledge-ignorance profile, a spot which will reflect their knowledge and ignorance of different objects.

To the knowledge-ignorance profile of objects, you must also add the knowledge profile of the Self. Here again, the spectrum can be broken down into countless parts, and each part will have a different amount of ignorance. An enlightened person will have 100% knowledge of the Self, while a completely ignorant person will have 0% knowledge or 100% ignorance.

If you combine the object profile with the Self profile, you will get a cumulative knowledge-ignorance profile. Within this cumulative profile, there is a spot for every living being. This spot is like a pixel of ignorance. As you can imagine, there are a countless number of pixels of ignorance. Each pixel of ignorance has its own unique mix of ignorance and knowledge. Each pixel of ignorance represents a single individual living being with their own knowledge-ignorance profile. You have a pixel of ignorance and I have a pixel of ignorance and, in the same way, every living being has their own unique pixel of ignorance.

Ignorance Is Dynamic: Each pixel of ignorance is not static; it is dynamic. It is conscious as it is in the presence of Awareness. The profile of ignorance keeps changing. If today you learn how to play tennis, you now have knowledge of playing tennis, so your ignorance of tennis is gone or reduced. This will affect your ignorance profile. If you study Vedanta and you gain an understanding of Self-Awareness, your ignorance profile will undergo change in a positive direction. If tomorrow you do something foolish, forgetting you are Self-Aware, your ignorance profile will move in a negative direction. Your day-to-day activity affects your ignorance profile. This pixel of ignorance is like an accounting ledger; it keeps track of all day-to-day activities and updates your pixel of ignorance on a continuous basis.

Vasanas and Pixel of Ignorance: Vasanas as taught in Vedanta are our tendencies–our strengths and weaknesses, our character traits. They make our personality profile. Vasanas are an accumulation of our tendencies over all our past lives.

The character traits or personality profile really depend on the knowledge and ignorance we have. As the knowledge-ignorance profile keeps changing, it impacts the accumulated vasanas. These vasanas reside within this pixel of ignorance. You own this pixel of ignorance with the vasanas and you carry this pixel with you. You had this pixel of ignorance in your previous births, you have the pixel in this birth, and you will have this pixel of ignorance in all your future births.

Pixel of Ignorance and Causal Body: There are a countless number of pixels of ignorance. Each living being has their own pixel of ignorance. We know there is only ONE Self-Awareness. When these countless pixels of ignorance come in the presence of Self-Shining Awareness, this Awareness is reflected in every pixel of ignorance. How does this happen?

The example taught in Vedanta–there are hundreds of buckets filled with water. You keep these buckets outdoors and you will see the reflected sun in every bucket. There will be no bucket without the reflected sun. The sun is reflected in every bucket. In the same way, the bulb of Awareness is reflected in each pixel of ignorance. There are countless pixels, and every pixel of ignorance has Reflected Awareness. It must be noted, it is not the "standalone" Self-Awareness but Reflected Awareness which is present in each pixel of ignorance. The presence of Reflected Awareness makes the pixel of ignorance conscious and sentient.

According to Vedanta, the human body or, for that matter, any living being is made of the following bodies:

- Causal/Seed Body or Karana Sharira
- Subtle Body or Sukshma Sharira
- Physical/Gross Body or Sthula Sharira

The Causal Body is also called the Seed Body because it is similar to a seed from which grows a tree, with branches, leaves, and fruit. A seed already has the potential form of the tree built in it. From a mango seed only a mango tree will grow and not an apple tree. In the same way, the Causal Body contains the human being in its potential form. Your Causal Body will have your potential form, my Causal Body will have my potential form. In this way, every living being has their own Causal or Seed Body. The Seed Body is the cause of the Subtle and Gross Bodies. That is why it is called the Causal Body. It is the starting point for any living being.

The pixel of ignorance with the Reflected Awareness is this Causal or Seed Body.

Pixel of Ignorance = Causal Body

This pixel of ignorance or Seed Body is the source for living out the current life. Under the right conditions, this Causal or Seed Body germinates and grows to play out the blueprint that is contained within it, using the Subtle Body and the Gross Body.

In many of the Vedanta scriptures, there is a reference to the "heart" or "cave." This heart is not the physical heart but refers to the pixel of ignorance, which is your Causal Body. In fact, Sri Ramana Maharshi teaches us that this pixel of ignorance is located two fingers from the center on the right side of your chest. Sri Shankaracharya teaches us that this pixel of ignorance is the knot which connects the living being with Self-Awareness.

Removing Ignorance

The only solution for removing ignorance is Knowledge. Knowledge is the only antidote to ignorance. We are not talking about the knowledge of objects but the Knowledge of our true nature, our inner core. Removing this ignorance is not easy. It is deep-rooted. This ignorance has accumulated over so many rebirths. A great deal of effort and dedication is required. Removing this ignorance is a two-step process:

Step 1: Purification of the Mind

Step 2: Direct Knowledge

Step 1: Purification of the Mind

To remove ignorance and gain the knowledge of Self-Awareness, the first step is to purify the mind. This is critical and important. Without purification, the knowledge of Self-Awareness will not sink in easily. Sri Shankaracharya taught that the following steps are necessary for the purification process:

1. Viveka–Discrimination
2. Vairagya–Dispassion
3. Sama–Quietude
4. Dama–Self-control
5. Titiksha–Tolerance
6. Samadhana–Well-placed mind
7. Mumuksutva–Desire for freedom

We have discussed these steps in detail in the essay “Understanding the Mind.”

Step 2: Direct Knowledge

Once we have started the process to purify our minds and we have studied the scriptures under the guidance of a well-established guru, we should begin to get a good understanding of our true nature as Self-Awareness or SatChitAnanda. Usually, the knowledge we gain at the beginning is indirect knowledge, it is not direct knowledge.

Indirect knowledge means that we are told by scriptures and teachers that the underlying reality of all of us is Self-Awareness or SatChitAnanda. We have the knowledge, but we have no experience of Self-Awareness. This knowledge is more theoretical. We are told that we are Self-Aware or the inner core of every living being is SatChitAnanda. All this knowledge is second- or third-person knowledge. It is still remote, and it seems it is the knowledge of something "out there." This knowledge is not related to me. What we must gain is direct knowledge–knowledge of my Self-Awareness, my SatChitAnanda/Brahman. Knowledge which is not remote but part of me.

Scriptures can only teach you indirect knowledge; you must convert this indirect knowledge to direct knowledge. The only method to convert this indirect knowledge to direct knowledge is self-enquiry. Self-enquiry is something you must do yourself. A guru or scripture can guide you, but self-enquiry must be done by oneself.

How do you do this self-enquiry to convert indirect to direct knowledge? Many scriptures teach us to focus on mahavakyas like "Tat Tvam Asi" ("That You Are") or "Aham Brahmasmi" ("I Am Brahman"). Sri Ramana Maharshi told us to focus on "Who Am I." In Chapter 7 of *Panchadasi* written by Sri Vidyaranya, a detailed analysis is given of how to convert indirect knowledge to direct knowledge. There are many paths, and you can choose the option which is best suited to you.

9 | Understanding the Pancha Koshas

If you are a student of Vedanta, you probably know that every living being is made up of five (pancha) koshas. Kosha is a Sanskrit word which means "sheath" or "layer." Based on this, the five koshas can be defined as follows (the word "maya" in the names below means "made of"):

1. Annamaya Kosha: sheath made of food–this is our physical body.
2. Pranamaya Kosha: sheath made of energy–to keep the physical body functional.
3. Manomaya Kosha: sheath made of mind stuff.
4. Vijnanamaya Kosha: sheath made of intelligence/ knowledge.
5. Anandamaya Kosha: sheath made of bliss.

The "made of" used above is not some abstract term. It literally means that the koshas are made of the things stated above. For example, the Vijnanamaya Kosha is made of intelligence. The substratum of the kosha is intelligence. Just like material is made of atoms and molecules, in the same way this kosha is made of intelligence. Intelligence is its essence. This logic applies to the other koshas also, and each kosha has its own building blocks. Most books describing the five koshas use the illustration in the next page. It may not be an accurate representation, but it does convey the idea quite well. Each outer sheath covers the inner sheath. If you peel off the outer sheath, you move to the inner sheath. The Food Sheath covers the Pranamaya Kosha, the Pranamaya Kosha covers the Manomaya Kosha, and so on. It is like peeling away the layers of an onion or unpacking a Russian matryoshka doll. If you peel away all the five layers, the image in the next page shows that you will reach your inner core, which is Pure Awareness or Self-Awareness.

Pure Consciousness = Self-Awareness

The concept of the five koshas was first revealed in the Taittiriya Upanishad, which was written around 600 BC. This Upanishad is the source for a detailed analysis of the five koshas. The great sages closed their eyes and meditated, looking for their innermost core. During this process, they gained tremendous insights into a wide variety of subjects. Insight into the five koshas is one of them.

The main purpose of discussing the five koshas is to show the correct path to reach your inner core, which is Self-Awareness. The strategy of "neti-neti"–"not this, not this"–is suggested in this Upanishad. In this methodology, you start eliminating what is not you, till you discover your inner self.

Each one of us thinks we are the physical body. We identify the physical body as ourselves. The Taittiriya Upanishad explains that the physical body is only made of food–the Annamaya Kosha. It is born out of food, it lives on food, and after dying it goes back into food. It is therefore impossible that your inner core, which is Self-Awareness, can be made of food. The Upanishad suggests you meditate on this idea, and when you are convinced that you are not the physical body, you peel away the Food Sheath as not being yourself.

The next inner layer is the Pranamaya Kosha. It vitalizes the body and keeps the body and the inner organs functioning. Blood circulation, breathing, muscle toning, etc. are some of the powers of this kosha. Without this kosha, the physical body is dead. The Upanishad explains that this layer is inert, it has no intelligence, it does its job like a robot. It is a slave doing its job faithfully. The Upanishad asks us to meditate on this idea and conclude that you are not the Pranamaya Kosha. In this way, you can eliminate this layer also as not being yourself.

The next sheath is the Manomaya Kosha or the mind stuff. The mind is continuously changing, it is changing with every thought. There is hardly a moment when there is no thought in the mind. We are taught that our inner core of Self-Awareness is unchanging. So, the ever-changing mind just cannot be our inner core. After meditating on this idea, you can peel away this sheath.

The next sheath you will encounter is the Vijnanamaya Kosha. This sheath is made of intelligence. During deep sleep (sleep without dreams), this kosha is no longer active, yet you still exist. Even if you have no thoughts, feelings, or emotions and your mind is absent, YOU still exist. Your inner core is always present. It cannot take a leave of absence. If the Vijnanamaya Kosha is absent during deep sleep, it only means that you cannot be the Vijnanamaya Kosha. In this way, you can negate this kosha too.

The next kosha is the Anandamaya Kosha. This is the innermost kosha, and it is closest to the inner core. Ananda means bliss but this meaning applies only in ideal conditions when there are no thoughts in the mind. This is impossible during the waking and dream states. During the waking and dream states, the mind is full of activity. During these active states, this kosha is the center of emotions or feeling. *I am tired, I am sad,* and so on. This means that this kosha has many different such attributes. We are taught that Self-Awareness is without attributes or qualities, therefore we cannot be this kosha. By meditating on this kosha, you can say “neti-neti” to this kosha too.

Once the identification with all the five koshas is removed, what remains is Self-Awareness. The Taittiriya Upanishad uses this teaching methodology of neti-neti to reach your inner core. This does seem logical and powerful. To better implement this teaching, it is a good idea to have a more detailed understanding of the five koshas. We will now analyze the five koshas in the following way:

- **Self-Awareness and the Five Koshas**
- **Five Koshas and Three Bodies**
- **Roles of the Different Koshas**

Self-Awareness and the Five Koshas

Self-Awareness is our inner core and Awareness is the nature of Self-Awareness. As we have discussed in other essays, Awareness is made of Subject, Object, and Intelligence. If any one of them is missing, there will be no Awareness. If you are currently aware of your surroundings, it is because there is a Subject, there is an Object, and there is Intelligence connecting the Object with the Subject.

Self-Awareness is much more complicated. *Self-Awareness means that "Awareness is aware of Awareness."* This implies that the subject is Awareness, the object is Awareness, and the intelligence is Awareness. Awareness plays the role of subject and object. In other words, both the subject and object are the same. This makes Self-Awareness complete, self-sufficient, and independent. Self-Awareness is therefore non-dual and homogenous.

Awareness = Subject + Object + Intelligence

In Self-Awareness, Self = Subject = Object = Intelligence

This Self-Shining Awareness is like a bulb of Awareness and it is our inner core. It is not dependent on anything else, and it generates its own light of Awareness.

Pixel of Ignorance and Koshas: If our nature and inner core is Self-Awareness, why don't we know it, why don't we feel it? The simple answer is that we are ignorant of our inner core. Since we have forgotten our true nature, Ignorance covers up Self-Awareness. When we forget who we really are, Ignorance pops up and, like a veil, covers Awareness.

As we have discussed in the essay "Ignorance Decoded," this veil of Ignorance is made up of a countless number of pixels, each pixel representing a living being. The pixel of ignorance is a mix of ignorance and knowledge. Each living being has their own unique pixel of ignorance. This pixel also contains the personality traits (vasanas) accumulated over all past births of an individual. It is like your passport, with all your prior travel details. We will see that this pixel of ignorance is our Seed Body.

Ignorance has a strange power. It can separate Subject and Object from the non-dual Self-Awareness. Yes, it has that power! How does this happen? Because of Ignorance, we forget we are both Subject and Object; we do not know that both Subject and Object are one and non-dual. If we do not know that we are both Subject and Object, it means that the subject and object are no longer a single entity but are separate and independent entities. Non-duality becomes duality by the simple fact of forgetting. This forgetting or not knowing is the power of Ignorance.

Although Self-Awareness is non-dual, it does have four parts.

In Self-Awareness, Self = Subject = Object = Intelligence

When Subject and Object separation takes place, the different koshas are created. The process of separation of Subject and Object is like refraction. Place a prism in front of a ray of light and we can see the seven different colors on the other side. In the same way, the pixel of ignorance refracts the light of Self-Awareness into the following three different koshas plus Sakshi as witness.

1. Manomaya Kosha–the home of the Object
2. Vijnanamaya Kosha–the home of the Intelligence
3. Anandamaya Kosha–the home of the Self
4. Sakshi (Witness)–the home of the Subject

These homogenous and integrated parts of Self-Awareness become the three koshas + Witness. Thus, we see that the above three koshas are a mix of Self-Awareness and the pixel of ignorance.

Koshas = Awareness + Ignorance

So, these three koshas evolve from a pixel of ignorance. What about the Annamaya Kosha and the Pranamaya Kosha? Their evolution is independent of the other three koshas. Let us discuss this further.

Annamaya Kosha: This is the physical or Gross Body. We know the starting place for the physical body is the mother's womb. It grows from a single cell to a complex physical body, all in the womb. The Garbha

Upanishad gives a detailed analysis of the growth of the fetus in the womb. It gives a comprehensive timetable of when the different parts of the body show up. It is quite amazing. It would be nice if the medical community could verify the timetable mentioned in this Upanishad.

Pranamaya Kosha: The Garbha Upanishad also indicates that, in the seventh month of being in the womb, the pixel of ignorance or the soul (jivatman) enters and connects with the Annamaya Kosha. How is the connection made? The connection is made by the Pranamaya Kosha. The Pranamaya Kosha is made of vital energy. It connects the soul with the Annamaya Kosha. The five senses–eyes, ears, tongue, nose, and skin–in the Annamaya Kosha are connected to the Manomaya Kosha. Also, organs of action like hands, legs, etc. are interconnected between the three koshas and the Annamaya Kosha. It is quite amazing how these connections are made seamlessly. So, the main role of the Pranamaya Kosha is to interconnect the three koshas from the pixel of ignorance with the Annamaya Kosha.

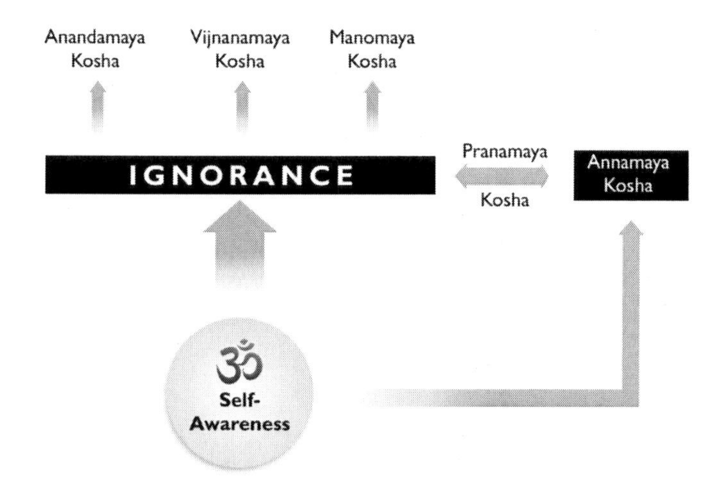

It is quite intriguing to learn from the Upanishad that the Seed Body only enters the body in the seventh month. Before that, the fetus is just a piece of flesh like any other part of the body. So, the baby in the womb has a soul, a personality, only after the seventh month. Before that, it is a body part within the womb. What is unknown and intriguing is how the selection is made. Which soul will enter which body? I am sure there must be a logical process which is controlled by some laws of nature.

Five Koshas and Three Bodies

To get a better understanding of the five koshas, it is important to correlate these with the three bodies. Vedanta teaches us that every living being has the following three different bodies:

1. Seed Body
2. Subtle Body
3. Gross/Physical Body

We saw earlier that due to the pixel of ignorance, the Seed Body is created. The Seed Body creates the Subtle Body. The Subtle Body creates the Gross Body.

What is the difference between a kosha/sheath and a body? A sheath is a covering of the body. A pastry or a cake is a body, and this pastry/cake may have different coverings like cream, chocolate, fruit, etc. In the same way, each of the three bodies has different coverings or koshas. Let us see each one of them in a little more detail.

1. Seed Body

The Seed Body is like any seed from which a tree with branches, leaves, and fruit is created. The seed has the potential form of the tree already built into it. You could say that the tree in an unmanifest condition is present in the seed. The Seed Body is also called a Causal Body because it is the cause of the tree. In the same way, an individual Seed Body will become a human being with all his or her tendencies and character/personality traits (called vasanas). This Seed Body will also contain the blueprint of one's life, including all the karmas that will be exhausted in this life. It is important to know that every object (living + nonliving) in the universe has a Seed Body. In fact, even the universe has a Seed Body. The Seed Body for the universe will be the total of all the seeds for individual objects.

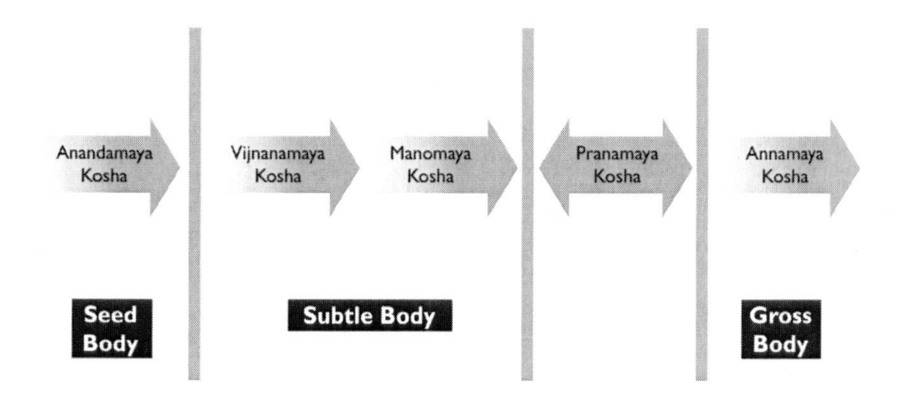

Earlier, we discussed the pixel of ignorance. This pixel of ignorance is the same as the Seed Body. Vedanta teaches us that the Seed Body is the spiritual heart or cave. The spiritual heart is not the physical heart. It is subtle, it does not have a physical form, and it is something we all have within us.

Seed Body = Pixel of Ignorance

When the Seed Body with the power of the Pranamaya Kosha connects with the fetus or the Annamaya Kosha, magic happens. The light of Self-Awareness refracts through the pixel of ignorance (Seed Body) and creates the Anandamaya Kosha, Vijanamaya Kosha, and Manomaya Kosha. The fetus is no longer a fetus but a living being with a personality, etc. When the refraction takes place and the three koshas are created, the integration is complete. At this moment, the Seed Body starts to germinate in the living being. The Seed Body blossoms to play out the blueprint of life.

The Anandamaya Kosha is within the Seed Body. It is the main layer within the pixel of ignorance. The Seed Body operates through the Anandamaya Kosha. The Anandamaya Kosha houses the feeling of "I-ness" and creates the feeling of "I" within us. The feeling of "'I" is also called the Ahamkara or Ego. Ahamkara in Sanskrit means the "I-Maker."

2. Subtle Body

As mentioned, the Manomaya Kosha and Vijnanamaya Kosha are created by the refraction of Self-Awareness. After refraction, these two are housed in the Subtle Body as two sheaths. A common name for the Subtle Body is the mind. From our experience, we know that the mind is located within the brain. So, when the refraction takes place in the pixel of ignorance, the two koshas are beamed as the mind within the brain.

We know the mind is rarely quiet; it is continually active. This means that the Manomaya Kosha and Vijnanamaya Kosha have a heavy load of activity. If you are a student of Vedanta, you will learn that the activity in the mind is made of vrittis or mental waveforms. These vrittis represent the different objects or combination of objects. The object waveforms are made of mind stuff–they are made up of the two sheaths in the Subtle Body. Manomaya Kosha helps create the material for the objects, while Vijnanamaya Kosha adds intelligence to the mind stuff.

Subtle Body = Manomaya Kosha + Vijnanamaya Kosha

Manomaya Kosha is the home of objects. The power to become objects is within the Manomaya Kosha. The input side of the Manomaya Kosha is connected to the five organs of sense and five organs of action. The five organs of sense are–nose for smell, tongue for taste, ears for sound, eyes for vision, and skin for touch. The five organs of action are–feet, hands, mouth for talking, organs for excretion and reproduction. The output side of the Manomaya Kosha is connected to the Vijnanamaya Kosha.

The Vijnanamaya Kosha is the home of intelligence. It is the storehouse of knowledge. The input side is connected to the Manomaya Kosha, while the output side is connected to the Anandamaya Kosha. We have seen earlier that the Anandamaya Kosha is a layer within the Seed Body.

3. Gross Body

The Annamaya Kosha is part of the Gross Body. We have seen earlier that the Gross Body is created in the mother's womb. It is connected to the other koshas through the Pranamaya Kosha.

In the three bodies, we have covered all the koshas except the Pranamaya Kosha. The question is, where does the Pranamaya Kosha fit? Is it part of the Seed, Subtle, or Gross Body? There is no clear-cut answer. Some believe it is part of the Gross Body and others think it is part of the Subtle Body. The Pranamaya Kosha comes into force when the Seed Body connects with the fetus in the womb. It is not really a sheath, but it is the interconnector between the Seed Body and the fetus in the womb. This fetus finally becomes the Annamaya Kosha. The Pranamaya Kosha sustains this Annamaya Kosha for the duration of its life.

Roles of the Different Koshas

Each kosha plays a different and distinct role. Let us try to understand this.

Perceiving: The perceiving of objects takes place in the Manomaya Kosha. We mentioned earlier that the Manomaya Kosha is connected to the five organs of the senses. It must be understood that the input signals from the five sense organs do not come from the Gross Body but from the subtle version of the five sense organs. Every gross object (living + nonliving) in the universe has a subtle version. This means every part of your body has a subtle version. There is a subtle version of your ear, eye, nose, and every cell and tissue and bone. Each of the subtle objects is made of vrittis or mental waveforms. Based on this reasoning, it is only logical to assume that there is a fully functional subtle universe made of waveforms. Everything that we experience really occurs in the subtle universe; the gross universe is only the manifestation of the subtle universe. This may seem radical, but it is the truth. These object waveforms are the building blocks of the subtle universe. Science, with its string theory, is moving in the same direction.

The input signal could be vision, sound, touch, smell, and taste; the perception of these objects takes place in the Manomaya Kosha. For example, when the input signal is for a tree, the Manomaya Kosha creates the required material which makes up the tree. This material is in the form of mental waveforms or vrittis. These mental waveforms have the required ingredients for the tree. If the input is music, it creates the material which makes up the sound for the music. In this way, it handles all the input signals coming from the outside world.

The perception does take place in the Manomaya Kosha, but the kosha has no clue what these objects are. It creates the source material, but it is clueless what it is. The Manomaya Kosha needs help; it therefore passes on the input signals to the Vijnanamaya Kosha for decoding.

Learning/Thinking: Vijnanamaya Kosha has intelligence. At the time of birth, the Vijnanamaya Kosha is a blank slate. With the power of intelligence, it learns continuously and acquires a great deal of knowledge. With this learning, it decodes the input signal. In the process of decoding, it adds intelligence to the object waveform. The object waveform is now made of knowledge. Knowledge is the substratum of the waveform. The object waveform has the knowledge of what the waveform represents. The object waveform has the knowledge, but there is no awareness. There is knowledge but no awareness within the Vijnanamaya Kosha. There must be an "I" or self who is aware. There is no "I" or self within this kosha.

The Vijnanamaya Kosha is powerful. It has the power of thinking, analyzing, and remembering. Some of these powers are as follows:

- Power of Cognition or Sensation
- Power of Imagination
- Power of Logic
- Power of Will
- Power of Memory

It is like a CPU in a computer, crunching and analyzing all sorts of numbers. Intelligence seems to be there but no awareness. In the same way, the Vijnanamaya Kosha has all these powers, but there is no self who is aware of these activities.

Feeling: Feeling and similar emotions take place in the Anandamaya Kosha. The name "Anandamaya" does not convey this idea. We have seen earlier that Anandamaya Kosha means "maker of bliss." This bliss can only happen when there are no vrittis or mental waveforms in the mind. Is this possible? Yes, only during deep sleep. During deep sleep there are no vrittis, no mental waveforms in the mind. The mind is blank. Only during that state, when there are no vrittis in the mind, can the Anandamaya Kosha experience bliss. During the waking and dream states, this is not possible. A continuous stream of object waveforms is being sent from the mind. The Anandamaya Kosha must react to these incoming vrittis.

We have seen earlier that the Anandamaya Kosha is made up of the feeling of "I." This feeling is nothing but the ego. The ego is looking for permanent peace and happiness in the world. We saw that the Vijnanamaya Kosha decodes objects (waveforms) coming in from the five sense organs in the Manomaya Kosha. These objects are presented to the Ahamkara or ego. What does the Ahamkara do with these object waveforms? The ego has a clear goal–it is looking for continuous happiness. It evaluates the object waveform against this key criterion. If the ego thinks the object can provide that happiness, it will like that object. If the ego thinks that it will not provide that happiness, it will dislike that object. In Vedanta this is called raga (like)/dvesha (dislike). The ego will run toward the object it likes and run away from objects which it dislikes. The ego undertakes this task for all the thoughts and objects which it encounters.

This is how the ego interacts with the object waveform presented by the Vijnanamaya Kosha, and it adds the sense of feeling to the object waveform with its likes/dislikes. This kosha starts to feel a range of emotions covering the entire spectrum. It feels happiness, sadness, anger, jealousy, attraction, repulsion, and so on. This sense of feeling takes place in the Anandamaya Kosha.

All living beings live within these five koshas. The ego operates within these five koshas. This does not help reach your innermost core, which is Self-Awareness.

The ego and the five koshas are not part of your Real Self. Self-Awareness is your Real Self. Ignorance is hiding the Real Self. The goal is to discover the Real Self and stay within that Real Self.

10 | Time (t)=0 Is Pure Awareness

To start this discussion, it is important to understand what we mean by t (time)=0. We can say that t=0 means that it is not the past, not the future, but the present. It means it is "now." Anything that is t=0+ or t=0- is not "now" but the future or the past. Even a nanosecond more or less than t=0 is not "now"–it would be past or future. Based on the Planck constant, the smallest possible time unit is t =10E-44 seconds. Even the passage of this extremely small time-unit would mean the event is not "now," but the past or the future.

So, where is t=0 for the universe? Where is the "now" moment of the universe? It cannot be the Big Bang moment. Time may have started with the Big Bang, but it is not the "now" moment. The Big Bang is 13.7 billion years old, which means t=-13.7 billion years for the Big Bang. Only the location of "now" can be t=0. Therefore, the Big Bang cannot be t=0. It may have been t=0 at the time of the Big Bang, but right now the Big Bang is 13.7 billion years old. It is an event in the past. So how do we understand t=0 or the "now" moment?

Any perception process must have the following two elements. Without these two elements, the perception process would be incomplete.

1. Subject or Observer
2. Object or Observed

In the following sections we will analyze and show where we can locate t=0 for the Subject/Observer and the Object/Observed.

Where Is t=0 for the Observer/Subject?

Even before we start understanding t=0 for the Observer/Subject, the question which must be answered is–what do we mean by an Observer?

According to Vedanta, Atma is the Observer which witnesses everything that is happening in the mind, and we know the mind is full of activity. This Atma is the Real "I"and it is our underlying reality. Atma is merely an Observer and it never influences, nor is it affected by what is happening in the mind. It is like a witness to a movie which is running in your mind.

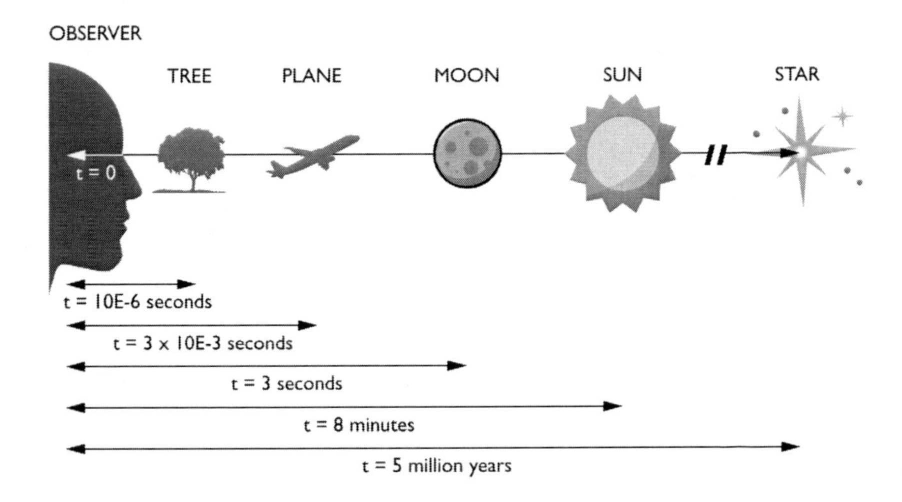

To locate t=0 for Atma/Observer, let us study the objects "out there." If we can see a faraway star, say, five million light-years away, it takes light from that star five million years to reach us. Now we see the sun; the light from the sun takes eight minutes to reach us. We look at the moon; light takes three seconds to reach us. We look at the plane flying in the sky at 30,000 feet; light takes about 300 milliseconds to reach us. As the distance of the object being viewed is reduced, the time taken for light to reach us is much less.

Now look at the tree outside the window; the time taken for light to reach you is 10 microseconds (10E-6). Looking at the computer screen one foot away and reading this essay, light takes about one nanosecond (10E-9) to reach you. You can even watch your thoughts–they too take some time to form; they are not instantaneous. As the distance reduces, the time taken for the light to reach our eyes reduces. If you extrapolate this backward, the only logical location for t to be equal to 0 is in the Observer, who is watching all these objects; t=0 is the only location where light takes zero seconds to reach the Observer. This must be the "now" location. Atma is the Observer, so Atma is t=0 within you. This t=0 is beyond time; it is always the "now" moment.

If you or anyone else looks around at the objects in the universe and uses the same reasoning as above, each one will reach the same conclusion: that the Observer within us is t=0. Everyone has their own t=0, which is within themselves. This will apply to every living being in the universe. It would, therefore, seem that I have my own "now" moment, you have your own "now" moment, and every living being in the universe has their own "now" moment. Does this mean that there are multiple t=0, one for every living being? Vedanta teaches us that Atma is the common Observer/Subject for every living being, and therefore there is only one t=0.

So how does Atma create the illusion of being a different observer within every living being? To explain this, the classic example given by Vedanta is that of buckets filled with water. Picture the sun shining over an unlimited number of buckets filled with water. What will you see? The sun reflected in each bucket. You will not see a partial image of the sun but the complete image of the sun in each bucket. Now imagine that the bucket represents our body and the water in the bucket is our mind. There are an unlimited number of living beings with a mind in this universe. The shining sun is the Atma. Atma is reflected in the mind of every living being. So, you can see how the Atma/Observer within each one of us is t=0.

Where Is t=0 for the Observed/Objects?

If you look closely, you will agree that whatever we see "out there" is all dated or past stuff. The faraway star is one million years old, the sun is eight minutes old, the moon is three seconds old, the plane in the sky is 300 milliseconds old, the tree outside the window is ten microseconds old, and the computer is one nanosecond old. This is because light takes that much time to reach us from different objects. We do not see any "now" objects where t=0; we only see "memory objects," which are no longer current. The universe is only made up of "memory" objects. It is just impossible to find a "now" object in the physical universe. These "memory" objects are for both living and nonliving objects.

The question is, does there exist a "now" version of any "memory" object, where t=0 for the object? Intuitively, you would think there should be a "now" object somewhere. But where is this "now" object?

Scientists add to the confusion. When they talk about "memory" objects, they make it seem as if they are talking about "now" objects. When a planet is discovered five million light-years away, it is referred to as if it is a "now" object, but it is a "memory" object. They are talking about an object which is five million years old; no one knows where that planet is "right now." Does it even exist, has it already been destroyed by a meteor? No one can be certain. One certainty is that the "now" object cannot be in the same location where the "memory" object is five million years ago.

So where is the universe where everything is "now" and where there are no "memory" objects? This is just not possible in the spacetime framework as we know it. To be in the "now" universe, every object in this universe must be at t=0. If t is not equal to 0, then it is not a "now" object, it is a "memory" object. We know t=0 for the Observer is within you, but where is t=0 for the "now" object?

We know that the sun we see is eight minutes old and it is a "memory" object. You see the "now minus eight minutes" version of the sun. This is because it takes light eight minutes to reach us. Let us play around with this. Now, for whatever reason, the sun is only "now minus four minutes" old; it would mean the sun has moved closer to the Observer (and is hotter). In the same way, if the sun is only "now minus thirty seconds" old, it would mean the sun is extremely close to the Observer, but it is still a memory object. If you keep extrapolating this backward, and finally if t becomes 0 for the sun, it will only mean that the sun is within the Atma. We have seen earlier that t=0 is the coordinate for the Observer/Atma. For the sun to be a "now" object, it must be within Atma.

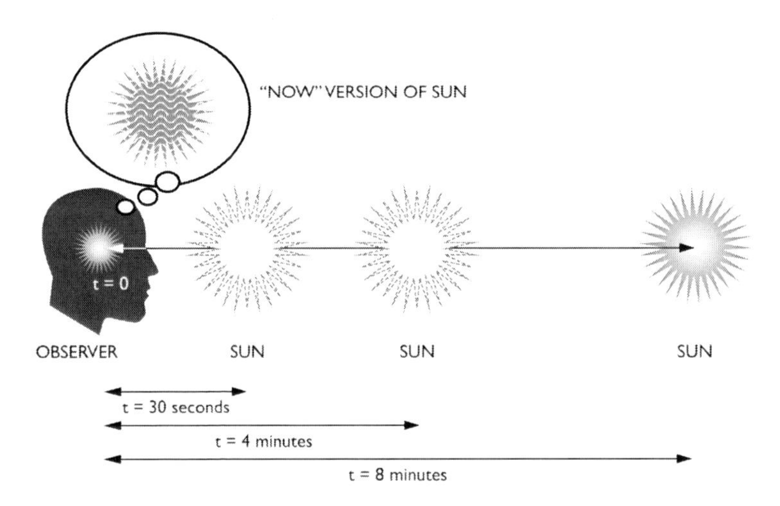

At t=0, the sun is a "now" object, and this "now" object is beyond the spacetime framework and is within Atma. This reasoning and logic will be applicable to every "memory" object in the universe. T=0 for all the memory objects in this physical universe is present within Atma. Atma is the Observer and this Atma is also the source for all the "now" objects.

For any object to be outside the spacetime framework, it must be in its "unmanifest" or "potential" or "seed" form. There is no actual sun, there is only the potential to become the sun. Just as Play-Doh used by kids has the potential to bc manipulated to become different objects, in the same way Atma has the potential to become any object in the universe.

T=0 Is Pure Awareness

We just saw that t=0 for the Observer is within each one of us. We also saw that t=0 for all the "now" objects is also within us. At t=0, both Subject and Object are the same. They are completely unified and homogenous with no separation whatsoever. What does this mean? This is the Singularity which science talks about. It is the unity of subject and object.

Vedanta teaches us that the essential nature of Atma is Awareness. If you look at Awareness more closely, you will realize that Awareness must always have the following two elements:

- If you are aware, then there should be someone who is aware. Awareness needs a subject.
- To be aware, there must be an object of which you are aware. Awareness needs an object.

Subject and object are needed to complete the Awareness process. To be Self-Aware, the subject and object must be within Awareness itself, with no separation. This is Pure Awareness. In our daily perception, we always feel that the subject is here while the object is “out there”; there is separation, we are therefore not Self-Aware.

Earlier, we saw that t=0 has both the Subject and Object as non-separate from each other. The only conclusion we can reach is that t=0 or the “now” moment is not only Aware, but it is Self-Aware. Vedanta teaches us that Atma is Self-Aware. Therefore, the location t=0 is Atma, and this Atma is the underlying reality of the universe, including for every living being.

If science does properly understand the concept of t=0 or the “now” moment, it will reach the conclusion that the location of t=0 is Awareness. This Awareness is the underlying reality of this universe.

11 | SatChitAnanda vs. Self-Awareness

If you are a student of Vedanta, SatChitAnanda and Brahman are the two terms which you will use often. Let us try and understand these two terms.

SatChitAnanda is our innermost core and is our true self. What does "Sat Chit Ananda" mean?

Sat: Sat means "Real." According to Vedanta, for anything to be Sat, it must exist in all the three tenses–past, present, and future. If you investigate Nature, you will not find anything which is Sat. There is nothing which is unchanging. Everything is changing. Everything is born and, therefore, everything dies. Our inner core is the only Sat, which is uncreated, unborn, and unchanging.

Chit: Chit means "Awareness." Many books also translate this as Consciousness. As we will discuss in this essay, Awareness is a better way to understand this.

Ananda: Our essential nature is Ananda or Bliss.

Brahman is another term which is meant to describe the same reality as SatChitAnanda. However, it takes a different approach. It does not talk about our inner core but, as the scriptures teach us, Brahman is the underlying reality of Nature. It is the substratum of the universe. It is the material cause of all the objects. The moment that terms like Nature or universe are used, the first instinct is to think that Brahman is something "out there." We need to investigate the universe to find Brahman. Investigating Nature or the universe is the realm of science. Does that mean science is going to help us discover Brahman? No, Brahman is beyond science. Brahman is outside space and time. It existed even when there was no space and time. Science can never discover Brahman.

There is SatChitAnanda which is our inner core, and there is Brahman which is the underlying reality of Nature. From this, it does seem that there are two realities. It looks like you must discover two things–SatChitAnanda and Brahman; SatChitAnanda within us and Brahman "out there." This does cause confusion. To resolve this confusion, the scriptures introduce the famous statement "Tat Tvam Asi" ("That You Are"). Vedanta makes a connection between our inner core SatChitAnanda and Brahman. That (Brahman) You (SatChitAnanda) Are. In this way, the underlying reality of the universe and the underlying reality of the self is the same. There is only one Reality. Vedanta explains that Brahman and SatChitAnanda are the same; there exists no dichotomy between the two, and they are identical.

Issues with SatChitAnanda or Brahman

- It is true, SatChitAnanda and Brahman are identical. Making the connection between SatChitAnanda and Brahman is not easy. It is not intuitive. We must first find SatChitAnanda within us and then try and locate Brahman within all the objects in the universe. This is not easy, but if you do manage to understand this, then you must find the common thread which connects them. What is that which makes SatChitAnanda and Brahman identical? There must be something which makes them identical, otherwise they would not be the same. Unfortunately, this is not very explicit in the scriptures.
- The scriptures teach us that our inner core is Sakshi (witness). It is the witness to everything which is happening in the mind. Since our inner core is SatChitAnanda, it does imply that SatChitAnanda plays the role of Sakshi. It is the Observer. As compared to SatChitAnanda, Brahman plays a different role. Brahman is the material cause of the objects in the universe. It is the substratum of all the objects. Can you see the difference between SatChitAnanda and Brahman? One is the witness and the other is the material cause of the objects. This difference is quite stark. Based on this, how does one understand that SatChitAnanda and Brahman are identical? It is not easy.
- The scriptures teach us that SatChitAnanda or Brahman is non-dual. Non-dual means there is no second thing. It is a single

entity. Unfortunately, we do not experience non-duality, we always experience duality. We experience subjects "in here" and objects "out there." This is our experience. For non-duality, it must mean that subject is equal to object and object is equal to subject. Both subject and object should be one homogenous entity. It is not easy for the human mind to experience non-duality, but you can try and imagine some entity in which subject and object are the same. This unique structure of Subject = Object is not clear within SatChitAnanda or Brahman. Sometimes SatChitAnanda is referred to as Sakshi (witness) and sometimes it is referred to as creator with Maya Shakti. This unity of Subject and Object is not very explicit with SatChitAnanda.

- The source of any mind is SatChitAnanda. Everything comes only from SatChitAnanda, including the mind. We know the mind is powerful. All these powers in the mind are solely due to the grace of SatChitAnanda. According to Vedanta, you can break down the mind into the following structure.
    - Manas (Mind)
    - Buddhi (Intelligence)
    - Sakshi (Witness)
    - Ahamkara (Ego)

Unfortunately, I have not come across any proper discussion in the scriptures on how SatChitAnanda, which is the source of everything, becomes the mind. How does a non-dual SatChitAnanda become manas, buddhi, sakshi, and ahamkara? Why not something else? What is the connection between SatChitAnanda and these four parts of the mind? How do these four parts interact with each other in the mind to create the universe "out there"? This lack of proper explanation causes confusion. It makes the proper understanding of SatChitAnanda or Brahman more difficult and makes the subject matter more mysterious. This subject matter is discussed in the essay "Understanding the Mind."

There must be a better way to understand our inner core and the substratum of the universe. If you are a follower of the great saint Sri Ramana Maharshi, you will learn to focus on Self-Awareness. Understanding Self-Awareness is a better way to know your inner core or your true Self. If you get a proper understanding of Awareness and the inherent powers within Awareness, it will answer the objections mentioned here and bring clarity to your understanding of your inner core or Self.

Understanding Awareness

As we have discussed in the essay "Understanding Self-Awareness," Awareness is made up of Subject, Object, and Intelligence. Knower, Known, and Knowing are the three powers of Awareness.

- Awareness = Subject + Object + Intelligence
- Power of Awareness = Power of Knower + Power of Knowing + Power of Known

It must be understood that Subject, Object, Intelligence, and the three powers are not something outside in the world; they are within Awareness and make up Awareness. At this moment, you are aware you are reading this essay. This means that the three powers of Awareness are functioning to make the reading possible. The essay is the object, and the observer within you is the subject. The power of reading within Awareness connects the subject and object. Whenever you have any experience, all three powers are operational to make you aware of the experience.

These are awesome powers, and they are part of Awareness. For this essay, let us discuss Power of the Knower and Power of the Known. Once these two powers are properly understood, you can make the connection between these two powers and SatChitAnanda and Brahman.

Power of Knower

To understand this, let us ask ourselves some questions.

- *When we see the tree, who is seeing the tree?*
- *When we listen to music, who is listening to the music?*
- *When we taste the sweetness of chocolate, who is tasting this chocolate?*

As we have discussed, there is an Observer within us that witnesses everything. This witness is the Subject. This Subject is part of Awareness. This Subject has Power of the Knower. This power is built-in within the

Subject. This power gives the Subject the ability to see, listen, and taste different objects. In fact, it is the knower of everything that is possible.

If you follow the Vedanta terminology, you can call Subject the Sakshi, the witness. Subject and Sakshi are synonymous. SatChitAnanda is the Sakshi; it is Power of the Knower which enables the subject to witness the objects. See some examples below of how the Observer/Subject undertakes this task. The Subject is one, but it plays different roles.

- When it is the knower of seeing, the Observer/Subject is a Seer
- When it is the knower of hearing, the Observer/Subject is a Hearer
- When it is the knower of reading, the Observer/Subject is a Reader
- When it is the knower of running, the Observer/Subject is a Runner

SatChitAnanda is the power which allows the Subject to be the seer, hearer, reader, or runner. Mind is limited by the five senses, but the power of knowing is much broader and wider. It is the observer of everything.

We have seen earlier that Awareness has three powers–Power of Knower, Power of Knowing, and Power of Known. Of these three powers, SatChitAnanda is Power of the Knower. With this power, the Observer can witness everything which happens in the mind.

Power of Known or Objects

Power of the Known is another power within Awareness. It has the power to become any object. It can take any form that we experience in the mind. A good metaphor to understand this is that it is like a lump of Play-Doh. You can manipulate the Play-Doh to any shape. You can make a car, a tree, a house. The Play-Doh can become any shape. It is important to understand that, whatever shape is given, the content is always Play-Doh. Make a car, the content is Play-Doh. Make a tree, the content is still Play-Doh.

In the same way, the content of all the objects in the universe is Awareness. How does one understand this? If you see a circle, then awareness cannot take the shape of a square. If it does, you will never experience the (round) circle. Awareness must also be a circle with exactly the same dimensions. If you see a tree, then awareness must also take the shape of the tree. This tree must be filled up with Awareness. If the tree is half-filled with Awareness, you will experience only a half-tree.

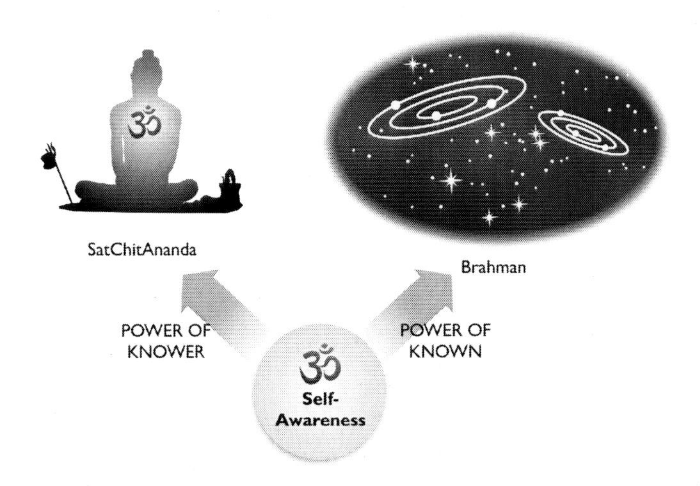

It is, therefore, correct to conclude that the content of the object must be Awareness. Awareness by itself is formless, but it has the potential to become any object. The power which manipulates Awareness to become any object is Power of the Known. If the incoming input from the senses is that of a car, Power of the Known will modify Awareness to take the shape of a car. If the input is that of music, Power of the Known will manipulate Awareness to that music. This Awareness allows you to be aware of these objects "out there."

Brahman is this Power of the Known. In this way, Brahman modifies itself to become any object. Brahman is the material cause of all the objects. Brahman, which is part of Awareness, is the substratum of everything in this universe.

So, we have seen that SatChitAnanda is Power of the Knower within Awareness, and Brahman is Power of the Known within Awareness.

Awareness is much wider; it contains all the three powers. Awareness is the underlying reality of both SatChitAnanda and Brahman.

That may be true, but how are SatChitAnanda and Brahman identical? From our discussion, it does not seem they are identical. Awareness is the common element between them, but they wield different powers. SatChitAnanda wields Power of the Knower and Brahman wields Power of the Known. They are not the same. However, the scriptures teach us that SatChitAnanda and Brahman are identical. How do we understand this? As we have discussed in the essay "Understanding Self-Awareness," Self-Awareness is non-dual. In this non-duality, Subject is equal to Object and Object is equal to Subject. Even the three powers of Awareness are non-dual. In Self-Awareness, Power of the Knower is equal to Power of the Known, and Power of the Known is equal to Power of the Knower.

In Self-Awareness, Subject = Object

In Self-Awareness, Power of Knower = Power of Known

Since Power of the Knower is identical to Power of the Known, it would mean that SatChitAnanda is identical to Brahman. Within Self-Awareness, both Brahman and SatChitAnanda are identical.

So, we can see that Awareness is the root of SatChitAnanda and Brahman. Understanding Self-Awareness is much easier than understanding SatChitAnanda and Brahman. Self-Awareness gives a much clearer picture and a deeper insight into our core and into the substratum of the universe. There is no separate SatChitAnanda for our inner core and for Brahman as the material cause of the universe. Awareness covers both these aspects. Therefore, there is less confusion. It is one entity, and it encompasses all the three powers. It is for this reason we will use the terms Self-Awareness and Awareness more often in these essays.

Having said this, the scriptures use SatChitAnanda and Brahman more often. To follow the scriptures, we have used the terms SatChitAnanda and Brahman at many different places. But they really mean Self-Awareness. Self-Awareness is the more accurate term. In the essays you will find all the three terms being used interchangeably.

12 | Knowing Is the Boss (of Everything)

Yes, Knowing is the Boss. Knowing means To Know. There is much more to Knowing than this simple definition. If you are a student of Vedanta, you will understand that Knowing is the same as Awareness or Consciousness or Chit. Knowing is the most powerful force in the universe and, surprisingly, this Knowing is our inner core. Knowing is the nature of the Real Self or I. The main goal of this essay is to understand the real meaning of Knowing. Understand the Power of Knowing. If you properly understand this, it is the most direct way to discover your Real Self.

Let us start our discussion with the following statements we make every day:

- I am listening to music.
- I am reading this book.
- I am thinking of traveling.
- I am talking on the phone.
- I am seeing a tree.

If you analyze these statements, you will notice that each statement has the subject "I am." Each statement has a different object–music, book, travel, phone, and tree, respectively. There is a verb which connects the subject with the object. More than a verb, there is an inherent power of intelligence which is connecting the subject with the object. This power reveals the object to the subject. How do we understand this power of intelligence?

Let us take the example of the power of listening, which is connecting "I am" with the music. If you follow science, it will tell us that the music waveform from the source will hit our eardrums. The job of the eardrum is to convert this into some form of an acoustic signal. This acoustic signal is then transmitted to the brain. What happens in the brain/mind is not known, but we do listen to music. There is an existent power in our mind which decodes and understands the incoming acoustic signal so that the subject "I am" can listen to the music. This decoding power and understanding within the mind are nothing but the power of listening, which makes the actual "act" of listening possible. This power of listening is made of intelligence with thc sole role of making listening possible.

Let us take another example, of seeing. The power of seeing has intelligence, which makes it possible for "I am" to know and see a tree. Without the power of seeing, none of us will see any object. Someone may argue that the eye provides this power. The eye does nothing other than converting the image into an optical signal and bringing the signal to the mind. What is the ability that decodes this optical signal into the understanding that this object is a tree? It is the power of seeing, which is within Intelligence and which allows us to know that there is a tree. This power of seeing knows that the optical signal is a tree.

The same similarly applies to reading, thinking, or talking. There is a power of reading, a power of thinking, and a power of talking. All these powers encapsulate the crux of intelligence. In fact, you can apply this logic to a much wider range of statements. Any statement which connects the subject with the object is connected by the power of intelligence.

Let us add another dimension by repeating the same statements in the following way. Please do not just read these statements but read them slowly, as if you are undertaking these tasks. I agree we do not talk in the following manner, but the sentences have been constructed in this manner to highlight the knowing part. Normally you would replace "I am knowing..." with "I know..."

- I am knowing that I am listening to music.
- I am knowing that I am reading this book.
- I am knowing that I am thinking of traveling.
- I am knowing that I am talking on the phone.
- I am knowing that I am seeing a tree.

1. There is a tremendous change in these statements as compared to the earlier statements. "I am listening to music," "I am reading this book,"

etc., are no longer self-contained sentences; they are the object in the statements. The "I am" in "I am listening..." is no longer the subject–it is part of the object. The "I am" in "I am reading..." is now part of the object. When you said "I am listening to music," you always felt that "I am" is really my inner core. You had the impression that "I am" referred to your own self.

2. However, the moment you apply the Knowing part to the sentence, everything seems to change. A new "I am" pops up, and the earlier "I am" becomes part of the object. Can there be two "I am" within you? Obviously not. Vedanta teaches that there is a universal Real Self which is our common inner core. The "I am" in "I am knowing..." is your Real Self, and the earlier "I am" in "I am listening..." is really part of the object. If this is understood, it can be a big change in our perspective.

This "I am" in "I am listening..." is really your ego. The ego always thinks it is the Real Self. Vedanta teaches that the ego masquerades as the Real I, but when you make a proper inquiry, you will find that the ego is like any other object. Ego is just another thought in the mind.

3. Daily, as you apply the Knowing part to every sentence you say or think, you will discover your Real Self within you. The "I am" in "I am knowing..." is your Real Self. Whenever you do any activity, watch carefully how the knowing part pops out within you. Repeatedly say "I know this," "I know that," and focus on the "I know" part; you will find that the Knowing part comes out from a spiritual heart.

You could live your entire life saying "I am listening to music," "I am reading this book," etc. This way you will never discover your Real Self. The Real Self will remain hidden. The moment you add "I am knowing" or "I know" to all your activities, the Knowing part pops out from the spiritual heart. The spiritual heart is not your physical heart but is your Seed Body. This is like how the seed of a tree has a potential of the tree within the seed. The tree seed can only become a tree, that too a specific type of tree. A mango tree seed cannot become an apple tree. In the same way, each one of us has a Seed Body. This Seed Body plays out the blueprint of our life. This Seed Body is our spiritual heart. According to Sri Ramana Maharshi, it is two fingers from the center on the right side in the rib cage.

4. Knowing is nothing but the intelligence which connects the subject "I am" with different objects. Knowing is the common element which connects the subject with all the different objects in the universe. If you study the statements made earlier, you will realize that Knowing is the ultimate intelligence. Knowing knows listening, Knowing knows reading, Knowing knows thinking, Knowing knows talking, and Knowing knows seeing. Power of Knowing includes the power of listening, reading, thinking, talking, and seeing. The scope and width of Power of Knowing is infinite, and it encompasses everything which is to be known in the universe. To put it differently, the power of listening, reading, thinking, talking, seeing, etc.–all these powers come out of Power of Knowing. Power of Knowing is the ultimate intelligence.

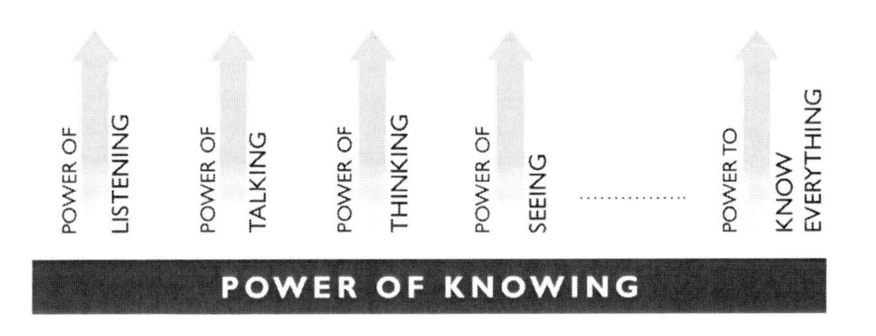

Someone might say, "I am knowing that I cannot speak Chinese." The ego "I" cannot speak Chinese, and the Real "I" knows that fact. This does not mean that the Real "I" does not know Chinese. The knowledge of Chinese is within Knowing. If you now learn Chinese, the ego "I" will speak Chinese and the Real "I" will know this fact.

Knowing is indeed the boss of all the knowledge and intelligence in the universe. The question to ask is, from where does all the knowledge and intelligence come?

The simple answer is: Awareness. Understand Awareness and you will learn that Knowing is a key ingredient of Awareness.

Understanding Awareness

As we have discussed in many essays, Awareness is the most powerful force in the universe, and it is the underlying reality of this universe. It has the power to connect with a form present in the mind and create an experience of which you are aware. Awareness is made of Subject, Object, and Intelligence. Knower, Known, and Knowing are the three powers of Awareness. It must be clear that:

- Awareness = Subject + Object + Intelligence
- Power of Awareness = Power of Knower + Power of Known + Power of Knowing

Wherever there is Awareness, there must be present Subject, Object, and Intelligence with all the three powers. At this moment you are aware you are reading this essay. This awareness has a subject, object, and intelligence.

Power of Knowing is the key power of Awareness. Power of the Knower only witnesses what is available to witness. Power of the Known has the power to become the different objects in the universe. Power of Knowing is crucial; it decodes the objects and lets the subject witness these objects. This intelligence or Power of Knowing is the driving force of Awareness and completes any experience in the mind.

The Knowing/Intelligence within Awareness has an unlimited range of power; in fact, it is infinite. We can comprehend only those experiences that our mind can handle. Our mind is full of ignorance and has a limited Power of Knowing. Awareness is not limited by the capacity of our mind. It is the source for intelligence; it has knowledge about everything possible. What is amazing is that this unlimited intelligence, this pure intelligence, this Knowing is available within each one of us. Remove the deep-rooted ignorance and the unlimited Power of Knowing will be available to everyone.

Knowing and the Five Koshas

In an earlier essay, "Understanding the Pancha Koshas," we saw that every living being is made up of the following five koshas (sheaths).

1. Annamaya Kosha: sheath made of food–this is our physical body.
2. Pranamaya Kosha: sheath made of energy–to keep the physical body functional.
3. Manomaya Kosha: sheath made of mind stuff.
4. Vijnanamaya Kosha: sheath made of intelligence/ knowledge.
5. Anandamaya Kosha: sheath made of bliss.

We saw that these five koshas covered our inner core, which is Self-Awareness. If you peel away the five layers, you will reach your inner core. The technique taught is that you learn and understand that you are not any of the five koshas. This allows you to peel each layer till you discover your inner self.

While discussing the five koshas, we saw that perception of external objects takes place in the Manomaya Kosha. The thinking, learning, and understanding takes place in the Vijnanamaya Kosha. The feeling and all the emotions take place in the Anandamaya Kosha.

What about Knowing discussed in this essay? Where does this fit in the hierarchy of these five koshas? Knowing is the ultimate level. This level is beyond the five koshas. It functions in our innermost core. It functions in the realm of Awareness. To function in this realm is the ultimate goal for everyone. The goal is to function in this realm.

13 | Life Is a Living Wave

Really! Yes, really, "life is a living wave" is the only truth. It sounds completely bizarre and even more difficult to comprehend. We are used to the physical world. We see all the activity taking place in the physical world; we daily live and interact in the physical world. We get up in the morning, go to work, return home, spend time with the family, and then go to sleep. All this happens in the physical world, so where and how does the "living wave" come into the picture?

Do we really live in the physical world? To answer this question truthfully, I have a challenge–show me a "real," "live" or "now" object in this world. Everything you see or interact with in this world is just a "memory" object. It is a dated object. There are no "now" or real objects in the physical world. The sun you see is not real, it is a "now minus eight minutes" version of the sun. Why? We know it takes light eight minutes to reach us from the sun, so the sun we see in the sky is a "now minus eight minutes" sun. It is not a "now" version of the sun.

The sun we see is not a "live," "real" or "now" sun; it is basically a memory object which is a "now minus eight minutes" version. In the same way, the moon we see at night is a "now minus three seconds" version of the moon, because the light takes three seconds to reach us from the moon. The plane in the sky is a "now minus 300 milliseconds" version, the tree outside my window is a "now minus 10 microseconds" version. This logic applies to every object in the physical world. It is just impossible for anyone to know or interact with a "live" or "now" object in this physical world. This not only applies to objects but also to people, animals, and any living being. Anything and everything in this physical universe is made up of only memory objects.

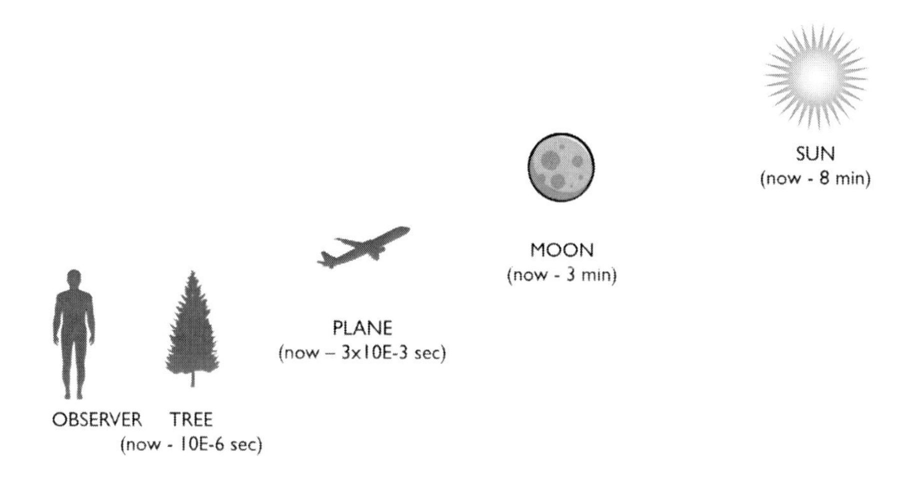

No 'Now' Objects in This Universe

You can compare the physical world to the playback from a digital video recorder (DVR). The DVR contains recorded events, and it is made up of only memory objects. When you are watching the DVR, you are never watching a "live" event, you are always watching the recording of a live event. So, it is correct to say that a DVR is made up of only memory objects; you will never find a "real" or "live" object by looking at a DVR recording. Like a DVR, the physical world is also made of only memory objects. It is never real; it is made of only dated objects.

If there is a recorded event in the DVR, there must have been a live event before. The live event is recorded in the DVR, and then the recorded event is played back as and when required. The same logic and reasoning apply to the physical world. We know the physical world is made of only memory objects or recorded objects. Like in the DVR case, there must be a "now" or "live" object/event for everything in the universe. The sun we see is a "now minus eight minutes" version of the sun, so where is the actual sun? Where is the "now" sun? It must be somewhere. In the same way, the moon we see is a "now minus three seconds" version; the actual or "now" moon must be available somewhere. This logic applies to all objects (living and nonliving). All these "now" objects in the world must exist somewhere–but where?

From the DVR example, it would seem that there are two types of events–the live event and the recorded event. They are both separate and distinct. If the live event is happening now, the recorded event is viewed later. In the same way, this world is also made of two types of objects–memory objects and "now" objects. They too are separate and distinct. The physical world around us is made of only memory objects. In the same vein, the "now" universe must be made of only "now" objects. A universe with the existence of memory objects alone is impossible.

Unfortunately, we know virtually nothing about the "now" objects and the "now" universe, and science has made little attempt to investigate this area. The focus of this article is to explore the "now" objects or the "now" universe. We will use both science and Vedanta to support our explanation. To get a better understanding, we will try to answer the following questions:

1. Where does the "now" universe reside?
2. Of what is the "now" universe made?
3. How does the "now" universe function?

1. Where Does the "Now" Universe Reside?

The first question to ask is: what is "now"? "Now" is something which is not the past or the future. It is not t=0+ or t=0–; it is t=0. It is the current moment. It is the present. It is now.

"Now" is time-based. It comes and goes rapidly, so it is not easy to grasp. But, then again, as one "now" goes away, another "now" moment takes its place. There is always a "now" moment. There is never an instant when there is no "now" moment. Do all the "now" moments need to be the same? The single-word answer is–No. They are never the same. The tree from this "now" moment to the next "now" moment is not the same, because it has grown older by the small time-fraction.

You can never compare two "now" moments. The preceding or coming "now" moment is either the past or the future; you can have only one "now" moment at any given time.

So where does the "now" moment reside? It is not incorrect to say that t=0 is the "now" moment. The start of the time meter is always at t=0, and this is the “now” moment. If time flows, as it always does, then t=0 becomes t=0+ and it is no longer the “now” moment. However, a new t=0 takes hold, and it replaces the old one. In this way, the “now” moment is always present. It is never not present. This “now” moment is t=0.

Okay, the “now” moment or t=0 is always present, but where is its location? One thing is clear: it cannot be present in space, because everything “out there” is only a memory object. If it is not “out there,” where else can it possibly be located? A clue: it must be outside space and time. Where is this outside? The surprising answer is that the “now” moment or t=0 is located within you. Vedanta has always taught this. To get a better understanding of this idea, let us investigate the “now” moment.

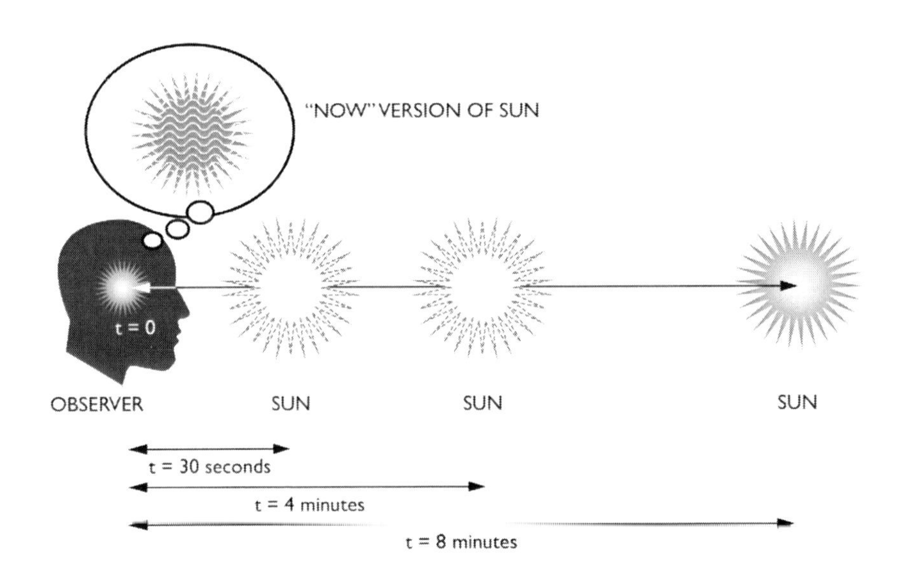

The easiest way to locate “now” or t=0 is to find the point where light will take zero seconds to reach us. We saw earlier that the sun is the “now minus eight minutes” version. This is because light takes eight minutes to reach us. Let us play around with this idea. Suppose that, for whatever reason, the sun could move and we could see a “now minus four minutes”

version of the sun ... what does this mean? It means that light would take four minutes to reach us and the sun would be located at the halfway mark, which will be nearer to us. If the sun moves even closer and we see the "now minus 30 seconds" version, it will mean that the sun is much closer to us. Using this reasoning, where do we find the "now minus zero seconds" sun? This must be the place where light will take zero seconds to reach us. The only correct answer is that the "now" version of the sun is within us as light will take zero seconds to reach us. This is the Observer within us. This is the Observer who is watching the sun and all other objects "out there." This logic and reasoning apply not only to the sun but to every object in the universe.

From the above discussion, it seems that the "now" location is within us. This location has all the "now" objects and the "now" universe. The "now" universe operates at this location. This "now" universe is beyond and outside of space and time. So, the question is, what is there which is beyond space and time? What is this location? Science does not have an answer. Vedanta does. Vedanta teaches us that Mind and Awareness are beyond space and time. Mind and Awareness is the t=0 location. Therefore, the "now" universe resides within the Mind and Awareness.

2. Of What Is the "Now" Universe Made?

We now understand that the "now" universe with all the "now" objects resides within the Mind and Awareness. The next question is: of what are the "now" objects made? What is the composition of the "now" universe? Surprisingly, you will get a clue to the answers from quantum physics.

"Now" Version Objects Made of Waves

Quantum physics teaches us that light has both wave-like and particle-like properties. Sometimes light is a particle and sometimes a wave. This idea was cemented when Louis de Broglie, a French doctoral student, wrote in his thesis that not only light but all matter must have both wave and particle properties. Here, matter means matter, including you, me, planets, cars–in fact, any living or nonliving object in this universe. In 1927, the de Broglie hypothesis was proven experimentally; thus, all matter is both a wave and a particle. In 1929, de Broglie was awarded the Nobel Prize for his theory. He is the only person to ever receive a Nobel Prize based on a doctoral thesis. If you are interested, you can read the essay "Quantum Physics–Overview" for more details.

Okay, that every object has a particle and wave duality is a fact. Is there a connection between the particle/wave duality and the memory/"now" object duality? Yes, there is. We have seen earlier that the physical world is made of only memory objects. These memory objects are the particle aspect of the duality. You will never see a wave in the physical world. In the physical world you will see only gross objects, which are the particle aspect of objects. So, we can agree that the particle aspect of the duality makes the memory object.

What about the "now" object? The "now" object can never be physical. It is outside the physical world. It is at t=0. The "now" universe cannot contain the particle aspect. So, what does the "now" object contain? Since the particle aspect is not possible, the only right answer is that the "now" object is made of the wave aspect of the duality. So, the correct conclusion is that "now" objects in the "now" universe are made of waves. Since the "now" universe functions in the mind, therefore these vibrating waves must reside within the mind. These waves are beyond and outside of space and time.

Quantum physics does show that the "now" universe is made of waves. Unfortunately, quantum physics does not give any details about these waves. What is the composition of these waves? Of what are the waves made? Luckily, Vedanta comes to the rescue and provides great insight into the wave aspect of matter.

Vedanta teaches us that all the objects in the mind take the form of waveforms or vrittis. Vrittis are vibrations in the mind caused by objects. These waveforms are made of "mind stuff." What is mind stuff? It literally means stuff that is made of mind. As explained in the essay "Understanding the Mind," these object waveforms or vrittis are sentient and made of intelligence. Knowledge is the substratum of the vrittis. Not easy to grasp, but these object vrittis are made of knowledge. Since they are made of knowledge, the vrittis know what object they represent. Every vritti is unique in representing a different object.

These object vrittis are complicated. Let us try and understand them. At any given moment, there is an object waveform. As time changes, the object waveform will also change. A new waveform is created with every passing moment. No object waveform is lost. All the past waveforms are still present within the object vrittis. All the past waveforms, right from the birth of the object to this current moment, combine to create a single cumulative waveform for the object. The object waveform or vritti is the total of all the waveforms for the object, right from its inception to the present time.

How do we understand this? Let us study an example–the sun is over 4.5 billion years old. The cumulative vritti of the sun will include all the waveforms for every moment in time. Every moment is part of the waveform for the sun. All these individual vrittis combine to create a "grand" waveform for the sun. As time passes, new waveforms are added to the cumulative profile of the sun. In the sun's cumulative vritti, the profile for each moment of the sun since inception is available. If you are on Earth, you will see the "now minus eight minutes" version of the sun. This version is present within the cumulative vritti of the sun. From Mars, you will see the "now minus 13 minutes" version of the sun. All the versions of the sun are present, and different versions are chosen depending on the distance from the sun.

We have just seen the example of the sun with all the historical waveforms or vrittis. This will apply to all the objects in the universe. Every object in the universe is a cumulative waveform of every moment in time. Your waveform will be a total of all the vrittis since your birth. The trees, cars, planets, galaxies–each one of them will have a time-wise total waveform.

To add to the complexity of the waveforms, all objects in the universe with their own cumulative waveforms will combine to create one big waveform for the universe. We can call this the "now" universe waveform. This "now" universe waveform includes everything which is contained in the universe. Nothing is left out.

A question can be asked: how does the gigantic "now" universe waveform keep track of the individual objects within the waveform? As mentioned earlier, each object waveform or vritti is made of Knowledge. Each subsection of the waveform has intelligence and knows what object it represents. Even if all the object wave functions combine to form a single "now" universe vritti, knowledge of each object is maintained.

Before we move forward, let us summarize what we know about the "now" universe.

- We know the "now" universe is made of vrittis or mental waveforms, and they reside within the mind.
- Every living and nonliving object has its own wave function. When waves are superimposed on each other, they form complex waveforms. The final "now" universe waveform contains the waveforms of everything in the universe. Nothing is left out.
- We know the "now" universe resides within the Mind. Awareness is the source of the mind. The "now" universe vrittis get their intelligence from Awareness. Therefore, the "now" universe is always conscious, sentient, and alive.
- We know there is a cosmic mind and an individual mind. The cosmic mind is the total of all the individual minds. The "now" universe operates in the cosmic mind; a small part of the "now" universe operates in the individual mind. What part would depend on what we are currently observing. Each one is observing a different part.

3. How Does the "Now" Universe Function?

So, how does the "now" universe function? We know there is a cosmic mind and an individual mind. The cosmic mind is the total of all the individual minds. The "now" universe operates in the cosmic mind; a small part, or the subsection of the "now" universe, operates in the individual mind.

All action happens only in the mind. This seems contradictory. It does appear that we perform actions in the physical world. However, the correct interpretation is that everything happens first in the subtle world or in the "now" universe. These "now" objects are then manifested as memory objects in the physical world. Any action seen in the physical world has already been completed in the world of vrittis. The subtle world with vrittis comes first and then the physical world. Even quantum physics supports this concept. Quantum physics teaches that any wave collapses in the presence of an observer to become a particle. This means that the particle comes only after a wave has collapsed. If there is no observer, there will be no collapsing of the wave and there will be no particle, and the wave will continue to be a wave. This shows that the "now" objects made of vrittis come first, and then these "now" objects become memory objects in the physical world.

We have seen earlier that the vrittis are made of knowledge, they are made of intelligence. What does this mean? It means that there is a software code within these vrittis which provides intelligence to any vritti. Artificial Intelligence, the trending technology, is a good comparison to understand this process. You can teach a robot to undertake a variety of actions. All this is possible because of the sophisticated software code written for the robot. The learning process happens in the software code. Once the process is learned in the software code, only then can the robot physically undertake the required action. The vritti has a similar type of software code which provides intelligence to the vritti. This software code is the backbone of the intelligence.

Each object vritti has a different role to play. It has different characteristics; it is made differently. The software code will reflect all these aspects for the object vritti. Every object vritti has its own software code. We already know how complex the universe is. We can only imagine the complexity of the software code that is required to cover everything in the universe.

To explain this, let us take an interaction between the ego and an object vritti. Let us take an example of cutting the branch of a tree with an ax. You see this action in the physical world. But we know that everything happens first in the "now" universe–the world of vrittis. How does this work? There is an ax vritti. By itself, the ax vritti cannot do anything. The ego with your body vritti combines with the ax vritti. Now the ax vritti is ready for action. The ax vritti has the software code for all the functions and features of the ax. One of the features is to cut and break objects apart. This feature is part of the software code for the ax vritti. The (body + ax) vritti interacts with the tree vritti. In this interaction, the (body + ax) vritti modifies the tree vritti. It modifies the software code of the tree vritti. In this process of modification, the tree vritti is without that branch. In the "now" universe, there is no actual cutting of the branch, but the modification of the software code reflects the change.

When this process is being projected, it will show the memory object of an ax. It will show the memory object of the person cutting the branch from the tree, which is also a memory object. This type of process is applicable to all the interactions among objects in the universe.

It seems clear that there is a fully functioning subtle world made of complex waveforms. This is the only real world. This is the "now" universe. This subtle world operates outside space and time, and this "now" universe is within us. So close but seems really far (another power of ignorance). The physical world is not that real; it is only made of memory objects. It always seems that we are interacting with the physical world, but this is untrue. The real interaction takes place in the "now" universe. The interaction of the subtle waveforms is projected out as the physical world by the power of Awareness. There is no denying that there is limited knowledge about the "now" universe. More efforts must be made to really understand the functioning of this subtle universe.

14 | Unity of Minds

We know each one of us has a mind. According to Vedanta, the mind is the subtle body, and it is made up of thoughts, perceptions, feelings, and emotions. In the same way, we have a gross body, which is the physical body we possess. There is no denying that each one of us is physically separated in space. Your gross body is there, my gross body is here, and in the same way, everyone is at a separate location in space. Yes, the physical body is separated in space. What about the mind? You will be surprised to learn that all the minds in this universe, at "this" moment, are at one location. Shocking, but true! Your mind, my mind, and everyone's mind at "this" moment is at one and the same location. There is unity of minds.

The only way to understand this is to think differently. Do not think about space or distance but think in terms of time. This is the key to understanding this concept. We have seen in other essays that the mind is always at t=0. Your mind, my mind, and all minds are always at t=0. We know t=0 is the "now" moment. So, for the "now" moment, there is unity among everyone's mind. It does not matter where your body is in space, but for the "now" moment there is unity of all the minds.

All the minds are at one spot (time-wise), which is outside space and time. The mind never moves; it is always at t=0, it is always outside the spacetime fabric. The body moves, and it operates inside the spacetime fabric. There is always a "now" moment, therefore the unity of all the minds is always maintained. We have also seen that the t=0 or "now" moment is within each one of us. This means that at this "now" moment, your mind and the entire cosmic mind which includes all the minds is present within us. Can you guess the number of individual minds in this universe? I think it is countless. Imagine the population of humans, animals, other creatures, plants, etc. To this you can add life on other planets. All these countless minds are within us at t=0 or the "now" moment. Wow–what a feeling!

If your friend is sitting in front of you, his physical body may be in front of you, but his mind is within you. Your friend will also have the same experience. He will see your physical body in front of him, but your mind will be within him. If there 10 people sitting in the same room, each one of them will have the same experience. Each of them will see the nine physical bodies "out there," but all the 10 minds will be within each one of them at t=0.

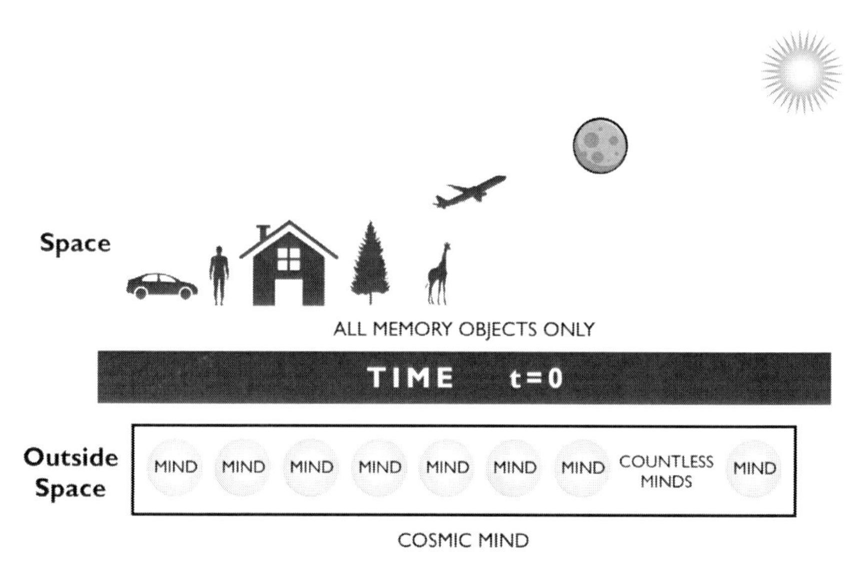

How do we understand this? We have discussed elsewhere that the physical universe "out there" is made of only "memory" objects. This means that all objects "out there" are dated stuff, and there are no "now" objects in the physical universe. Why? Because it takes light a finite amount of time to reach us. So, we always see the dated version of the object.

We know that light takes eight minutes to reach us from the sun. The sun we see is a "now minus eight minutes" version of the sun, it is not the "now" version of the sun. In the same way, the moon we see is a "now minus three seconds" version of the moon, the tree outside the window may be some milliseconds old, the computer in front of you may be some nanoseconds old. There is nothing which is "now" in the physical universe.

The mind resides outside the spacetime fabric and it is t=0. Therefore, from your point of view, the person in front of you is a memory object, but his mind is at t=0, which is within you. The person in front of you will have a similar experience. He will see a memory object of you, but your mind, which is at t=0, is within him. This will apply to each living being in the universe. Basically, each person creates their own universe on the spacetime fabric, and this fabric starts with the individual mind.

In the essay "Life Is a Living Wave," we have explained that there is a fully functioning subtle universe, which is made of waveforms. The waveform of the objects in the universe is available to the cosmic mind and individual minds. The waveform of all the objects is within the cosmic mind, but a subset of this will be available in the individual minds.

Once the unity of all the minds is properly understood, then the interaction of the mind with the "now" universe waveform becomes clear. All the minds are at one place and the subset of the "now" universe waveform is present in the individual minds at t=0. The subset waveform would depend upon what each mind is watching. Once the waveform in each mind enters the presence of the Observer, the waveform collapses in every mind and then each mind projects its own spacetime fabric and the physical world (depending upon the waveform being watched) "out there."

Space is created with the collapsing of the waveform. Your body, my body, and all the objects being viewed are placed at different locations in space. It must be understood that all the minds are still at t=0–it has not moved. From your viewpoint, you are always carrying both the mind and the body. Wherever you go, the t=0 is still with you. All the people you see–they are all memory objects, and their minds are within you. All the people will have the same experience; their mind and all the minds are within them, and all the people around them are memory objects.

It is interesting to note that the Observer or Sakshi is common for all the minds. There is no separate Observer for each mind, but one Observer for all the minds. All the minds are at the same spot at t=0; the single

Observer collapses all the waves simultaneously in each mind and watches all the minds simultaneously. What can one say—this is sheer magic; this is the power of Awareness! Vedanta calls this Maya Shakti.

To conclude, there is complete unity of minds, and all the minds of every living being are at the same spot outside the spacetime fabric. Each mind projects and creates its own universe.

15 | Understanding the Five Elements

The five elements usually refer to space, air, fire, water, and earth. Interestingly, reference to these five elements is found in most of the ancient civilizations, including Greece, Egypt, Persia, Babylonia, Japan, Tibet, and India. The list is not the same, but they are similar. How and why this happened is a mystery.

The terms space, air, fire, water, and earth by themselves do not indicate any common thread. They do not have any commonality between them. This has meant that there is no proper or consistent interpretation for these five elements. The Chinese interpretation is that there is a connection between these five elements and the life force. Yoga interprets that understanding these five elements is the key to proper health and spiritual advancement. Ayurveda bases its entire theory on the five elements. The human body is made up of these five elements and managing them effectively is the goal of Ayurveda.

So many different interpretations do cause confusion. There is no proper consensus on what these five elements really mean. The five elements really represent the building blocks of Nature and all the matter "out there." Everything in this universe is made up of these five elements.

I am sure science will disagree. Scientists will not agree that these are the five basic elements. Over the years, science has developed a detailed periodic table with 118 basic elements. All of us have studied these elements of the periodic table at school. Each element in the periodic table has a different atomic structure. These basic elements mix and combine to create all the possible matter in this universe. So, according to science, these 118 elements are the basic elements and not the five elements as indicated by the ancient civilizations.

Agreed, all the visible matter "out there" is made up of these 118 elements. Just to show the limitations of the periodic table, the following questions can be asked:

- What is the common building block of these 118 elements?
- Of what is sound made?
- Of what is smell made?
- Of what is taste made?
- Of what is touch made?

How should we answer these important questions? The elements in the periodic table do not cover these questions. Science does not really investigate these questions. So, the interpretation of the periodic table is limited and incomplete.

Vedanta Interpretation

One of the best explanations for the five elements is given by Sri Vidyaranya in Chapter 2 of *Panchadasi*. This chapter is called "The Differentiation of the Five Elements." According to Sri Vidyaranya, the gross elements are space, air, fire, water, earth, while the inner qualities are sound, touch, form, taste, smell. The qualities of these elements are, in respective order: sound, which is the quality of space; touch, which is the quality of air; form, which is the quality of fire; taste, which is the quality of water; and smell, which is the quality of earth. These are the qualities of the five elements. Let us understand each element briefly.

Space: Space has only one quality and that is sound. Space does not make sound, but it does reverberate sound like an echo. We cannot touch, taste, or smell space. Sound alone is the quality of space. There is a humming sound in space. Some people say that OM is the sound heard in space.

Air: Air has two qualities. It can make sound, and it can be felt. You can hear the air (the wind blowing) and you can feel the air, whether cold or hot. Therefore, sound and touch are the qualities of air. The main quality of air is touch, as sound is also available within space.

Fire: Fire has three qualities: form, touch, and sound. You can see the form of fire, you can feel the heat of fire, and you can hear the crackling sound of fire. Form is the main quality of fire. Sound is available within space, and air and touch are available within air.

Water: Water has four qualities–taste, form, touch, and sound. You can touch water, see its form, taste water, and also hear its sound. The main quality of water is taste. The other qualities are present in the other elements.

Earth: Earth has five qualities: smell, taste, form, touch, and sound. Hardness is the touch of earth; the breaking of an object is the sound. A variety of forms are made of earth. Earth has taste, such as sweetness, bitterness. It also has a smell–a good smell, a bad smell, a fragrance, or a bad odor. These are the five qualities of earth. Smell is the main quality of earth, as it is not present in the other elements.

Find below a quick summary of the elements and their qualities.

Element	Main Quality	Other Qualities
Space	Sound	
Air	Touch	Sound
Fire	Form	Sound, Touch
Water	Taste	Sound, Touch, and Form
Earth	Smell	Sound, Touch, Form, and Taste

There are five qualities in earth, four in water, three in fire, two in air, one in space. You will notice that space is the most subtle element, and earth is the most gross element. There is a steady progress in grossification as you move from space to earth. Air is more gross than space. Fire is more gross than air. Water is more gross than fire and, finally, earth is more gross than water.

Vedanta teaches that if you mix and combine these qualities in the elements, you get all the different objects in the universe. This process is called Panchikarana. Panchikarana is the method of transforming subtle matter to gross matter. Adi Shankaracharya, a great saint of ancient

India, wrote a treatise on this theory, titled *Panchikaranam*, which was elaborated and commented on by many of his students and followers.

Panchikarana is based on the quintuplicating of the five subtle elements–space, air, fire, water, and earth. The five elements first divided themselves into two parts of 50% each, one 50% part of which was further divided into four parts. Four parts of 50% make one-eighth parts. In the 50% part you can have one of the elements; in the one-eighth parts, you can have the other four elements. For example, in the 50% part you can have fire, while in the other four parts of one-eighth each you can have space, air, water and earth. This process of division and combination goes on till the gross elements are produced. Understanding the Panchikarana process is not easy. The best takeaway from this could be that the five elements mix and match to create different objects.

Understanding Panchikarana or the five elements is not clear-cut or well-defined. Studying the different commentaries about the five elements, I feel that these elements are just symbols representing a category of objects. Nothing more, nothing less. For example, earth represents solid objects, and these solid objects must have all the five qualities–sound, touch, form, taste, and smell. In the same way, water represents all liquids. All liquids must have the four qualities–sound, touch, form, and taste. To put it differently, if an object has all the five qualities, it must be a solid object. The proportion between sound, touch, form, taste, and smell could be different, but it will have all the five qualities.

It does seem that the names of the five elements are more symbolic, and that what is important is the qualities which make up the objects. Sound, taste, form, smell, and taste are the five building blocks for all the objects in the universe. The only thing we know about objects is these five qualities. We perceive these five qualities in objects. Our connection to the external world is through these five qualities.

Let us take the example of a mango. How does one describe a mango? It is by describing the five qualities. The form of the mango, the taste of the mango, the smell of the mango, and so on. All these are qualities which are built into the mango. These qualities define a mango. In the same way, every object will have its own unique mix of all or some of these qualities. All the qualities will not be present in every object. Some objects will have only one quality, others two, three, four, or five, depending on the type of object.

To understand how these qualities are built into different objects, let us look at it from two different perspectives:

- Energy and Qualities
- Vibrations and Qualities

Energy and Qualities

We have seen that space has one quality, i.e., sound. How do we understand this? Science will tell you that if you shout in deep space far away from Earth, no one can hear because there is no sound in space. Yes, sound is there within the atmosphere of Earth, but no sound is possible outside this bubble. In other essays, including "Projection–The Only Truth," we have shown how space is created. It is created by stretching the spacetime fabric, which is made of time. The energy stretches out time, so that one second of the fabric will create 186,000 miles of space. Another interesting fact is that the undercoating of the spacetime fabric pulsates with energy. The pixels within the spacetime fabric, which are 10E-44 seconds apart, combine with energy to create the undercoating for the spacetime fabric. Every possible frequency is available at each pixel point on the spacetime fabric. Even science now acknowledges the presence of this undercoating of energy, and they call it the vacuum energy. This vacuum energy is in every part of space. There is no place which is untouched. Our understanding of space is that there is nothing present. This is incorrect; the undercoating of space is full of energy. This undercoating is pulsating, vibrating, and bubbling with energy.

We know that sound is caused by vibrations. Anything which vibrates must have a frequency or a combination of frequencies. Here the term "sound" is more generic, representing the full spectrum of frequencies. We are used to understanding sound with a frequency range of 20 Hz to 20 kHz, which is what humans hear. The generic sound used in the five elements covers the entire spectrum of frequencies. Based on the Planck constant, the maximum possible frequency is 10E+41 Hz. This would mean that the frequency spectrum in Nature is up to 10E+41 Hz.

The ancient Indian rishis were clear about this and covered this entire frequency spectrum with the term OM. If you chant OM by breaking down OM into three syllables (A,U,M), you will cover the entire frequency range which is achievable by human beings. Start with A, which is low frequency, then move on to U, which is midrange, and finally M, which is high frequency. The sound frequency range for humans is limited. OM truly signifies the entire possible frequency range (0 to 10E+41Hz.)

Everything in this universe is caused by vibrations. Sound, we know, is caused by vibration; even taste, form, smell, and touch are caused only by vibration. If vibration is the cause, it must have a frequency. This frequency must be part of OM. All the possible vibrations are part of OM. It is for this reason that OM is given such importance in the Indian scriptures–because it represents everything that is possible. OM therefore represents the divine because it covers everything which is possible. Putting it another way, everything in this universe is made of vibrations and hence must be part of OM.

The sound quality within space is all-encompassing. The vibration for touch, form and taste are part of OM.

Vibration and Qualities

We have just seen that vibrations are the real source of five qualities–sound, touch, form, taste, and smell. This is not our experience. We do not experience these vibrations. Instead, we see forms, we hear sound, we smell, we taste, and we feel a touch. So how does vibration fit into this full process? To understand this, it is important to know the correct perception process.

Science teaches us that a fully functioning universe exists "out there." This universe is full of objects. We perceive these objects through our five senses–eyes for form, ears for sound, tongue for taste, nose for smell, and skin for touch. Unfortunately, this is not correct; it is not how perception really works. There are many limitations. In the essay "Projection–The Only Truth," we have explained through the following five methods why the current perception method is not correct:

1. By using science
2. By using logic
3. By using math
4. By using quantum physics
5. By using neuroscience

The only truth is that each individual projects their own universe. There is a fully functioning subtle universe which is projected. This subtle universe is made of vibrations. Each object in the subtle universe is made of vibrations. A detailed analysis of these vibrations is given in the essay "Life Is a Living Wave." Let us now connect these vibrations with the five qualities.

The vibrations are full of energy. The five qualities are superimposed on these vibrations. The energy is like the content of the vibrations, while the five qualities are the form superimposed on it. This energy and these qualities are the definition of subtle objects. An object is nothing but a grouping of these five qualities.

Going back to the example of the mango, there is a subtle version of the mango. The subtle version of the mango will have the five qualities. The sweetness of taste, the beautiful aroma in smell, the form of the mango, the touch, and the sound. All these qualities are built into the subtle version of the mango. Each quality in the object is like DNA–it is unique. The DNA represents the characteristics of that quality in the subtle object. The DNA for form will be different from the DNA for sound. Each object will have a mix of these independent DNAs, representing different qualities. If you ask of what an object is made, the simple answer is that it is made up of just these five qualities. There is nothing other than these five qualities in the object. The sound quality will have the sound characteristics which are inbuilt in the product. Say you drop a glass–it will shatter. The type of sound it will make is part of the DNA of glass. The smell emitted by roses is part of the DNA of roses. The vibrations which represent an object will have the DNA of the five qualities.

Vibrations and the Five Senses

We have just seen that all subtle objects are made of vibrations and the five qualities. These objects are available in the subtle universe. So how does the living being perceive these objects? The perception takes place in the subtle universe. There is the physical ear, and there is a subtle ear. There is the physical eye, and there is a subtle eye. There is a subtle version of all five senses. These five senses scout for the subtle objects. The subtle eye will look for the form characteristics in the subtle objects. The subtle objects may have all the five qualities, but the subtle eye will look for the form part in the object. The subtle ear will look for the sound characteristics in the object. In the same way, the five subtle sense organs are continuously looking at objects and looking for the matching characteristics in these objects. Once they find the matching characteristics, they will filter that part and send it to the mind for processing. The subtle sense organs will scout for the objects which are in their vicinity. Someone sitting at home can scout for the objects nearby, while someone in a restaurant will scout for the objects in that place. In this way, each living being scouts for a different set of objects.

After passing through the five subtle sense organs, the vibrations are presented to the mind. In the essay "Understanding the Mind," we have a detailed analysis of how the mind processes the incoming signals from the sense organs. Here is a quick recap. The mind has the following four parts:

1. Manas
2. Buddhi
3. Ahamkara
4. Sakshi

The incoming vibrations from the different sense organs are presented to Manas. Manas has Power of the Known. This power allows the vibrations to become the object which is presented to Manas. If the vibration has been received through the ear, then the ingredients to make sound are added to the vibrations. If the vibration is received through the nose, the ingredients to become smell are added by Power of the Known in Manas. The smell could be sweet or sour; this would depend on the DNA of the incoming vibration. Manas does not know what the object is, it just adds the code for the material ingredient depending on the type of quality.

Buddhi is intelligence. It adds the intelligence to the vibrations. With this intelligence, the vibration now knows what object it represents. The vibration is now made-up intelligence. These vibrations with intelligence are nothing but vrittis, which we have discussed in other essays.

When these vrittis are presented to Ahamkara and Sakshi, awareness is created. This awareness is what is projected "out there."

In conclusion, the five elements are really a discussion about the five qualities–sound, touch, form, taste, and smell, which combine to create all the objects in the universe.

Science

Unfortunately, science does not fully appreciate the importance of the teachings of Vedanta. If the teachings are applied with logic, reasoning, and scientific rigor, they can add a new dimension to understanding science. As you will see in these essays, this knowledge dramatically changes many aspects of science. The best part is that it resolves many of the stumbling blocks being faced within science.

Since the changes are quite dramatic, the reader is requested to keep an open mind while reading these essays. Also, to ensure that logic and reasoning are maintained, I have tried my best to make each essay self-contained. This has meant that many of the concepts are repeated in different essays.

16 | Understanding Photons

A photon is unique. It is the only particle in the universe which travels at the speed of light–186,000 miles per second. According to science, it is physically impossible for anything to travel at the speed of light. This is because it will require an infinite amount of energy to push something to achieve the speed of light. Infinite means infinite; therefore, it is just impossible to achieve the speed of light for any object. At the Large Hadron Collider in CERN, Switzerland, it has been possible to achieve 99.999% of the speed of light–achieving 100% is impossible.

This really makes you wonder–if it is impossible to achieve the speed of light, how come the photons achieve this speed so easily? And, to top it all, they seem to be everywhere in the universe. Anything traveling at the speed of light must have infinite energy or mass, but photons have zero mass. If you apply the tool kit of the Theory of Special Relativity to the photon, the implications are profound and breathtaking. Let us talk about this now.

Einstein's Theory of Special Relativity

The Theory of Special Relativity, introduced in 1905, deals with the connection between space and time. The major finding is that wherever there is motion, time slows down and space shrinks. The faster the motion, the slower the time, the more compressed the space. Yes, time does slow down. We will not notice these changes in time in our day-to-day motion. You need to achieve speeds closer to the speed of light to notice the change in time. It is impossible for cars or rockets to reach speeds anywhere close to the speed of light. Einstein provided a thought experiment to explain the implications of this theory.

You are on Earth and your twin brother goes into space in a rocket. Both of you have top-of-the-range atomic clocks. Your twin brother's rocket is traveling at the speed of 0.8 c. You, on Earth, measure the speed of light, and you find it to be c. Your twin brother also measures the speed of light; he also finds that it is c. How come? The clock in the rocket slows down, and the space gets compressed and is much shorter so that the speed of light is still c. His spacetime framework is more compressed, but the speed of light is still c. Your twin brother returns to Earth. Your clock shows he traveled for 10 years, while his clock shows that he traveled for only six years.

Earth Clock and Rocket Clock Are Ticking at Different Rates

Your twin brother goes on another trip, and now he increases his speed to 0.9999 c. He measures the speed of light, and he still finds it to be c, the same as you will find on Earth. His clock will be running very slowly as compared to your clock on Earth. He returns after 50 days, according to his clock. Your clock on Earth will show he has traveled for 10 years. Amazing stuff! His spacetime is extremely compressed.

Here is an addition to the Einstein thought experiment. Your twin brother enjoys being in space. He goes back for another trip, and now his rocket travels at the speed of light, c. He tries to measure the speed of light, but he is unable to do so. Light travels at c and his rocket is also traveling at speed c; both are going parallel to each other, speed-wise. To make a measurement, you need light to bounce off an object, but if the rocket and light are going at the same speed, it is impossible to take this measurement.

When he returns to Earth, your clock shows he has traveled for 10 years, but he will find his clock is at a standstill–no time has passed for him. Also, according to him, he has covered no distance because there is no space. You aged 10 years; he felt he did not go anywhere either timewise or distance-wise and, therefore, did not age at all.

Now replace the rocket and the twin brother with a photon. The photon will have the same experience as your twin brother traveling at the speed of light, c, in a rocket. Let us imagine that we have put a tiny camera on a photon and this photon is traveling at its usual speed (of light). What will this camera capture? It will capture a universe whose size is smaller than a dot. The dot in this case is zero, which means there is nothing–no space. Nothing means nothing, but we know there is something: there is a photon. What you could say is that the photon "experienced" the following according to the Theory of Special Relativity:

- Distance traveled by photon = 0
- Time experienced by photon = 0 or standstill
- Energy content of photon = infinity. The formulas for the Lorenz Transformation will confirm this.

What is your experience as an observer stationed on Earth, tracking a photon traveling for 10 years?

- Distance traveled by photon = 10 light-years
- Time traveled by photon = 10 years
- Mass of photon = 0
- Speed of light = c

According to the photon, it feels it is at a standstill, not covering any distance. However, the observer feels the photon is covering a large distance traveling at the speed of light. How do we interpret this information? Based on the information we have understood, we can make the following important conclusions:

- The photon travels only in the presence of the observer (ego). If there is no observer, then the photon remains at a standstill. The presence of an observer is a prerequisite for the photon to travel. The source of the observer is Awareness. So, whenever a photon comes in the presence of Awareness in any mind–your mind, my mind, or the cosmic mind–the photon becomes conscious, and then and only then are we aware of the photon. It is this photon which zips around at the speed of light.
- From the photon's perspective, it is at a standstill in time and covers no distance. In fact, for the photon, there is no time and no space. It must be beyond the spacetime framework. If it was within the spacetime framework, time for the photon would change. What does this really mean? Anything beyond time must be in a dormant condition; it could also be called an unmanifest condition. According to Vedanta, the photon is in its potential form, just like a tree is in an unmanifest, potential condition within a seed. The physical tree still has not come out, but the tree is there in a potential form in the seed. The photon is also in the same potential form. What potential form does the photon represent? All aspects of the universe are the "potential" within the photon.
- Where does the photon reside in its unmanifest condition? It is beyond the mind. Since the unmanifest photon is beyond the mind, it is only logical to conclude that the unmanifest photon exists within SatChitAnanda or Self-Awareness, which is unchanging, limitless, without boundaries.
- According to the mind, (ego) the energy level or mass of the photon is zero, but according to the photon, its energy level is infinite. This photon with infinite energy is lying dormant within SatChitAnanda in an unmanifest condition. Whenever the observer has the desire to view the universe, this unmanifest photon will come into the observer's mind, it will become conscious, and then it will manifest to become the universe we see around us. This manifested universe will have a part of the infinite energy.

We have analyzed that from the photon's point of view, it remains in an unmanifest condition within SatChitAnanda. When this photon enters your mind, it becomes conscious and manifests itself.

Photons and Energy

Within SatChitAnanda, the photons have a potential for infinite energy. These photons are the source of all the energy required to sustain this universe. The photon has an infinite amount of energy, but this finite universe can use only a finite amount of energy. You, as an observer, can only see a part of the universe and, therefore, only a finite amount of

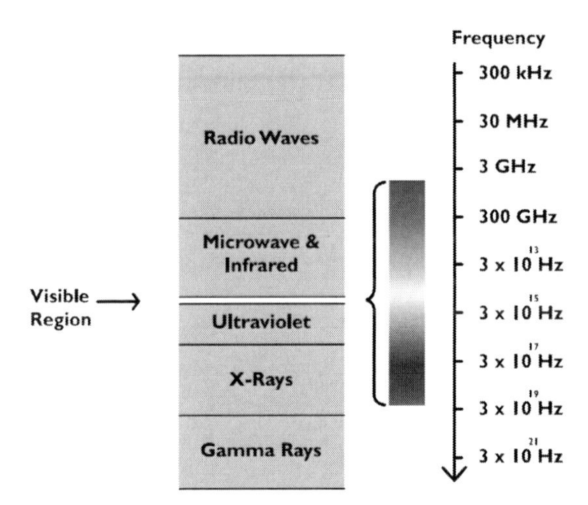

energy is required. The unused energy of the photon remains in an unmanifest condition and is used for other purposes. Please read the essay "Unlocking Dark Energy and Dark Matter" to understand the other applications of this infinite energy.

It must be understood that the only energy available in the universe is the energy provided by photons.

A photon in a waveform is also known as an electromagnetic energy wave (EMV). The known spectrum of light ranges from radio waves (300 KHz) to gamma rays (3 x 10E+21) Hz. This spectrum of energy covers the universe. It is the source of everything. All objects are made of energy, and this energy comes with the manifestation of the photon in the presence of Awareness.

17 | Quantum Physics and Vedanta

On the surface, quantum physics and Vedanta may look quite different. One is part of the scientific tradition, and the other in some ways is philosophy–some may even call it religion. Science is trying to understand the universe "out there" and Vedanta is trying to understand the universe "inside you." Everyone will agree that there is only one universe; both "out there" and "in here" are parts of the same universe. If this is true, both must have the same underlying reality. If you are part of the universe, then your underlying reality must be the same as the underlying reality of the universe "out there." There cannot be two independent realities for the same universe. Both science and Vedanta are looking for the same underlying reality. Besides, they share common ground which we will explore in this essay.

Basically, science started from "out there" and then moved inward to find the underlying reality. Vedanta started from "in here" and then moved outward to understand the universe. The goal for both is the same.

Subatomic particles behave in unpredictable ways. Quantum physics is trying its best to provide a proper explanation which is rooted in science and supported by experiments. Sometimes a particle is a "wave." At other times, it is a "particle." This discovery marked the starting point of quantum physics, which has explored this contradiction over the past century. Many questions have been successfully answered, but with every answer new questions come up. And, so, the search for answers does not seem to end. Some of the questions cannot and will not be answered by science, because they are outside the scope of science.

In many ways this is quite like Vedanta. Vedanta teaches us that the mind is made of waveforms or vrittis, and these "mind waves" become the objects which we see around us in this physical universe. Are the "waves" described by quantum physics the same as the "waves" in the mind? The focus of this essay is to show that this is true.

Quantum Physics and Waves

The birth of quantum physics took place at the beginning of the 20th century, when scientists found that light showed both wave-like and particle-like properties. Sometimes light is a particle, and sometimes it is a wave. This idea was cemented further when Louis de Broglie, a French

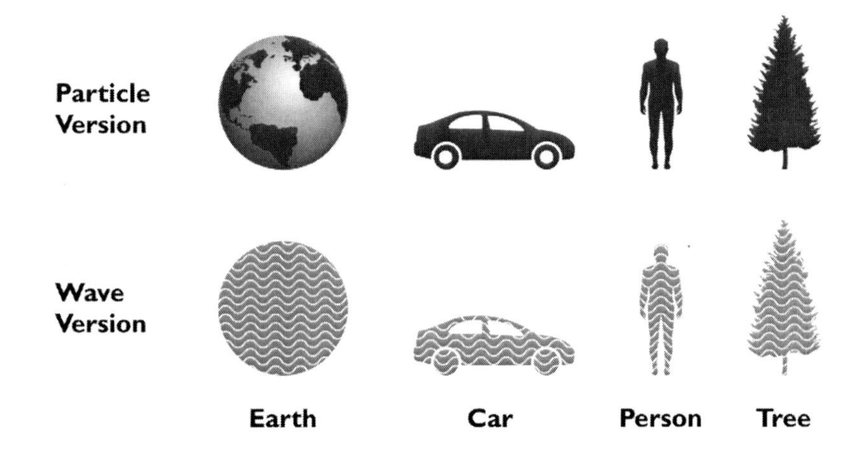

doctoral student, made a bold assertion that not only light but all matter must have both wave and particle properties. Here, matter means matter including you, me, planets, cars–in fact, any living or nonliving object in this universe. In 1927, the de Broglie hypothesis was proven experimentally; thus, all matter is both a wave and a particle. For details, please read the essay "Quantum Physics–Overview."

In this essay, we will focus on the wave part of the wave/particle duality. The wave and particle are two sides of the same coin. All matter can be a wave or a particle. In 1925, Schrodinger formulated a complex equation to understand the wave part of the wave/particle duality. Schrodinger's wave equation is a generic equation which can represent all the possible object wave functions in the universe. Schrodinger's wave equation represents a physical system consisting of the following two parts:

1. Observed system
2. Observing system

Observed System: The observed system is a wave which represents the object. This wave can be represented by Schrodinger's wave equation. This wave function is the energy profile of the object with time as the variable. The wave equation for subatomic particles like electrons, photons, and molecules has been determined by physicists. However, macro-objects like you and me or cars and planets have more complex wave functions, and it is much more difficult to input their variables to create the Schrodinger wave function. Nevertheless, there is a Schrodinger wave equation for every object in the universe.

1. Schrodinger's wave equation represents only "standing" waves and not "traveling" waves. We see traveling waves when we throw a stone in a pond and see the waves traveling outward, or when we see waves in the ocean. Standing waves, on the other hand, are waves which propagate in an enclosed environment; they keep bouncing off the enclosing walls. Electrons, as waves, are standing waves because they are enclosed within an atom. For the observing system to observe a standing wave, it must be enclosed in some type of environment.

2. You can convert Schrodinger's wave function into a probability wave function by squaring the wave function. The probability wave function contains all the possible outcomes. There could be infinite possibilities. To explain this, the famous "Schrodinger's cat" example is given. A cat is enclosed in a box which contains a vial of poison attached to an atomic trigger. The atomic trigger can randomly trigger the poison vial. One is never sure if the cat is dead or alive at any given time. As per the probability function yielded by Schrodinger's equation, the cat could be dead or alive, and it could also be half dead or half alive, one-third dead or two-thirds alive, and all the other different possible mixes of ratios between dead and alive. It has infinite possibilities, but only a few logical possibilities. You cannot have anything one-quarter alive and three-quarters dead.

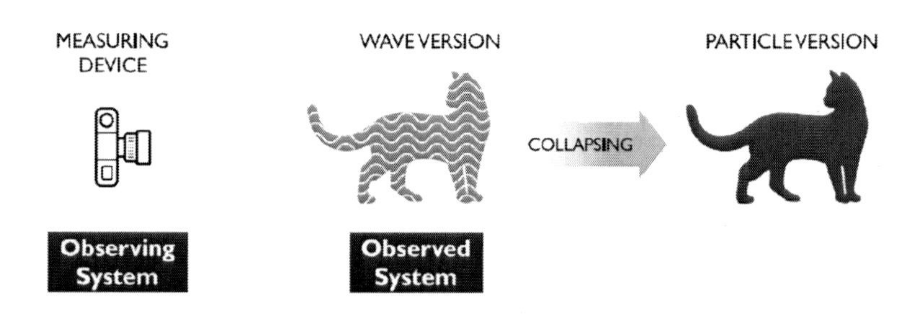

Wave Collapsing in the Presence of Observing System

Observing System: Another important aspect of the physical system for Schrodinger's wave equation is the observing system. When this observing system interacts with the observed system at any given time, the wave function of the observed system collapses to only one of the logical possibilities at that given time. In the example of Schrodinger's cat, if you open the trapdoor to see the cat, the cat will be alive or dead. If it is found alive, all the other possibilities become zero. In other words, when the observing system interacts with the observed system, the wave collapses to one of the possibilities for that given time, and then all the other possibilities have a zero chance of occurring. Till the trapdoor is opened, the cat is in a waveform with infinite possibilities. When the door is opened by the observing system, the cat wave collapses into being alive, and then all the other possibilities become zero.

Here is a direct hint that the wave function only collapses in the presence of an observing system. If there is no observing system, the observed system will continue to be a wave function. Before interacting with an observing system, the observed system is a wave, and the moment after interacting with the observing system, the observed wave function collapses to become a particle.

With this proper understanding of Schrodinger's wave function, many further questions come to mind.

Question 1: A prerequisite for Schrodinger's wave function is that it must be a standing wave. To be a standing wave, it must be enclosed within some type of "wall." We saw that the electron wave function operates within an atom. But the atom is also a wave, so where are the walls for the atom? You might say, the molecule. But the molecule is also a wave function, so where are the walls for the molecule? As you keep moving from micro to macro, you can keep asking the same question for every macro-object in this universe. Where is the wall for the standing waves of the objects in this world?

Question 2: Besides the wall, there are many other questions one can ask about the wave function.

- Of what are the waves made? Nobody has seen a wave, but it must be made of something; it cannot be made of nothing.
- The waves need some sort of medium to propagate. What is this underlying medium? At one time, scientists speculated that there was some sort of ether in which the light waves traveled. Experiments have proven that there is no ether underlying this universe. So, what is the medium through which waves travel?
- Where do the waves reside? "Out there" or "in here"? One thing is clear: it cannot be within the particle object, because the particle objects only show up when the wave function collapses in the presence of the observing system. The wave comes first and then the particle; therefore, the wave cannot exist within the particle.

Question 3: Quantum physics provides little understanding of the observing system. In the famous double-slit experiment (please read the essay "Quantum Physics–Overview" for details), it is suggested that the photographic plate is the observing system. The photographic plate interacts with the incoming light wave, and this wave function collapses at the photographic plate. Science assumes that the photographic plate is the observing system. If you examine this closely, does a man-made photographic plate have the capacity to collapse a wave function to become a particle? What unique quality of the photographic plate allows the wave function to collapse? Another question to ask is: what is the exact meaning of the statement "collapsing wave function"?

If you take the broader viewpoint, you will realize that the photographic plate itself is matter, and therefore it also has a wave function. So, what observing system collapses the wave function of the photographic plate?

The logical answer would be your eyes. But the eye is also matter and therefore it also has a wave function. So, what observing system collapses the wave function of the eye? The answer would be your brain. But the brain is also matter and therefore it also has a wave function. So, what observing system collapses the wave function of the brain? I think that at this point, science has come to the end of the road; it cannot explain what or which observing system collapses the wave function of the brain.

If we understand Vedanta properly, most of these questions can be answered. In the coming sections we will try to explain some of the key teachings of Vedanta that help answer these questions.

Vedanta and Mental Waveforms

Vedanta teaches us that all the objects in the mind take the form of waveforms or vrittis. Vrittis are vibrations in the mind caused by objects. As explained in the essay "Understanding the Mind," these object waveforms or vrittis are sentient and made of intelligence. Knowledge is the substratum of the vrittis. Not easy to grasp, but these object vrittis are made of knowledge. Since they are made of knowledge, the vrittis know what object they represent. Every vritti is unique in representing a different object.

These object vrittis are complicated. How do we understand them? Let us study an example. The sun is over 4.5 billion years old. The cumulative vritti of the sun will include all the waveforms for every moment in time. Every moment is part of the waveform for the sun. All these individual vrittis combine to create a "grand" waveform for the sun. As time passes, new waveforms are added to the cumulative profile of the sun. In the sun's cumulative vritti, the profile for each moment of the sun since inception is available. If you are on Earth, you will see the "now minus eight minutes" version of the sun. This version is present within the cumulative vritti of the sun. From Mars, you will see the "now minus 13 minutes" version of the sun. All the versions of the sun are present, and different versions are chosen depending on the distance from the sun.

We have just seen the example of the sun with all the historical waveforms or vrittis. This will apply to all the objects in the universe. Every object in the universe is a cumulative waveform of every moment in time. Your waveform will be a total of all the vrittis since your birth. The trees, cars, planets, galaxies–each one of them will have a time-wise total waveform.

To add to the complexity of the waveforms, all objects in the universe with their own cumulative waveforms will combine to create one big waveform for the universe. We can call this the "now" universe waveform. This "now" universe waveform includes everything which is contained in the universe. Nothing is left out.

A question can be asked: how does the gigantic "now" universe waveform keep track of the individual objects within the waveform? As we mentioned earlier, each object waveform or vritti is made of Knowledge. Each subsection of the waveform has intelligence and knows what object it represents. Even if all the object wave functions combine to form a single "now" universe vritti, knowledge of each object is maintained.

Correlating Quantum Physics and Vedanta

Schrodinger's wave function represents a system which consists of an observed system and an observing system. The observed system is a waveform representing micro- or macro-objects. In the presence of the observing system, the observed collapses to become a particle. Now look at what is happening in our minds. The mind is the observed system and is made of vrittis or waveforms representing complex objects. The Subject is the observing system looking at what is happening in the individual mind. In the presence of Atma, the observed waveform in the mind collapses to project the world "out there" as a particle.

It would seem that Schrodinger's wave function represents the wave function of what is happening in your mind. Even the time variable in Schrodinger's wave equation is the same as the historical timeline for the object vrittis in the mind. They are similar in every way. This is the only correct conclusion. Schrodinger's equation only deals with waveforms. We know from Vedanta that the waveforms operate in the subtle universe, and this subtle universe resides either within the individual mind or the cosmic mind. The waveforms cannot operate "out there" in a yet-non-existent physical entity; they can only operate within the mind. The locus of waveforms is in the mind. Simple wave functions for electrons, protons, and other micro-objects reside within the mind, and the complex wave functions for you, me, and other macro-objects also reside within the mind.

With this understanding, let us see if we can answer the questions which were raised earlier in the overview of Schrodinger's wave equation.

Answer 1: For Schrodinger's wave equation to operate, the waveforms must be standing waves and not traveling waves. Standing waves need "walls" to operate. As we saw earlier, we will not find the walls for the standing waves "out there." The only place you find walls for the standing waves is the individual mind or the cosmic mind. The waveforms bounce within these walls. Therefore, the only place for Schrodinger's wave equation to operate is the individual mind and the cosmic mind. This means that Schrodinger's wave equation represents the vrittis or waveforms operating within the mind.

Answer 2: Of what are the waves made? According to Vedanta, the vrittis in the mind are made of mind stuff. Mind is part of the Subtle Body and is made up of subtle elements. Vedanta teaches us that the universe is made up of five elements: Space, Air, Fire, Water, and Earth. These five elements come in both subtle form and gross form. The individual mind and the cosmic mind are made up of the subtle form of the five elements. Even the food we eat has a gross form and subtle form. The gross form of the food nourishes our body, while the subtle part of the food nourishes the mind or the Subtle Body.

Atma is the light of Awareness. When the mind comes in touch with this light of Awareness, the mind becomes Conscious. The mind is filled with this Consciousness. This Consciousness is the underlying "ether" or "medium" of the vrittis within the mind. In the presence of this Consciousness, the vrittis become active or "conscious."

We saw earlier that standing waves cannot operate "out there" in the space of the universe. The only place the vrittis can operate is within the individual mind or the cosmic mind. In the wave/particle duality, it is quite clear that the wave creates the particle. The underlying cause of the particle universe is the wave universe. Maya Shakti projects the wave universe as the particle universe or the physical universe that we see.

Answer 3: Science must clearly understand that a measuring system like the photographic plate in the double-slit experiment does not have the power or mechanism to collapse the light wave into a photon. The photographic plate itself has a wave component operating within the mind. Who collapses the waveform of the photographic plate? The only correct answer to that is Atma. Atma is the observer of all the activity within the individual and cosmic mind, and Atma is the only source with the power to collapse a wave function.

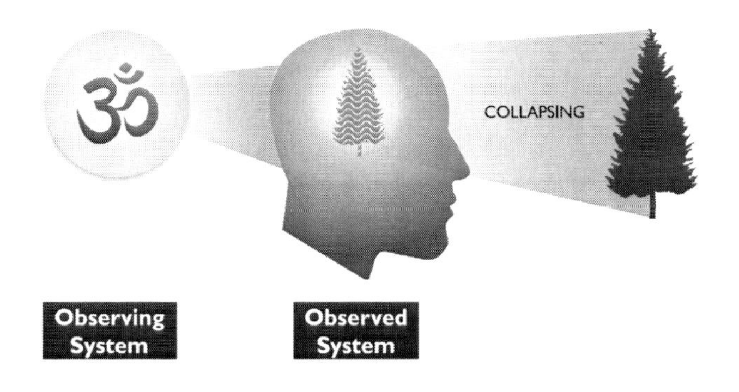

Wave in Mind Collapsing in the Presence of Self-Awareness

The other question which needs to be answered is, what is meant by collapsing of the wave? Science suggests that when the wave changes from a wave to a particle, the wave collapses. Vedanta has a two-step process:

Step 1: Vritti Vyapti: This means "wrapping" of the vritti or waveform by the mind. When a vritti is formed in the mind, the mind goes into its "memory database" and checks what this vritti represents. The mind then takes the shape of that object. At this stage, it only takes the shape of what the wave represents. It does not have any content. It is like a wire diagram with no content.

Step 2: Phala Vyapti: Phala means fruit, but a better translation would be the yielding of a result from the wrapping. The shape of the mind object comes in the presence of Atma, which is the light of Awareness. When anything comes in the presence of Atma it becomes conscious, and this wire diagram of the mind object is now filled with Consciousness. You can be aware of something only when it is conscious. With this step, Atma/Observer is now fully aware of the subtle objects in the mind.

In Vedanta, this two-step process does not mean that the waveform collapses, but that Atma becomes aware of what the vritti or waveform in the mind really means and represents. When science says that the waveform collapses, it really means that the observer is aware of what the waveform represents. For the observer to be aware of the observed, both the observer and the observed must be conscious. If either one of them is not conscious, the observing process is not complete. Atma is the Self-Aware Observer, and the mind with its content is also conscious in the presence of the observer. This completes the cycle and, therefore, Atma is aware of what is happening in the mind. This also means that the process of observing can only happen in the mind.

The only conclusion from all these answers is that Schrodinger's wave equation represents the wave functions operating within the mind. The vrittis in the mind are the same as Schrodinger's wave equation. This common ground could be a step forward for quantum physics.

18 | Projection—The Only Truth

Vedanta teaches us that the universe "out there" is the projection of the mind. This is completely contradictory to what science teaches us. Science teaches us that there is already a universe "out there" made up of an unlimited number of objects. To perceive this universe, light travels from these objects and hits the retina of our eyes. The image in the retina is upside down; this image is reversed and the optical signal from the retina is transmitted to the brain. What happens in thc brain is still unknown, but, somehow, we perceive the image of the universe "out there."

Vedanta teaches that the "inside" subtle objects in the mind come first, and these become the "outside" gross objects. Science teaches that the "outside" gross objects become the "inside" subtle objects in the brain. These are completely opposite statements. Only one of them can be true. Which one? It is important to resolve this issue before we move forward with the discussion in this essay. Since we are talking about projections, Vedanta's teaching is the only correct way to understand this issue. Projection of the universe by the mind is the only truth. We will now analyze this issue from different angles to show this hypothesis as correct.

1. By using science
2. By using logic
3. By using math
4. By using quantum physics
5. By using neuroscience

1. By Using Science—Theory of Special Relativity

Einstein's Theory of Special Relativity was a major discovery in science; it discovered a connection between motion and time. The underlying theme of this discovery was that the speed of light is fixed at 186,000 miles per second, irrespective of the frame of reference. Because of this, if you have motion (of any sort), time slows down. Even if you are walking or traveling at 40% of the speed of light, time slows down. How much it slows down depends on the speed. The higher the speed, the more the slowing of time. At the speed of light, time does not move, it remains stationary. The higher the speed, the more that space gets compressed.

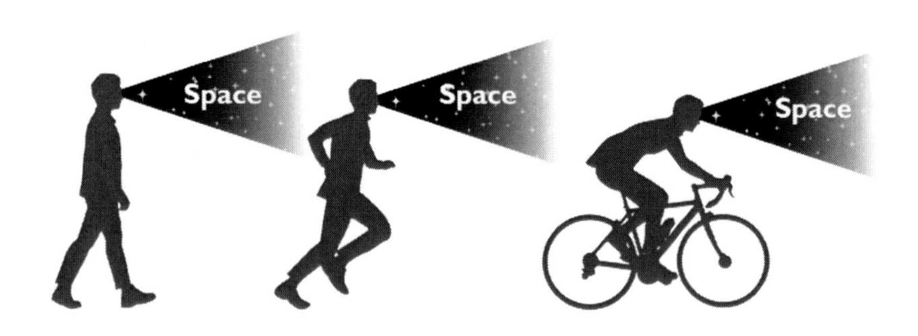

We do not realize this, but the connection between motion and time has tremendous implications in our daily life. Do we see motion in this universe? Of course, there is motion everywhere. We see an ant crawling, we see a person walking, and someone else is cycling or going in a car. Some are going faster while others are slower. If you apply the principles of Einstein's theory, it will mean that the time clock for each person is ticking differently. If two people are stationary, their clocks will tick at the same rate; the moment one of them starts walking, the clock for the person walking will slow down.

If you are stationary and I am walking, my clock is different, the atoms in the universe that I am seeing are vibrating differently, so all my objects are completely different from your objects. What does this mean? It means that I project my own objects and universe, and you project your own objects and universe. In the same way, every living being creates their own universe.

The only correct conclusion from this discussion is that each person is projecting a different universe based on their internal clock. Einstein's Theory of Special Relativity therefore supports what Vedanta is teaching us about the projection of the universe.

2. By Using Logical Reasoning

We have discussed this elsewhere, but we will repeat this reasoning once again to make sure it is properly understood. Let us study the external objects "out there." If we can see a faraway star, say, five million light-years away, it takes light from that star five million years to reach us. Now, we see the sun; the light from the sun takes eight minutes to reach us. We look at the moon; its light takes three seconds to reach us. We look at the plane flying in the sky at 30,000 feet; its light will take about 300 milliseconds to reach us. As the distance of the object being viewed is reduced, the time taken for light to reach us or for us to see it is much less.

I now look at the tree outside the window; the time taken for light to reach me is 10 microseconds (10E-6). I am looking at the computer screen one foot away while typing this essay; light will take about one nanosecond (10E-9) to reach me. As the distance reduces, the time taken for light to reach me also reduces. If you extrapolate this backward, the only logical place for t to be equal to 0 is the observer, who is watching all these objects. This means that the observer within you is the starting point of space. This starting point is t=0.

If you or anyone else looks at the universe, they will reach the same conclusion. The starting point for space is within themselves. This will apply to every living being in the universe. It would seem, therefore, that I have my own starting point of space at t=0, you have your own starting point t=0, and every living being in the universe has their own starting point of space at t=0. The only way to understand this is that every living being creates their own universe, and the space for this universe starts with t=0.

This logical reasoning does show that each individual living being projects their own universe, and the space of this universe starts with the observer within you.

3. By Using Mathematical Calculation–Hubble Constant

To understand the rate of expansion of the universe, scientists came up with the Hubble constant. The Hubble constant states that the rate of expansion is about 72 kilometers per second per megaparsec. A megaparsec is a million parsecs, or about 3.3 million light-years. It means that objects 3.3 million light-years away are expanding at 72 kilometers per second. The Hubble constant is based only on observation. Scientists have not come up with any mathematical proof for this observation.

If you understand the fundamentals of the universe's expansion, it is possible to calculate and prove the Hubble constant. Please read the essay "Hubble Constant–A Mathematical Proof," where we have shown that the Hubble constant is indeed correct. The mathematical calculation shows that, at 3.3 million light-years away, space is indeed expanding at 72 km/second. This means that the expansion model used for the calculation of the Hubble constant must be correct.

The expansion model used to calculate the Hubble constant shows that the starting point of space is the observer within you. The t=0 for space is the observer within you. Since each one of us has our own observer, so each one projects our own universe. Each one creates the space and projects the required objects on this spacetime fabric.

So, the mathematical model for the Hubble constant supports the concept of projection of the universe by each observer.

4. By Using Quantum Physics

Quantum physics was born when scientists discovered the wave/particle duality for light. They found that light sometimes behaved as a wave and sometimes it behaved like a particle. Louis de Broglie, who won the Nobel Prize in 1929, showed that not only light but all matter in the universe has the wave/particle duality. It means that you, me, the trees, the car, the planets, the house–every object in this universe has both wave and particle duality. We are both wave and particles.

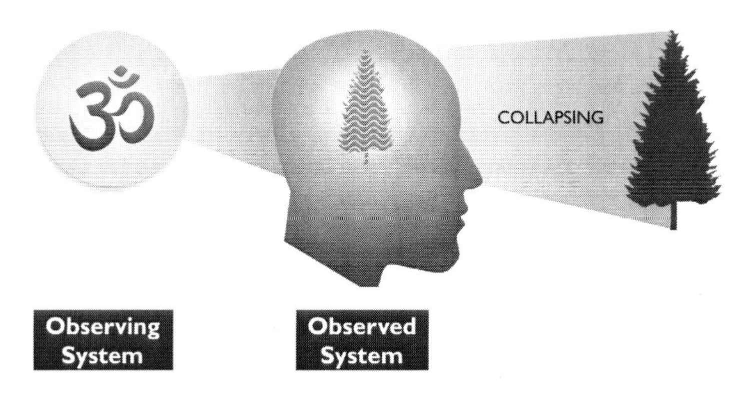

The wave comes first. This wave collapses in the presence of the observer to become a particle.

To get a better understanding of this wave/particle duality, several experiments were conducted by Schrodinger. Schrodinger's famous equation represents the wave part of the wave/particle duality. According to this wave function, the wave representing an object collapses to become a particle in the presence of a measuring device or observer. This is how a particle is created from a wave.

The biggest takeaway from this is that the wave part comes first. This wave collapses in the presence of the observer to become a particle. This shows that the particle comes later. Therefore, the wave is the cause and the particle is the effect. The wave comes first and the particle comes second. As we have discussed in my essay "Quantum Physics and Vedanta," the wave is nothing but the waveforms in the mind, and the particle is nothing but the world "out there." The mental waveforms collapse in the presence of the observer (Atma) to become the physical world "out there" made up of particles.

Thus, quantum physics also shows that the subtle world made of mental waveforms comes first, and then these mental waveforms are converted to particles as the world "out there." The individual mind projects the mental waveforms as the world "out there."

Quantum physics thus supports the idea of projection of the universe by each observer.

5. By Using Neuroscience

Benjamin Libet, a well-known neuroscientist, conducted a wide variety of experiments over many years to show that an event occurs in the brain/mind complex before we are aware of it.

Experiment 1: A person touches a hot rod. The signal is transmitted to the brain in 100 milliseconds. The brain instructs the hand to remove it from the rod; this takes another 100 milliseconds. All this action takes place, but the person becomes aware of the pain caused by the hot rod only after 0.5 seconds. So much is happening in the brain and we become aware of it after the event has happened. This shows that there is a fully functioning subtle universe in the mind of which we are not aware.

Experiment 2: A person's brain is all wired up with electrodes, and he is instructed to look at a clock and decide to press a button. When he decides to press the button, he makes a note of the time on the clock. The experimenters found that it took 200 milliseconds to press the button after the person decided to press it. They also found that 300 milliseconds before this person made the decision to press the button, there was activity in the brain–the electrodes in the brain were lighting up. This suggests that, on the subtle level, the decision to press the button was made much before the person's awareness of having made the decision.

These experiments clearly show that activity takes place first in the mind and then in the physical world. What conclusion can we draw from this? The subtle universe in the mind comes first and then the physical universe, and not the other way around. Further, this subtle world controls and creates the physical world.

We have just proven in different ways that there is no single universe "out there." Each living being creates and projects their own universe. This may not be easy to digest but this is the only truth. The only universe you know is what you project "out there." It is impossible to know the universe other people are seeing. Everything is a projection from the mind. For this projection to work, it is only correct that subtle objects come first, and this is converted to gross objects "out there." So, subtle objects come first and then the gross objects. This shows that what science has been teaching is inaccurate and incorrect.

So, how does this projection work? We can divide the projection process into two steps:

Step 1: Pre-projection activity in the mind

Step 2: Projection by the mind

Step 1: Pre-projection activity in the mind

It is easy to compare this step to a digital projector. There are two elements to any projector—a light source or bulb and the content which must be projected. The mind also has a similar structure:

- A bulb of Awareness
- Content which must be projected

Let us discuss these two parts in detail.

A Bulb of Awareness

Awareness is the innermost core of any living being. It is like a bulb shining within our inner core. The bulb of Awareness radiates Awareness. Vedanta teaches us that our inner core is SatChitAnanda. The bulb of Awareness is the same as SatChitAnanda.

Bulb of Awareness = Self-Awareness = SatChitAnanda = Atma

Self-Awareness is non-dual, homogenous, and it has many inherent powers. We will discuss a few of them here, which will be useful for this essay.

- Formless
- Unchanging
- Infinite Energy Source

Formless: Awareness is formless. Because it is formless, Awareness has the potential to take any form. The possible forms are limitless. If Awareness had some type of form, then possible forms would be limited. For example, if Awareness had the shape of a cube, then this building block could be combined in different ways to create only a limited number of shapes. It would not be possible to create every possible shape. In the same way, if the building block of Awareness was a sphere, the possibility of creating different shapes would be limited. Only something which is formless has the potential to create an unlimited number of shapes and sizes. There is no restriction on the possibilities. Awareness is formless and therefore Awareness has the potential to become any object. The possibilities are unlimited.

Unchanging: Awareness is unchanging. It remains the same and it will never change (no change over past, present, or future). In something which is unchanging, time must be static; it does not move. The only reason something is unchanging is because this time factor is not moving. If, for whatever reason, this "unchanging" starts "changing," time will and must "pop out" from this unchanging entity. If something is changing, it means that what is "now" is no longer the same. Since the two events are not the same, the time factor comes into play to connect the two events. It is not incorrect to say that time drives the change between two events. Awareness is unchanging and the only reason it does not change is because the time factor is static.

Infinite Energy Source: Does Self-Awareness or SatChitAnanda have infinite energy? Yes, it does have infinite energy. Please read the essay "Awareness–Infinite Energy Source" for a detailed analysis.

This infinite energy stored in Self-Awareness is the source of the energy in the universe. This energy within Self-Awareness is in an unmanifest condition and is in potential form. This energy is inactive; it is dormant, but it is present. Vedanta calls this infinite energy stored within our inner core Maya Shakti. We will shortly see how this energy is activated and how it is used in different ways to power the projection of the universe "out there."

Content Which Must Be Projected

We have just seen that the bulb of Awareness or Self-Awareness is the power source for the projection of content. What about the content which must be projected? Vedanta teaches us that there are individual minds, and the sum of individual minds can be called the cosmic mind. The cosmic mind is the source of content. A good way to understand this is to compare this with Google Maps. Somewhere in the cloud, there is a complete software or code for Google Maps. This software will show the roads for almost every city and country in the world. If we move to a different location, Google Maps will show the map for only that location.

The cosmic map is like Google Maps but more extensive, complex, smarter, and dynamic.

- The cosmic map covers the entire universe. It is extremely detailed and covers every inch of the universe. There is no place which is left out. It cannot be more complete. Every tree, every mountain, every planet, and every living being is covered by the cosmic map.
- Every perspective and view is covered in the cosmic map. If you are flying at 30,000 feet, that view from the window is covered. If you are underwater and look upward, that view is covered. If you are moving in a train, that view is covered. If you go into space, that view is covered. If you are underground inside a cave, that view is covered. There is nothing which is missing in this cosmic map.
- The cosmic map is not static. It is dynamic. Everything in this universe ages. Every living and nonliving being in this universe ages. As time flows, every object in the universe grows and changes. The cosmic map reflects this for every object in this ever-changing universe.
- The cosmic map is always up-to-date. If you cut a branch or move a stone or if anyone makes any change to any aspect anywhere in the universe, the cosmic map will reflect those changes instantaneously. The cosmic map is never outdated. It is updated continuously and immediately.

The cosmic mind stores the complete map of the universe. The individual mind covers a subset of the map, which depends on what the individual person wants to view. The content within the individual mind is used for the projection.

Step 2: Projection of the mind

Once the content in the individual mind encounters the bulb of Awareness, you have magic, you have awareness of the content. This awareness is displayed in the world "out there." Sri Vidyaranya, the great sage from the 14th century, in the sixth chapter of *Panchadasi* has compared the image "out there" to a painting. If you think about it, this is a perfect analogy. Anything and everything we see "out there" is like a painting. In fact, the painting "out there" is superior to any painting that a human being can create. See the variety, see the shades, see the beauty of nature. It is breathtaking.

Sri Vidyaranya has analyzed the following steps needed to create any painting:

1. You need a canvas for the painting. Sri Vidyaranya talks about a piece of cloth as the canvas.
2. You need some sort of starch to harden the canvas to make it painting-ready.
3. You make a line drawing of the sketch you want to create.
4. You add color to finish the painting.

The projection of the content from the mind follows the same four steps.

Step 1: You need space–the canvas

Step 2: Harden the canvas with energy

Step 3: Create the subtle image of the painting

Step 4: Add awareness to finish the projection

Let us discuss each of the steps in more detail to understand how the actual projection takes place. This discussion is rooted in science so that this does not remain abstract and philosophical.

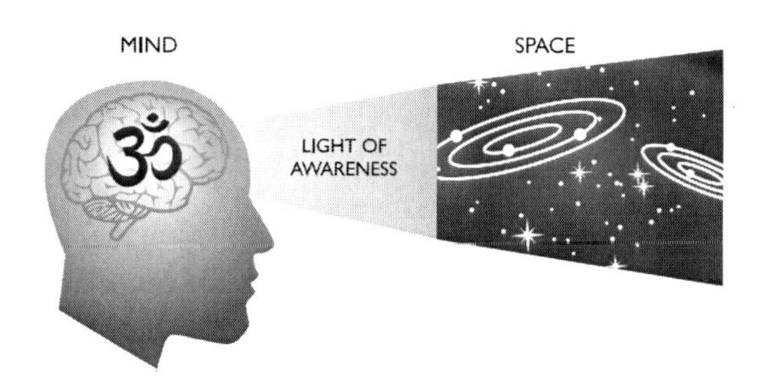

Projection by Mind

Step 1: You need space–the canvas

There is no denying that all the "painting" or "image" being projected "out there" is in space. Space seems to be the canvas for the projection. It is the screen on which the painting is created or projected. We see space everywhere but do not have much of an understanding about 1) the fabric of space and 2) how space is created. Let us try and understand these two aspects.

Fabric of Space: You will be surprised to learn that time is the underlying cause of space. Einstein understood this, and he referred to space as spacetime. When we look at space, we mostly see distances. The tree is 100 feet away, the person standing "out there" is 300 feet away, and so on. This perspective does not give a proper understanding of space. We should look at space in terms of time. If we can see a faraway star, say five million light-years away, it will take light from that star five million years to reach us. Now, we see the sun; the light from the sun takes eight minutes to reach us. We look at the moon; light takes three seconds to reach us. We look at the plane flying in the sky at 30,000 feet; light takes about 300 milliseconds to reach us. As the distance of the object being viewed is reduced, the time taken for light to reach us or for us to see it is much less. Time is the actual fabric of space. Time is the cause of space. Space is just the result; it is the effect of time.

- **Space vs. Spacetime:** People use space and spacetime interchangeably. This causes confusion. Let us clarify this. When you look at space in terms of distances, it is space. However, when you look at the same space in terms of time, that space is spacetime. Space is "out there"; you can see it. Spacetime is not "out there"; it is within your mind. It is a mental thing. You imagine the sun is eight minutes away from you. You imagine objects are so many seconds away from you. All this imagination takes place in the mind. Spacetime is in the mind first and then this spacetime is converted to space "out there."
- **Pixels of Spacetime:** We know an LCD monitor is made up of pixels. Pixels are picture elements which make up the surface of the monitor screen. In the same way, spacetime is also made up of pixels. Since spacetime is time-based, the pixels must also be time-based. The starting pixel will be at t=0, which is the start of the spacetime fabric, and the value of the time pixel will increase as you move further away on the spacetime fabric. How far apart are these pixels in space? Well, based on the Planck constant, the smallest division of time is 10E-44 seconds. So, spacetime is not continuous. It is made up of time-based pixels which are 10E-44 seconds apart. The entire spacetime is made up of pixels which are 10E-44 seconds apart. The first pixel will be at 10E-44 seconds, the second pixel will be at 2 x 10E-44 seconds away, the third pixel will be at 3 x 10E-44 seconds away. This progression will continue till the end of the spacetime fabric.

How Is Space Created? You will be surprised to know that space is created because of our ignorance of our true nature. We have discussed that Self-Awareness is formless, unchanging, and it has infinite energy. All these powers are within Self-Awareness. If all this is true, why do we not know this or why do we not experience this? The simple answer is that we are ignorant. We are ignorant that we are non-dual, that we are both the subject and object. Since we are not aware that we are both the subject and the object, this means that the subject and object are no longer one entity; they are separate. Ignorance separates the subject and object.

With the separation of subject and object, all powers within Self-Awareness manifest themselves. All the powers pop out in the mind.

- The infinite energy is now available in the cosmic mind and a limited subset of this energy in the individual minds.
- The unchanging Self-Awareness becomes the changing cosmic mind. With the changing mind, the time clock is now active. This clock in the mind has the power to create or generate time.
- The formless Self-Awareness becomes the cosmic mind with the potential to take an unlimited number of forms.

The energy which is available in the mind is pure energy. This energy plays different roles within the mind. It must be understood that this energy is independent of time; it is raw or pure energy which is available in the mind.

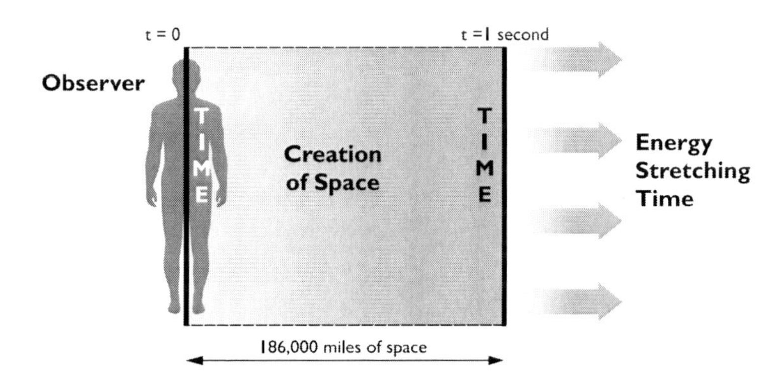

We know spacetime is made up of time. Let us see what happens when part of this energy interacts with the spacetime fabric in the individual mind. This energy stretches out the spacetime fabric so that every second in time is equal to 186,000 miles (speed of light). Just like a rubber band can be stretched outward, in the same way the fabric can be stretched outward by this pure energy. With this stretching of spacetime fabric, space is created. One second of the fabric becomes 186,000 miles of space. This is the space we see "out there." This space is the canvas which is used for the projection of the painting or image. So, space is created when this pure energy stretches out the spacetime fabric.

Step 2: Harden the canvas with energy

Like starch is used to harden the canvas made of cloth, energy is used to harden every part of the spacetime fabric. Part of the pure energy is used to stretch time to create space. Another portion of this energy combines with the time pixels to create electromagnetic (EM) waves. How does this happen? We saw earlier that the spacetime fabric is made of time-based pixels which are 10E-44 seconds apart. This pure energy combines with each time pixel in the spacetime fabric to give energy to the pixels. This energy is nothing but the source of the electromagnetic waves. The moment energy combines with time pixels, you get frequencies and wavelengths.

A wide range of frequencies and wavelengths make up the spectrum of the EM energy. The known spectrum ranges from radio waves (300 KHz) to gamma rays (3 x 10E+21) Hz. Each time pixel in the spacetime fabric oscillates; this oscillation is a combination of all the possible frequencies in the EM spectrum. Each time pixel is a source of the complete range of EM frequencies. There is no place in the spacetime fabric where there is no energy. This energy is bubbling under the surface of the spacetime fabric. This EM energy provides the undercoating for the spacetime fabric–it hardens the spacetime fabric. This canvas is now ready for painting.

Step 3: Create the subtle image of the painting

The sketch of the painting must come first. In the same way, the subtle image of the painting is created first on the spacetime fabric. Everything subtle must happen only in the mind. Let us see how this works.

A portion of the cosmic map which we discussed earlier presents itself in the mind. When the cosmic map combines with the mind, mental waveforms are created. Vedanta calls these mental waveforms vrittis. These vibrations in the mind are made of intelligence. Intelligence is the ingredient or substratum of the waveforms.

Any scene is usually a total of many individual objects. Each object has its own mental waveform or vritti. They superimpose on each other and form complex vrittis representing the scene. Since these are mental waveforms, they must have energy to exist. Without energy, the mental waveforms cannot function. Each vritti representing an object has a unique energy profile. The total of the individual objects will have a complex energy profile representing the scene. These complex mental waveforms are placed on the spacetime fabric. Objects closer to the observer are placed first, and objects further away are placed afterward. In this way, all the required objects become part of the spacetime fabric.

Energy and Spacetime: How do these mental waveforms interact with spacetime? Einstein had already answered this question. In his Theory of General Relativity, Einstein concluded that when energy or mass is placed on the spacetime fabric, the spacetime fabric curves. It is like a stretched rubber sheet. If you place a ball on this rubber sheet, the weight of the ball will curve the rubber sheet around it. The heavier the ball, the greater the curvature. The spacetime fabric behaves in the same way in the presence of energy. The energy from the mental waveforms will leave an imprint (or curvature) on the spacetime fabric. Wherever there is a concentration of energy, the spacetime fabric will curve. The higher the amount of energy, the greater the curvature. The less the amount of energy, the smaller the curvature. Even a tiny amount of energy will leave a dent on the spacetime fabric.

The imprint of the mental waveforms on the spacetime fabric is like the sketch we make before adding paint to a painting.

Step 4: Add Awareness to finish the projection

If you look at any painting, you will notice that the painting is made up of the following two things:

1. Form
2. Content

The trees, people, houses, or any other object you see in the painting is the form present in the painting. The paint is the only content of the painting. If you think about it carefully, nothing else is present in the painting other than the paint. There may be different colors, but all these colors are still only paint. As another example, when you see a movie, you see so many characters and objects on the screen. All these are different forms in the movie. The content of these forms is nothing but light. Light with different shades and colors is the content of the movies.

We have compared the projection of the world "out there" with a painting. So, like the painting or the movie, everything in the world "out there" is only made up of form + content. Let us discuss this further.

Form: In the last section, we saw that the intelligent mental waveforms or vrittis make an imprint on the spacetime fabric. This imprint curves the spacetime fabric. We saw that each time pixel in the spacetime fabric is an outlet for the EM energy. The knowledgeable imprint of the mental waveforms interacts with the EM energy. What happens? It sucks out the EM energy stored in the pixels and uses that energy to become the form of the object. The mental waveform knows what form it must take; it uses the EM energy and becomes that required form. This form is no longer subtle; it is gross. The gross form of the object is created by the interaction of the mental waveform with the EM energy. The imprint of all the mental waveforms will interact with the EM energy and create gross forms, and these forms will be located at appropriate distances in space.

Science has discussed this interaction between mental energy waves and EM energy. They call this the Quantum Field Theory (QFT). Simply put, QFT states that when two energy fields interact with each other, particles are created. This is exactly what is happening here. The mental energy wave and the EM energy are the two fields. When they interact, the gross form of the object is created.

Content: So, what is the content of the object form? If you are a student of Vedanta, the answer would be that the content is Awareness. Awareness is the ingredient of every object in the world "out there." If you have an experience of objects, you must be aware of that experience. Awareness is the prerequisite of any experience. If there is no Awareness, there can be no experience. The following equation links experience with Awareness.

Experience = Awareness + Form

We just saw that forms are created by the interaction of mental waveforms and EM energy. For us to experience these forms, they must be filled with Awareness. Without Awareness, there cannot be any experience. To experience any object, Awareness must take the exact shape of the form. If the form is a circle, Awareness cannot be a rectangle. Awareness must also be a circle. Therefore, Awareness must take the exact shape of the form. Just like the forms in the painting are filled with paint, in the same way all forms are filled with Awareness.

When Awareness fills up the object form, the painting is completed. This completes the projection of the objects “out there.” This completes the picture on the canvas of space.

It must be understood that the projection we have seen is that of only a single frame. A single frame by itself is static. We want to see continuous motion. To see continuous motion, science tells us that there must be at least 24 frames per second. How many frames are projected by the mind is unknown, but there must be at least 24 frames per second. The complex process of creating space and gross forms is repeated for every frame. Each frame is different from the previous frame.

19 | Awareness—The Infinite Energy Source

Awareness is the substratum of this universe. In fact, Awareness is the content of each object in the universe. Without Awareness, you cannot experience anything in the universe. Wherever there is Awareness, the subject, object, and intelligence must be present. This Awareness is present in the mind. The source of this Awareness is Self-Awareness. Self-Awareness is like a bulb of Awareness, radiating Awareness on a continuous basis. It does nothing except shine Awareness. This bulb of Awareness is non-dual. To be non-dual, subject = object and object = subject. Subject and object are one entity. Please read the essay "Understanding Self-Awareness" for a detailed explanation.

Does Self-Awareness or SatChitAnanda have infinite energy? Yes, it does have infinite energy. How can we understand this? Obviously, there is no direct scientific proof, but we can use logic and correlate with other scientific investigations.

Using Logic

To understand this, a good example is to see how the atomic nucleus works. In school we learned that the atomic nucleus is made up of neutrons and protons. Different elements have a different combination of neutrons and protons. Neutrons have a neutral charge, while protons have a positive charge. We also know that positive charges must repel each other. If they are supposed to repel each other, how come they stick together within the nucleus? The answer is that there is a strong nuclear force which keeps these protons together within the nucleus. This nuclear force binds the protons together. This force is 100 times greater than the repulsive force between the protons. This nuclear force is within the atomic nucleus and is always present in the nucleus. In fact, this strong nuclear force is the source for the atomic bomb.

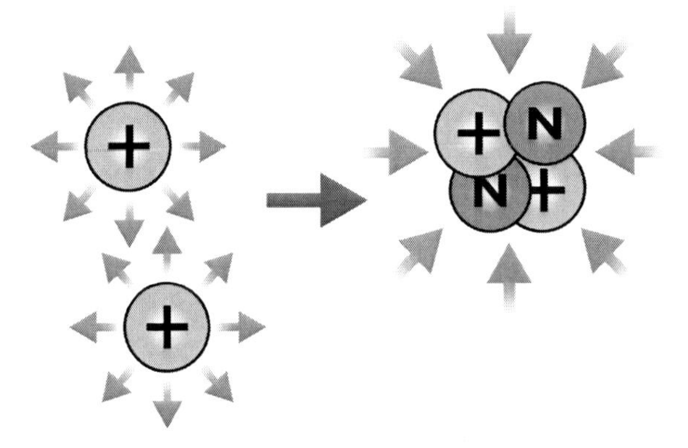

Binding Protons in Atomic Nuclei

This concept can be applied to keep the object and the subject together as one entity within Self-Awareness. In Self-Awareness, the subject is the same as the object and the object is the same as the subject. Logically, they must be separate. The subject is "in here" and the object is "out there." Can you imagine the energy required to bring the subject and

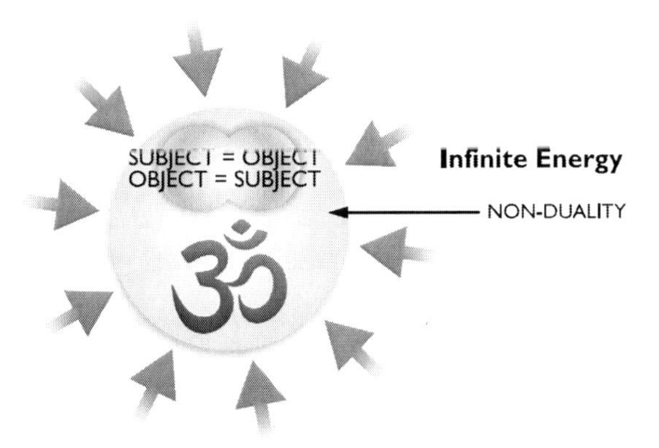

object together as one homogenous entity? To force them to become one entity? To make the subject into an object and the object into a subject? It seems like an impossible task, but it does happen within Self-Awareness. It is not wrong to predict that the energy required to undertake this task is infinite.

An infinite amount of energy will be required to keep the subject and object as one unit within Self-Awareness. Like the nuclear force is present within the nucleus, Self-Awareness is a storehouse for an infinite amount of energy to keep the subject and object as one homogenous unit. This infinite energy stored in Self-Awareness is the source of the energy in the universe. This energy within Self-Awareness is in an unmanifest condition and is in its potential form. This energy within Self-Awareness is inactive; it is dormant, but it is present. Vedanta refers to this infinite energy stored within our inner core as Maya Shakti.

How Is the Infinite Energy Activated?

The simple answer is Ignorance. We are ignorant of our true nature of Self-Awareness. We are ignorant that we are non-dual, that we are both the subject and object. Since we are not aware that we are both the subject and the object, the subject and object are no longer one entity; they are separate. Ignorance separates the subject and object. We then feel this duality with objects "out there" and the subject "in here."

With the separation of subject and object, this infinite energy pops out and is now available in the cosmic mind and a limited subset of this energy in the individual minds. This vast energy reservoir plays different roles within the mind.

- Part of this energy is used to stretch out time, to create the space "out there."
- Another part of this energy combines with the time pixels in the spacetime fabric to create the full spectrum of the electromagnetic waves. The known spectrum ranges from radio waves (300 KHz) to gamma rays (3 x 10E+21) Hz. Each time pixel in the spacetime fabric oscillates to generate all the possible frequencies in the EM

spectrum. This energy is the substratum of the spacetime fabric. There is no part of the fabric where this energy is missing.

- Another part of the energy is used to power up the object mental waveforms or vrittis in the mind.

A detailed explanation of these bullet points is available in the essay "Projection–The Only Truth."

Okay, we have shown that Self-Awareness is the storehouse for an infinite amount of energy, and this energy is present in the cosmic and individual minds. Is there any way to corroborate this assertion? Anything which will support this? Yes, there is. For this we need to understand photons and Einstein's Theory of Special Relativity. This will show and support that there is infinite energy in the mind.

Photons and Infinite Energy

We have discussed this subject matter in the essay "Understanding Photons." We repeat some parts of it to show that photons are the source of infinite energy and these photons function within Self-Awareness.

A photon is unique; it is the only particle in the universe which travels at the speed of light–186,000 miles per second. According to science, it is physically impossible for anything to travel at the speed of light, because it will require an infinite amount of energy to push something to achieve the speed of light.

If you apply the Theory of Special Relativity to the photon, you get a better understanding of energy and photons. The Theory of Special Relativity deals with the connection between space and time. The major finding is that wherever there is motion, time slows down. The faster you go, the slower the time. At the speed of light, time comes to a standstill. As it was impossible for cars or rockets to reach speeds anywhere close to the speed of light, Einstein provided a thought experiment to explain the implications of this theory.

You are on Earth and your twin brother goes into space in a rocket. Your twin brother's rocket is traveling at the speed of 0.8 c. You, on Earth, measure the speed of the light, and you find it to be c. Your twin brother also measures the speed of light; he also finds that it is c. This happens because the clock in the rocket slows down, so that the speed of light is still c. Your twin brother returns to Earth. Your clock shows that he traveled for 10 years, while his clock shows that he traveled for only six years.

If your twin brother goes back for another trip, and now his rocket travels at the speed of light c, what will happen? At the speed of light, his time will not move, his clock will be at a standstill, and he will not be moving because there is no space.

When your twin brother returns, your clock shows he has traveled for 10 years, but he will find his clock is at a standstill; no time has passed for him. Also, he has covered no distance. You aged 10 years; he felt he did not go anywhere either time-wise or distance-wise and therefore did not age at all.

Now replace the rocket and the twin brother with a photon. The photon will have the "same experience" as your twin brother traveling at the speed of light, c, in a rocket. The photon will also experience no time and no distance. From the perspective of the photon, there is no time and there is no space. This understanding is important.

Here is what you could say the photon "experienced" according to the Theory of Special Relativity:

- Distance traveled by photon = 0
- Time experienced by photon = 0 or standstill
- Energy content of photon = infinity. The formulas for the Lorenz Transformation will confirm this.

What is your experience as an observer stationed on Earth, tracking a photon traveling for 10 years?

- Distance traveled by photon = 10 light-years
- Time traveled by photon = 10 years
- Mass of photon = 0
- Speed of light = c

Amazing conclusions–you think the photons move around at the speed of light, but "according" to the photons, they do not move, they are stationary. According to the photon, it has an infinite amount of energy.

If time does not move for the photon, it must be outside time and it must be beyond the spacetime framework. If it is within the spacetime framework, time for the photon must change. Time changes for everything in space. Where is beyond spacetime? According to Vedanta, Self-Awareness, the cosmic and individual minds are beyond time and the spacetime framework. This means that the infinite energy of the photon is present only in the mind.

So, the infinite energy of the photon is present in the mind. We saw earlier that the infinite energy "popping out" from Self-Awareness is also in the mind. This means that the infinite energy of the photons is the same energy which is released by Self-Awareness due to ignorance. Therefore, the energy for the photons comes from Self-Awareness.

The mind is a powerhouse, and it has the capacity to handle and manage the infinite amount of energy. It is not easy to fathom how there can be infinite energy in the mind. Looking at the sun, we see the awesome energy it has, the power of destruction it has. The sun's energy is just a tiny, tiny, minuscule part of the total energy of the universe. How can this infinite energy be stored in the mind? The cosmic mind stores all the energy and just a small subset is available in the individual minds. It must be understood that the energy in the mind is in the subtle form and not in the gross or physical form. The subtle form is part of the subtle universe. Little is known of the subtle universe. Whatever the format of the energy in the mind, it is a fact that the source of the infinite energy is Self-Awareness. Self-Awareness is the source of infinite energy.

20 | Understanding Motion

Motion is part of our daily life. We see motion or movement everywhere. What causes this motion? How does it happen? You will be surprised; it is completely opposite to our conventional understanding.

Frames of Reference

If two cars are traveling abreast at 60 mph, they will not experience any motion with respect to each other. They will feel that they are stationary. They will only feel motion if they pass a stationary person on the roadside. If one driver is driving at 60 mph and the other at 55 mph, they will only experience a speed of 5 mph. To explain this, physics teaches us that there are two frames of reference. One frame of reference is the observer, and the other frame of reference is the object. If both the reference frames move at the same speed, there will be no relative motion. If they are not moving at the same speed, motion will be experienced.

Motion has a knack of playing tricks on us. There are two stationary trains at a platform. You are sitting in one of them, and the other train starts moving. Why do we feel that we are moving and the other train is stationary? The observer frame is stationary and the object frame is moving, but we feel that the object frame is stationary and the observer frame is moving with respect to the object frame. We look through the window on the other side and then realize that we are stationary and the other train is moving. If there were no windows on the other side, we would think that we were moving. If there is no frame of reference except the other train, we will really think that we are moving. The conclusion is that if there are *only* two frames of reference, then each frame of reference thinks it is moving with respect to the other reference frame.

As the train on the next track moves, we feel that we are moving and the other train is stationary.

Apply this logic to our daily life. We are walking toward some trees. Are we really walking toward the trees or are we stationary and the trees coming toward us? The idea that we are stationary and the trees are moving toward us is a possibility based on the frames of reference we discussed for the trains at the platform. But can this be true? Yes, it is true, and it is the only truth. It is difficult to digest this. How can the trees move–they seem stationary.

The teachings of Vedanta can help us in this regard. We have seen in the other essays that the Observer, which is Awareness, is within each one of us. This Observer is outside the spacetime fabric and is always t=0. This Observer is not the body or mind and is always stationary; it never moves. It cannot move because it is outside the spacetime fabric. If the Observer frame is always fixed, it is only logical that the trees are moving closer to us to give a sense of motion. But how can the trees and other such fixed objects in the universe move? As we have discussed in the essay "Projection–The Only Truth," there is a fully functioning subtle universe made up of mental waveforms which is operating in the mind. These subtle mental waveforms are then projected "out there" as the physical world. Believing in the idea of the projection of the universe is critical to properly understanding motion.

Based on this, there are subtle waveforms of the trees in our mind. In some way (which is discussed later) the subtle waveforms of the trees move closer to the fixed Observer in the mind. When this happens, the projected physical trees will be closer to the Observer. Since the physical trees have moved to be closer to the fixed observer, there is a sense of motion or movement of the trees. We do not feel this; we feel the trees are fixed and we have moved closer to them. This is the same way that you feel your fixed train is moving compared to the other train at the platform. This is the grand deception of motion, played by Maya Shakti.

The Observer frame is always stationary, and the movement of the object frame gives the impression of motion for the Observer frame. So, how does the object frame really move? What is the cause of the object frame's movement?

Time and Motion

We have seen from other essays that, if you understand the Theory of Special Relativity, we can conclude that motion and time are interconnected. When motion speed increases, then time slows down. It seems that motion comes first and then time slows down. Motion is the cause, and the slowdown of time is the effect. Is this the correct interpretation? I do not think so. Motion is gross; we see motion everywhere. In contrast, time is subtle–you cannot see it, touch it, or feel it. Time is present in the mind as a mental waveform. This waveform has the power to create time. It is quite difficult for us to understand or visualize the composition of this waveform, but one thing is certain–that time is subtle and, therefore, it is a waveform and is present in everyone's mind.

Vedanta teaches us those subtle mental waveforms come first, and that the subtle waveforms are the cause of the gross world around us. The subtle waveform projects the physical world "out there." If you apply this reasoning, time must come first, and the time waveform is the cause of motion. So, the correct way to interpret the connection between motion and time is that when time slows down, then motion is created.

When time slows down, it is only logical to expect that the objects will be closer to the Observer. The physics equation $s = v*t$ will support this.

When time t is a smaller value, the distance s will be smaller, meaning it is closer to the Observer.

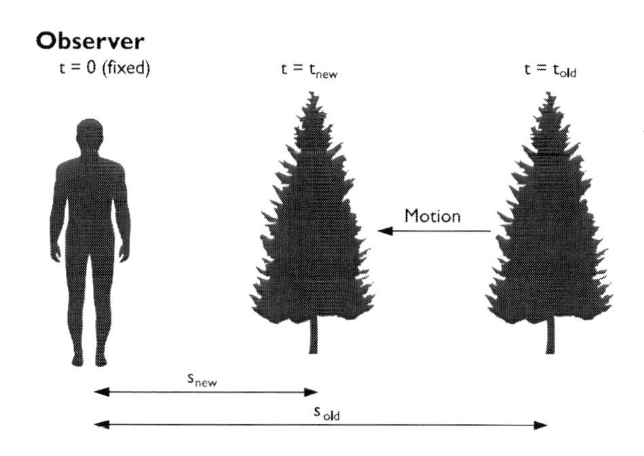

The Observer is fixed at t=0; it does not move. Before motion, the tree is at s_{old} distance away and time taken is t_{old}. To reflect motion, time has slowed to t_{new} and the distance of the tree is now s_{new}. S_{new} is closer to the Observer; this means that the tree has moved from its old position to the new position. The objects have moved, meaning there is motion. However, we feel the opposite–that the objects are fixed, and the Observer has moved. This is exactly the way we feel when the other train moves from the platform. We are fixed and the other train is moving, but we feel that the other train is fixed and we are moving.

So, time controls motion and not the other way around. Time is the cause of motion. Increase or decrease the time factor in the mind, and the resulting motion (or speed) of the objects will change in the physical world. Time is also the cause of the spacetime fabric expansion or contraction. Increase or decrease the time, and spacetime fabric will also expand or contract. This corroborates Einstein's Theory of Special Relativity.

The next time you are walking or running, just imagine that you are fixed at your location but the objects around you are moving closer to you. It will seem true. Isn't it amazing?

The same logic also applies to acceleration. Acceleration is a type of motion, so here too time controls motion. In the earlier discussion, time slowed down by a fixed amount and this resulted in motion at a fixed speed. But, in acceleration, time slows down by squaring itself; this results in motion being accelerated, and objects move closer in an accelerated matter.

So, time is king; it controls both motion and acceleration.

21 | Are We Robots?

Are we robots? It is a strange question. The answer is yes and no. The answer would depend on how the question is asked and about whom we are talking. Let us understand this.

A robot is nothing but a machine that can replicate certain human movements and functions. These movements and functions are pre-programmed in a robot. What is the difference between us and a robot? The main difference is the mind. We have a mind, and the robot does not have a mind. The mind is a complex instrument. This mind allows us to think, make decisions, be aware of ourselves, has feelings and emotions and exercises our free will. The robot does not have a mind and therefore lacks these functions. Its functions are limited to what has been pre-programmed for the robot.

Let us ask the following two questions to set the discussion:

Ask yourself if you are a robot. The answer would be a definite *No*. We are aware of everything around us. We make our own decisions. We have free will, allowing us freedom of speech and movement. We have emotions and feelings. We also have a mind, and we know we have a mind. We know the mind is within our bodies. Anything without a mind must be a robot. Since our body and mind are rolled into one unit, we are not robots. This seems logical.

Are people around you robots? I am sure your first reaction will be that people around you are human beings and so they are not robots. Okay, people around you are human beings, but are the mind and body of these people at the same location? I am sure you cannot guarantee that. You can see the body of the people around you, but you cannot see their minds. You cannot be 100% sure if the mind is with them. You do assume that, since you have the body-mind complex within yourself, all the people around you will also have the body-mind complex within themselves. It does seem that way. Unfortunately, this is a wrong assumption. You may have the body and mind in one place, but the people around you do not have the body and mind in one place. Yes, this is true!

Let us discuss this further. We will show that the mind of everyone around you is within you, and their body is in the space "out there." The body and mind are separated.

Location of the Mind

Where is the mind located? Intuitively we know that the mind is not located in space. You cannot find the mind anywhere in space. Why? What you find in space is only gross matter. Visible objects. The mind is subtle; it is not something you can touch or see. It is therefore impossible to find the mind in space. The mind must be outside space. How to find something outside space? The best way would be to find the starting point of space. When this is found, we can guess that the mind will be outside that starting point.

To look for the starting point of space, you must look at space "out there" in terms of time and not distance. We must look for t=0 for space. We can easily say that light from faraway objects will take more time to reach us than light from objects which are close to us. The light from the sun takes eight minutes to reach us, while the light from the tree outside the window will take 10 microseconds (10E-6). As the distance reduces, the time taken for light to reach us also reduces. The size of the space gets reduced. If you extrapolate this backward, the only logical place for light to take zero seconds to reach us is the mind. At t=0 there is no space. This means that the mind within you is the starting point of space. The mind is the t=0 for space. The mind is just outside space, and space starts where the mind ends. This will apply to every living being. Each must understand that t=0 for space is within him or her. It does seem that space is everywhere, but the starting point of this space is within each one of us. This does seem counterintuitive, but we have just shown that the starting point for space is within us.

We have just seen that the t=0 or "now" moment is within each one of us. This means that at this "now" moment, your mind and the entire cosmic mind which includes all the minds is present within us.

Location of the Human Body

So, the mind is outside space. For me, my mind and all the minds in the universe are within me. For you as well, your mind, my mind, and all the minds in the universe are within you. This will apply to each living being. What about the body? The body is within space. We see our body; we see the bodies of other people. We have just seen that our mind is outside space, but our body is within space. How do we understand this?

Our Own Body: We always know that our mind is within our body. We know this for a fact. We never experience our body to be here and the mind somewhere else. We never have an out-of-body experience. The mind and body are always together, and they are never separated.

See the contradiction–the mind is outside space, but the body which contains the mind is always within space. In fact, the body is all over space. Today it is here, tomorrow it is flying to India, going to a restaurant, always moving within space. How should we understand this issue? If the mind is outside space, then the only logical way to understand this issue is that the body is always at the starting point of space. The start of space is always your body. The first object in space is your body, and then follow all the other objects you see "out there." In this way, both the mind and body remain in one place.

Since our body-mind complex is in one place, we are not robots. We have free will and self-awareness.

Bodies of Other People: If your friend is sitting 100 feet away, does he have his body and mind in one place? Not really. Why? You are not seeing the "now" version of a friend. Light takes 0.10 μs (microseconds) to reach you. You will see the "now" version of your friend only when light takes zero time to reach you. That is impossible. You will always see a dated version of your friend. In this case, you see the "now minus 0.10 μs" version of your friend. Not only friends but all the people around you are also dated versions of themselves. You might say 1 μs = 10E-6 seconds is a small number and the human mind cannot discern these small time-scales. That is true, but nature does not operate with this time scale. Based on the Planck constant, the smallest time frame is 10E-44 seconds. Nature operates with this time scale. Compared to 10E-44 seconds, 10E-6 seconds is like an eternity. We may not notice it and be unable to discern it, but it must be clear that we are always seeing a dated version of the people around us.

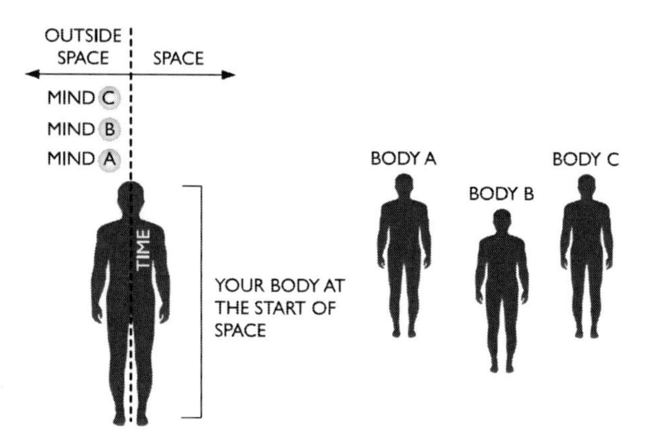

Mind outside Space. Body inside Space.

Let us compare this with the actors in a movie. When you watch a movie, you never see the live version of the actors; you will always see a recorded or dated version of the actors. If I ask you if the mind of the actors is with them on the screen, your answer will be a "no." You only see the body version of the actors. The mind will be available only with the live or "now" version of the actors. The live or "now" version of the actors is somewhere else and not on the screen. The actors on the screen do not have the mind; they only have the dated version of the body.

This is exactly what is happening to your friend and the people around you. They are like the actors on the screen. Like the actors on the screen, you only see the dated version of your friend and the people around you. They are the dated version because light takes a finite amount of time to reach us. If this is correct, you only see the body of your friend and the people around you. Their mind is not with the dated version of the body. Their mind is elsewhere. Where? It is outside space; it is at the t=0 location. We have seen that the t=0 location is only within each one of us. So, the mind of your friend and of the people around you is within you. It is not easy to accept or grasp, but if you think about it, this reasoning is correct and logical. So, your friend and the people you see are just a body, and their mind is located within you, which is outside space.

So, your friend and people around you are really robots, with a body. Their mind is within you and the dated version of the body is in space. This mind is like a remote control; it manages all the activities of the remote body. All the intelligence which the body shows is controlled and managed by the mind from a remote location. The remote mind tells the body to speak, and then the body speaks. The mind thinks and signals the body to get in the car, or to get an ice cream. The mind controls all the actions of the body. Any human body you see around is just the body with no mind in it. The mind is at a remote location.

If your friend is sitting in front of you, then his/her physical body may be in front of you, but his mind is within you. Your friend will also have the same experience. He/she will see your physical body in front of him/her, but your mind is also within him/her. If there are 10 people sitting in the same room, each one of them will have the same experience. Each of them will see the nine physical bodies "out there," but all the 10 minds will be within each one of them at t=0.

To conclude, each one of us knows that we are not robots because the pivot of the body-mind complex is at one place. But the people around us, they are really like robots. Their mind is within you and this mind is like a remote control; it manages all the activities of the body which is scattered all over space.

22 | Are We Looking at the Same Objects?

Imagine that each one of us is looking at the same scene, maybe a group of trees. Are we looking at the same trees? If we are looking at the same scene, I am sure most people will answer, "Yes, we are looking at the same trees." The correct answer is a qualified "yes." We may be looking at the same trees, but each one of us is looking at a different version of the trees. In other words, we are not looking at "exactly" the same trees but at different versions of the same trees.

How do we understand this? The problem is the way we look at the vast and intractable space. We are used to seeing space in terms of distance. This tree is 100 feet away, that house is one mile away, that plane is flying at 30,000 feet. There is nothing wrong with this, but this vision hides the complexities of the space "out there." The interesting truths about space get hidden with this perspective.

Another way to look at space is in terms of time. Measure distance by the amount of time light takes to reach us from different objects. Einstein taught us that space and time are the same things, and he coined the term "spacetime." This would mean we can measure distance in space both in miles/km and in seconds. Things become interesting and the inner complexity of the universe becomes evident when you look at the universe in terms of time.

To get the ball rolling, let us look at some trees in terms of time taken by light to reach us from the trees. For instance, suppose you are standing at Location A and your friend is standing at Location B, and you are looking at a group of trees located and rooted at different distances. We know that light travels at 186,000 miles/second. Even though the trees are not far, a single beam of light will take some time to reach us. See below the results of the trees in terms of distance and time taken by light to reach us.

	Location A		**Location B**	
	Distance	Time	Distance	Time
Tree 1	100 ft	0.10 μs	600 ft	0.60 μs
Tree 2	300 ft	0.30 μs	800 ft	0.80 μs
Tree 3	500 ft	0.50 μs	1000 ft	1.0 μs
Tree 4	1000 ft	1.0 μs	1500 ft	1.5 μs

Note: μs = microsecond (1 μs = 10E-6 seconds)

You are standing at Location A and Tree 1 is 100 feet away. Based on the speed of light, it will take approximately 0.1 μs for light to reach you from the point where the tree is located. Since light has taken some time to reach you, the version of the tree you will see is not the current version but a dated version of the tree. You will see the current version of the tree only if the distance between the tree and you is zero and light will take zero seconds to reach you. We can call this the "now" tree. It is the current version of the tree. The simple explanation is that if light must travel any distance (however small), you will never see the current or "now" version of the tree. It will always be the older, dated version of the tree.

Based on this, for Tree 1, which is 100 feet away, you will see the "now minus 0.1 μs" version of the tree. This is because light takes 0.1 μs to reach us, so what we see is not the "now" version but a "now minus 0.1 μs" version of the tree. Light from Tree 3 at 500 feet will take 0.5 μs to reach us, so the version of the tree you see is the "now minus 0.5 μs" version of the tree. This logic will apply to all the objects in the universe.

Now, suppose your friend is standing at location B, which is 500 feet behind you. For him, tree 1 is 600 feet away. Since your friend is standing 600 feet away, light will take 0.6 μs to reach him. This would mean that your friend will see the "now minus 0.6 μs" version of the same tree. The version of his tree is different from the one that you are seeing. You, at

100 feet away, see the “now minus 0.1 μs” version of the tree, and your friend, at 600 feet, will see the “now minus 0.6 μs” version of the tree. Since light travels a longer time to reach your friend from the same tree, he will see a different version of the same tree.

This may sound strange, but it is true that if we are standing at different distances from the tree, we will see a different version of the same tree. This logic applies to all objects in the universe.

You may argue that 10E-6 seconds is a small number, and a human being cannot discern these small-time differences. This is true, and that is why there is no confusion between the different versions of the same objects. We all think we are seeing the same version of the tree. The human mind has a limited capacity to distinguish between these minor changes. If the human mind cannot distinguish between these minor changes, that does not mean that Mother Nature is also limited. Based on the Planck constant, the smallest possible time slot in nature is 10E-44 seconds. This is a small number, and nature is constructed based on time increments of 10E-44 seconds. If you compare 10E-6 seconds with 10E-44 seconds, 10E-6 seconds seems like eternity. This is the discerning capacity of nature.

The point being made is that the tree you see at 100 feet is the “now minus 0.1 μs” version of the tree, and your friend sees the “now minus 0.6 μs” version of the same tree at 600 feet. If each of you takes a photo of the tree, you might not notice any difference. This is expected because the distances are not much. The human mind cannot distinguish these minor changes, but nature provides different versions of the same tree.

If these minor version changes for small distances are difficult to accept, let us conduct a thought experiment where the object distances are large, and the time taken for light to reach us is significant. Let us assume that human beings are living all over the universe; even the faraway planets are inhabited by us. Let us say that at this very moment, four people are looking at the sun. Person 1 is stationed on Earth. Person 2 is stationed on Mars. Person 3 is on a planet which is one million light-years away. Person 4 is living on a planet which is four billion light-years

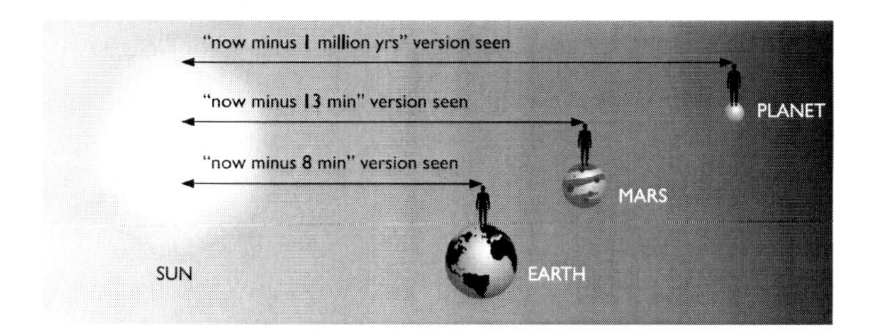

away. At this "now" moment, all of them are looking at the sun. What will each person see?

- Person 1 will see the "now minus eight minutes" version of thc sun, because a single ray of light takes eight minutes to reach Person 1 on Earth.
- Person 2 is on Mars and light takes 13 minutes to reach Mars. This person will see the "now minus 13 minutes" version of the sun. It may not be noticeable, but the sun from Mars will look five minutes younger compared to the sun that Person 1 sees from Earth.
- Person 3, who is one million light-years away, will see the "now minus one million light-years" version of the sun. This is because it has taken light one million years to reach Person 3.
- Person 4, who is four billion light-years away, will see the "now minus four billion light-years" version of the sun. We know that the sun is about 4.5 billion years old. So, right now, Person 4 will see the version of the sun which was four billion light-years ago. This person sees the infant version of the sun, which is totally different from the sun that Person 1 is seeing from Earth or Mars.

All four people are looking at the sun right "now," but they are seeing different versions of the sun. Not only the sun, but this same explanation also applies to every object in the universe. Whether you are a few millimeters away or light-years away, each one of us will see a different version of the same object.

Some more intriguing complexity of the world yet remains unsolved. You are standing 600 feet from Tree 1. We have seen that at this distance, you will see the "now minus 0.6 μs" version of the tree. Now you start walking toward the tree. What happens? As you walk, the tree gets closer to you. This means that the beam of light will take less time to reach you and, therefore, you will see a different version of the same tree. With every step you take, you will see a different version of the tree. It is indeed amazing stuff, but entirely true. When you are 100 feet from the tree, you will see the "now minus 0.1 μs" version of the tree. What is happening? The tree looks fixed, stationary; how is it possible that the tree is changing its version continuously? It would almost seem as though the current version is being physically uprooted and replaced by a newer version of the tree.

How do we understand this reality? We can see that the universe "out there" looks different when space is viewed with the eyes of time and not distance. How do we understand that when you see a version of the tree, your friend sees a different version of the same tree? That a person who is four billion light-years away will see the infant version of the sun, while you on Earth will see the "now minus eight minutes" version of the sun? How are we to comprehend that when you walk, run, or drive a car, the version of the tree and every object "out there" keeps changing its version on a continuous basis?

This is intriguing because this perspective is never discussed. If you want a simple answer–it is called projection. It means that each one of us projects our own universe "out there." Our mind projects the universe, and that is what we see. I am projecting a version of the tree along with other objects; you are also projecting your own version of the tree depending on the distance at which the tree is located from you. In this way, each one of us is projecting their own version of the tree along with other objects. There is no other way which will explain why you see a different version of the tree as compared to others. Also, if you are moving at any speed, how will versions of the objects keep changing? The entire phenomenon is possible only because each one of us is projecting the universe "out there."

Vedanta teaches us that there is a fully functioning subtle universe made of waveforms which is operating in the cosmic mind, and a subset of this subtle universe is operating within individual minds. Also, each object in the universe has a gross form and a subtle form. The subtle form is made up of waveforms. Each object has its own unique waveform. These object waveforms make up the subtle universe.

In the cosmic mind and in all individual minds, there is also a time waveform. This waveform is the source of time. This time waveform superimposes on the object waveform to form a combined time-object waveform. This time-object waveform is powerful, and it maintains the full historical timeline record of the object, right from its birth to the "now" moment. All the versions of the objects are available or stored in the combined time-object waveform. For example, if Tree 1 is 70 years old, the combined time-tree 1 waveform will have the complete record of all the versions of the tree from its birth to the current moment. This applies to every object in the universe.

When you are seeing Tree 1, the "now minus 0.1 μs" version of the time-tree 1 waveform will be available in your mind. Your mind will then project this tree at 100 feet. When your friend sees Tree 1, the "now minus 0.6 μs" version of the time-tree 1 waveform will be available in his mind. Your friend's mind will project this tree at 600 feet. Thus, projection varies from one individual mind to another.

The next time you look at space, please look at it through the lens of time. You will get a different perspective of the world "out there." If you do this regularly, you will understand the actual construction of the universe. You will realize that objects are placed at different distances because of the time that light takes to reach us. If you think deeply about this, you will be convinced that your mind is projecting the different version of the objects "out there."

23 | The Large Hadron Collider and the Truth

If you follow science, you must have heard of the Large Hadron Collider (LHC). It was built in 2008 by the European Organization for Nuclear Research (CERN), with the collaboration of 10,000 scientists from over 100 countries. It is an underground tunnel, with a circumference of about 27 km, in which scientists smash elementary particles to study their construction with the goal of finding the substratum of the physical world, to find out the building blocks of the universe.

To understand how the LHC works, the famous equation $E=mc^2$, discovered by Einstein, is a good starting point. We know that atoms are made up of protons and neutrons, which are in the nucleus and that the electrons rotate around the nucleus. The idea is to find out the substratum of these particles. To get the ball rolling, elementary particles like neutrons and protons are energized in the LHC. As the energy provided to the particles is increased, based on the Einstein equation, the speed of these particles increases. By continuously providing more energy, the speed of these particles nearly achieves the speed of light–not the speed of light, but almost the speed of light. To achieve the speed of light is impossible because you would need infinite energy.

After achieving this high speed, any further increase in the energy to the particles does not cause the particle speed to increase much, but the mass of the particles keeps increasing. At this high level of energy, the elementary particle has both a very high speed and a very high mass. In the early years of 2008 to 2013, the particle energy achieved was four teraelectronvolts (4 TeV). Two beams of these high-energy, high-mass particles were sent in opposite directions and then smashed against each other to observe the particles breaking up into smaller particles, so that the inner construction of these particles could be discovered. This was done repeatedly to attain consistency and surety in the findings. There is no denying that many new particles were discovered. Some people call these the particle zoo–fermions, bosons, tau, anti-tau, muon neutrino, quarks, etc. The list keeps growing.

This obviously did not satisfy the scientists. Between 2013 and 2015, they upgraded the LHC to make the particles accelerate at energy levels of 6.5 TeV, a more than 50% increase in the energy level. During this phase they discovered the Higgs boson, the particle which provides mass to all the objects in the universe. After three years of continuous smashing of particles, the scientists were not satisfied. They decided that they needed to further upgrade the LHC particle accelerator. Now, the LHC is in upgrade mode for the next few years. They are hoping that the new, more powerful LHC will answer all the remaining questions.

The question is, will the scientists ever be able to discover the substratum of the universe by smashing these high-energy particles? The simple answer is *No* and *Never*. They can spend billions of dollars and make the particle accelerator more powerful, but they will NEVER discover the substratum of the universe; they will never find out the building blocks of the universe. They are looking to discover the truth in the wrong place.

DVR and Recording

The current strategy being followed by science will never be successful because it approaches the problem in the wrong way. Let us try and understand this. Suppose you are looking at a playback of an event from a DVR, and someone asks you to find out the number of bones a human being has by looking at an image of the person on the TV. Will you be successful? Never. Whatever you may try, you will never find out the number of bones in that human being. You may try to digitally zoom into the image to blow it up, hoping to see the inside of the human being. There is no doubt you will be unsuccessful, but you will discover that the image of the human being is made of pixels. This discovery will lead you to further investigate the pixels, hoping to find the number of bones in the human being. You are trying to find out the number of bones in a human being, but you are now focused on investigating and discovering everything about pixels. This is what is happening with science when scientists continue to smash particles at the LHC, discovering new particles—they are moving further away from understanding the real substratum of the universe.

Universe and Recording

How does this example help us in understanding this universe? If you study it carefully, you will discover that this universe is also made of "recorded" or "memory" objects. There are no "real" or "live" or "now" objects in this universe. As discussed in previous essays, the sun we see is a "now minus eight minutes" version of the sun. It takes light eight minutes to reach us, therefore the sun is a recorded image and not a "live" or "now" image or "now" sun. Take the moon; it takes light three seconds to reach us, so the moon we see is a recorded image of the moon and not a "live" image of the moon. The plane flying at 30,000 feet is a "now minus 10E-3 seconds" version of the plane, because light takes that much time to reach us, so the plane is also a recorded image.

This concept applies not only to the stars, sun, and the moon, but to every micro- or macro-object in this physical universe. The moon, the trees, stars, animals, human beings—every living and nonliving object in this world is a "recorded" or "memory" object. This means that the physical universe "out there" is only made up of "recorded" or "memory" objects. However hard you try, you will never discover a "live" or "now" object anywhere in this physical universe. Like you will discover only pixels if you investigate a human being in a recorded image, in the same way you will discover only atoms and subatomic particles if you investigate the "recorded" or "memory" objects in this universe.

So, how does one investigate to find out the real substratum of the universe? There must be a different and better strategy to discover the underlying reality of the universe and the construction of objects.

Objects and the Truth

Science is trying to find out the composition of the physical objects in the universe. Scientists will never find this by smashing particles in the LHC. It is exactly like trying to find the number of bones in a human body by exploring a recorded image. It is just not possible. Since smashing particles in the LHC is not the solution, we must look elsewhere. But where? Fortunately, we can find the solution within Vedanta. The ancient rishis in India contemplated and came up with the correct way to fully understand the composition of any object. So, what is the truth behind any physical object?

The best way to start this discussion is to understand the popular Vedanta metaphor of pot/clay. We know that clay pots come in many different sizes, shapes, and designs. Some are tall, some are short, some are round etc. There seems to be an unlimited possibility for shapes and sizes. If you study all the clay pots carefully, you will see that each clay pot has the following two components: content and form. So, which part is the content and which part is the form? The answer is obvious–the clay is the content, and the pot is a form of the clay. With different shapes and sizes, the form of the pot could vary, but the content of all the pots will always be clay.

Clay Pot = Clay (content) + Pot (form)

Content Is Clay for All Pots

A simple question: in the clay pot, what is the weight of the clay, which is the content, and what is the weight of the pot, which is a form? The answer is obvious; the clay has all the weight, and the pot has no weight. Another question: can you separate the form of the pot from its clay content? The answer is that it is impossible to separate the pot form from the clay content. They are inseparable. The pot form is an idea or concept which has been superimposed on the clay.

This Vedantic metaphor can help us understand the underlying components for every object in this physical universe. Every object in the universe must have the following two components:

1. Content
2. Form

Of What Is Content Made?

So, what is the content of all the objects in the universe? Vedanta teaches us that a good starter question is: how do we know an object exists? The simple answer is that we are aware of the object. We see it, we know it, we can touch it.

How do we know the tree is green? Because we are aware of it.

How do we know sugar is sweet? Because we are aware of it.

How do we know we have two legs and two hands? Because we are aware of them.

How do we know the weight of the chair is 20 lb? Because we are aware of it.

How do we know the smooth touch of silk? Because we are aware of it.

How do we know we are listening to music? Because we are aware of it.

The common thread that connects all these questions is Awareness. Awareness is a prerequisite to observe any object. Awareness is a prerequisite for the existence of any object. Without Awareness, we would not know any objects which are perceived by the five sense organs–eyes, ears, nose, tongue, and skin. The objects coming in from the sensory organs must encounter Awareness; only then can we observe the object. For an analogy, think of the sun. When there is no light from the sun, you cannot see anything, but in the presence of sunlight everything becomes visible. In the same way, when any form enters the presence of the light of Awareness, we become aware of the object. If there is no light of Awareness, you will perceive nothing, and no object will exist.

So, what is Awareness and what does Awareness have to do with the content of the object? Everything. Awareness is the content of all the objects in the universe. The content of the objects from the five senses is simply Awareness. To any newcomer, Awareness is just another English word, with a dictionary meaning of "knowledge or perception of a situation or fact." Awareness is much more than an English word.

Awareness is the most powerful force in the universe, and it is the underlying reality of this universe. It has the power to connect with a form present in the mind and fill up the object with Awareness. As we have discussed in the essay "Understanding Self-Awareness," Awareness is made up of a Subject, Object, and Intelligence.

- Awareness = Subject + Object + Intelligence
- Power of Awareness = Power of Knower + Power of Known + Power of Knowing

Awareness is made of Subject, Object, and Intelligence, and it has three different powers–Knower, Known, and Knowing. It must be understood that the Subject, Object, Intelligence, and the three powers are not something outside in the world; they are within Awareness and make up Awareness.

Wherever there is Awareness, there must be present Subject, Object, and Intelligence with all the three powers. To understand how the content of every object in this universe is only Awareness, we need to understand Power of the Known.

Power of Known

Power of the Known is a power within Awareness. It is a power which deals with objects. It deals with the objects received from the five senses. A better way to understand Power of the Known is that it is a power to become any object. This power does not create any object but becomes the object which is superimposed on this power by the five senses.

Awareness by itself is formless, but it has the potential to become any object. The object it will become depends on the input received from the five senses. A good metaphor to explain this is that Awareness is like a lump of Play-Doh, which is formless, but you can manipulate the Play-Doh into any shape. Whatever shape you create, the content is always Play-Doh. In the same way, the content of all the objects in the universe is only Awareness. It can take any shape or form, but the content is always Awareness.

The next time you see a tree, or listen to music, or feel the cold water, you must be clear that the tree, music, or water is made up of only Awareness and nothing but Awareness. It is the content of every object.

Of What Is Form Made?

We now know that the content of any object is Awareness. So, of what is the form of the object made? What is the source of the form? To understand this properly, you need to understand how the mind functions. As we have discussed in other essays, the mind is made up of mental waveforms or vrittis. The ingredients of these waveforms are knowledge and intelligence. These waveforms come into the mind from the five input or sensory organs–eyes, nose, tongue, ears, and skin. These intelligent mental waveforms are the bases of the form. When these intelligent waveforms come in touch with Awareness and they superimpose themselves on Awareness, the intelligent waveforms become the form of the objects that we see in the physical world. The content is Awareness, but the form comes from the five senses. The waveforms from the ear become the sound we hear. The waveforms from the eyes become the form of the objects we see. The waveforms from the tongue become the taste we feel. In the same way, smell and touch also function using the input waveforms from the nose and skin.

We saw in the earlier metaphor that clay is the only content in the clay pot. The pot is only a form which is superimposed on the clay. In the same way, Awareness is the only content of all the objects, and the form comes from the five senses which are superimposed on Awareness.

This is true, but why don't we feel that the content is Awareness during our daily interaction with objects? This is because our attention is always focused on the form part of the object and, in the process, we ignore the content part. As an example, if you go to a furniture shop, your attention is always focused on the different designs of furniture. I like this design, I do not like this design. This design will look nice in the house. The focus is on the form part of the furniture and not on the content part. Our focus on the form of the object is so deep-rooted that we do not know and understand that Awareness is the only content of all objects.

Content Is Awareness for All Objects

If you think about it, even science has been focusing exclusively on the form of objects. Scientists have been investigating the form of objects, and they have made great strides by discovering all the different inner layers of the form. Molecules, atoms, and all the subatomic particles. The problem is that science has been investigating the form of objects, but they want to discover the content of objects. They are not going to find Awareness by smashing subatomic particles in the LHC. They are working at the wrong end of the objects. They are working with the form of the objects and not the content of the objects.

You do not have to hunt for Awareness; it is hiding in plain sight. If you see an object, Awareness is already present in that object. It is right in front of you. You are already aware of the object. The next time you see an object, do not focus on the form but focus on the fact that you are Aware of the object. If you do this regularly, you will realize that Awareness is everywhere, and objects are just a skin on top of Awareness.

24 | The Real Perception Process

Experience has a knack of fooling us on a regular basis. We see the sun setting every day, but we know very well that the sun never sets. It is Earth rotating backward which gives us the experience that the sun is setting on the horizon. The sky looks blue, but we know that in reality there is no sky, and neither is it blue. There are many such examples where our experiences are false. The same is also true of how we visually perceive the world.

Science has taught us that light is reflected from any object in this universe that we observe, and it travels to the retina in our eye. There are 120 million rods which are sensitive to black and white, and there are about seven million cones which are sensitive to color. These rods and cones convert the incoming light into an optical signal. This optical signal is transmitted to the visual cortex in the human brain. This is the end of the journey of the perception process. There is no explanation of what happens to the optical signal and how the brain decodes the optical signal and reconstructs our visual world. Science also never tells us who is at home within the brain who finally sees the reconstructed visual image. Who is the final observer of this image?

The way the perception process is currently described is incomplete and has shortcomings. The objective of this essay is to give a fresh and different outlook to the perception process.

Limitations of the Current Perception Process

Besides the lack of understanding of the observer and of what happens in the mind/brain in the reconstruction of the outside world, there is this unanswered question: does the incoming light reflected from objects have the capacity to generate the awareness of those objects? It would seem that this reflected light is our only connection with the outside world. We are aware of all the objects, both far and near, only because of this reflected light. Is it asking too much of the reflected light?

1. If you look at a faraway star, the light traveling from there can take a long time to reach us. For Star A, which is 10 light-years away, the photon would have had to start traveling 10 light-years earlier so that it could hit the retina in our eye now to make Star A visible. Now we turn around and try and see Star B, which is one million light-years away. That photon would have needed to start its journey one million light-years earlier, so that it would be available to our eyes now. This is a long journey for the photon passing through space containing dark matter, galaxies, and planets. The photon must keep its purity of wavelength and energy level. Now if you can imagine millions of people spread over many different galaxies looking at the same stars at the same time, different photons from Star A and Star B should also travel from the past to the present to reach these millions of viewers. It would seem that these photons from anywhere in the universe are available to viewers everywhere on demand, and that too instantaneously. This makes you wonder–is there is a limit to the number of photons the reflected light can generate from the object and travel to all corners of the universe?

2. We know that light is made up of different colors and each of the colors has a different wavelength. When light passes through a prism (basically from one medium to another), the wavelengths for each color bend differently and we see the rainbow effect on the other side of the prism. Light breaks up and moves in scattered directions. It is more than likely that the light coming from distant objects will pass through different media, which only means that the photons of different colors will scatter and move in different directions. The probability of scattering is much higher if the light must travel from stars which are light-years away. If this is really happening, what is the accuracy of the photons reaching the human eye? Are they really representing the objects accurately? It is taken for granted that the photons reaching us from distant objects are an accurate representation.

3. Another critical question: how can the photon accurately represent the distance and time it has traveled? The object could be close by or a distant star. Physics tells us that these particles are continuously destroyed to become other particles, and then they combine once again to become a

photon. Such a dance is going on continuously. Keeping the dance in mind, there is no way to know if the original photon has traveled to reach the human eye. As of now, there is no indication that the photon has some sort of memory of its origin. There are millions of photons hitting the rods and cones in the retina, but there is no way to know which photon comes from which object and how much distance it has traveled. If this critical information is lacking, it is impossible for the eye to reproduce the image we are trying to perceive.

You could say that this is perhaps unknown to science, and that the photon does have memory to know the distance it has traveled. If so, how does it transfer this distance data to the retina? The retina, in turn, must add the data regarding distance to the optical signal being sent to the brain. Only in this way can the brain reconstruct the visual image accurately.

All the above arguments show that it is just not clear how we really perceive the objects in the universe. What science tells us so far is full of problems and shortcomings.

4. Let us now look at the same problem from a more radical point of view, which is fully supported by science. Einstein postulated that nothing in this universe can travel faster than the speed of light. He also explained that if anything travels at the speed of light, for that object, space will be smaller than the smallest dot. Now, the only particle we know which can travel at the speed of light is a photon. Let us play around with this proven fact. Imagine that we have put a tiny camera on a photon and this photon is traveling at its usual speed (of light). What will the camera capture? It will capture a universe whose size is smaller than a dot. Let us apply this logic to all the available photons in the universe. All these photons will see the same universe, which will be smaller than the smallest dot. Even the dot is an exaggeration. Actually, the dot is zero in size, which means there is nothing–no space. Nothing means nothing, but we know there is something; there is a photon. The only way to understand this is that the photon is in an unmanifest or dormant condition; it is in its potential form, just like a tree is in an unmanifest condition within a seed. The physical tree has still not come out, but the tree is there in a potential form in the seed.

From the photon's viewpoint or from its frame of reference, there is nothing out there; there is no space, no universe, no distance, and no time. This is because the photon is in an unmanifest condition.

However, if you look at it from the observer's point of view, from the observer's frame of reference, we see a vast, huge universe. In this frame of reference, the photons manifest themselves, and we think that the photons are zooming around at the speed of light. How do we understand this?

It must be understood that this availability of the photon is completely dependent on the observer or perceiver. When the observer wants to see a faraway star, only then is the photon from that star readily available. The observer's mind thinks it has taken all this time for the photon to reach it from the star, but, from the photon's point of view, it is already here. This applies to any object the observer wants to see. When the observer wants to see an object, the photon is readily available from that object. This clearly shows that the existence of the photon completely depends on the observer.

We think that photons and the universe are independent of the observer, but this is just not possible.

The Real Perception Process

From the photon's frame of reference, there is no universe. However, if we take the observer as the frame of reference, we see the universe. The logical conclusion is that the observer/mind is creating this universe. In this section, we will discuss how the observer/mind creates this universe. We can divide our discussion into the following three-step process:

1. Mind Activity
2. Projection of Content
3. Closing the Loop

1. Mind Activity

It is uncanny that what is taught in quantum physics applies to what is happening in the mind. It is almost as though all the discoveries made in quantum physics are to understand what is going on in the mind. Maybe it is so, and the physicists who made all these discoveries never realized it.

Quantum physics began with the basic goal of understanding the wave and particle duality. Sometimes matter behaves like a wave and at other times it is a particle. There is an observed system which can be represented by a wave function. The form of the wave function of the observed system can be calculated via Schrodinger's wave equation. When the observer system interacts with this wave function by looking at the observed system, the wave function collapses into one entity, and the probability of all the other possibilities becomes zero. In quantum physics, the observer system is usually some type of measuring device which interacts with the wave function, thereby collapsing the wave function.

If you replace the observer system of the measuring device with the ultimate Observer, the Awareful Brahman, the above paragraph could describe what happens in the mind. The similarity is remarkable. An argument could be made that quantum physics has not fully understood this–that the final and the only measurement/observer system is Brahman. We saw earlier in the essay "Quantum Physics and Vedanta" that the unmanifest photon becomes manifest only in the presence of the observer and not in the presence of any measuring system. No physical measuring system has the power to convert an unmanifest photon into a manifest photon. Besides, the measuring system itself is made up of photons, which are made manifest in the presence of the Observer/Brahman. Everything must and does collapse in the presence of the Observer/Brahman.

The mind is made up of waveforms called vrittis (which means "whirlpool"), just like the waves in a pond. If we analyze this, we realize that so much is happening in the mind. All the thoughts, feelings, and perceptions coming from various sources like the senses, emotions, and memories are in the mind. All these are vrittis and have their own waveforms. If you mix and match these waveforms, you will get complex wave patterns in the mind. All these vrittis combine to generate one complex vritti. As in quantum physics, we now collapse this vritti or wave function.

2. Projection of Content

Once the conscious mind and the conscious object in subtle form have been created, the next step is the projection of the object outside the mind, like a hologram or a painting. This projection is done by the power of

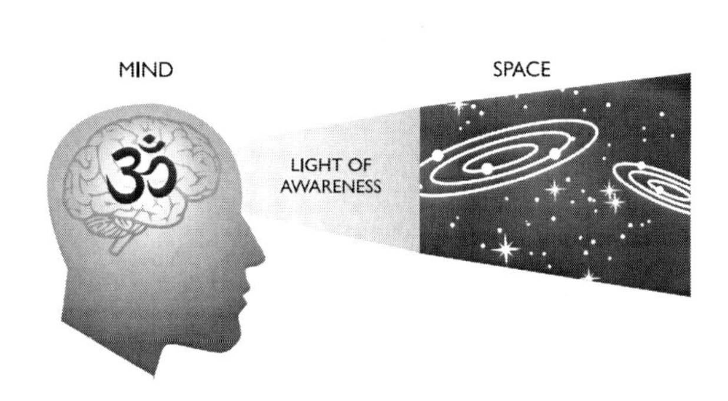

Projection by Mind

Awareness. The power of Awareness is the creative power of the Observer/Brahman. As we have discussed in other essays, the power of Awareness has the following powers:

Power of Awareness = Power of Knower + Power of Known + Power of Knowing

What you see outside in the universe and in the objects there is the projection of your mind. The power of Awareness has the capacity to do this. The projection of the content from the mind follows these four steps:

1. You need space—the canvas
2. Harden the canvas with energy
3. Create the subtle image of the painting
4. Add awareness to finish the projection

Please read the essay "Projection—The Only Truth," where a detailed science-based explanation has been given on how projection works.

The mind with the vrittis is filled with Awareness/Consciousness. This Awareness/Consciousness is being projected outside by the power of Awareness to form the fabric of the universe. In the presence of Awareness, these subtle objects in the mind take up gross forms. These gross forms are the objects we see around us.

3. Closing the Loop

Now that we have a much better understanding of how the real perception process works, it may be worthwhile to pause and answer some questions which may come up.

Q1. If the real perception is done when the Observer/Brahman witnesses the objects in the mind, then the question is: why is there the need of the gross universe? It seems redundant.

A1. The answer is ignorance. We forget that we are SatChitAnanda or Brahman. We do not know that we are Observer/Brahman witnessing the objects in the mind. The subtle world is unknown to us. Instead of Observer/Brahman, we become Observer/Mind. This Observer/Mind is looking for eternal happiness. To find this happiness, we take up a physical body; we also want desirable objects in the world so that we can interact with them and find this happiness. It is with this desire that we use the power of Awareness to create this universe. Obviously, we will not find this true happiness in objects outside, but the quest continues. This quest will come to an end only when we realize our true nature as SatChitAnanda.

Q2. It seems there are two types of objects–mind objects and world objects. Is this correct?

A2. Not really. The world object is the "grossified" version of the mind object. It is the same thing, except that the mind object is subtle with no awareness, and the world object is gross and filled with awareness.

Q3. We know we have eyes with retinas. How is it possible to disregard these gross objects in the perception process?

A3. There is no denying that eyes are gross objects and the source of the optical signal from external objects. Based on quantum physics, all matter has particle and wave properties. Even the eyes have a wave version. The wave version of the eyes has all the intelligence and functionality of the eye. The wave version of the eyes is a vritti in the mind. This vritti has the software code to take care of all the features of the eye. The wave version of external objects interacts with the wave version of the eyes in the retina. Everything happens first in the subtle universe made up of vrittis. A detailed analysis of the subtle universe is given in the essay "Life Is a Living Wave."

The perception process happens in the subtle universe first and then that is projected as the gross objects "out there." The current perception process being taught by science has defects. The projection of the universe by the Observer/Brahman is the only correct way to understand the perception process.

25 | The Theory of Everything

The Theory of Everything is the final goal for science. Scientists want to discover a framework through which they can explain everything that is possible in physics, a framework that will work for both classical and quantum physics at both the macro and micro level. It is one all-encompassing theory explaining all of physics, a unified approach which explains the laws of the universe. It also has Singularity and includes all the laws of physics.

This is a lofty goal. The goal is to find the underlying reality of matter, energy, and all the forces in the universe. Basically, find the substratum, the source of the universe. This substratum or source should explain everything in the universe. Both living and nonliving beings should evolve from this source. This is a tough task. There is no denying that science has made a great deal of progress. The question is, is it ready to reach for the final frontier–the Theory of Everything. The focus of this essay is to make an in-depth investigation and see if science is ready to climb the final mountain and uncover the Theory of Everything.

A lot has happened over the past 125 years. A great deal of progress has been made to understand the buildup of matter. Knowledge has been gained regarding the building blocks of the universe. Let us trace some of the key milestones in our long scientific journey so far:

390 BC – Democritus, a Greek philosopher, suggested that the smallest particle in the universe was what he called an “atomos.” The word “atom” comes from here.

1890s – J. J. Thomson discovered the negatively charged electrons.

1910s – Ernest Rutherford discovered the positively charged protons.

1930s – James Chadwick discovered the neutron to complete the atomic structure.

1950s – A wide range of new particles was discovered, which led to the coining of the phrase "particle zoo."

1960s – Discovery of the different types of quarks, which make up protons and neutrons.

1970s – All the new particles were arranged as the standard model of particle physics.

2010s – Discovery of the Higgs boson, which is added to the standard model.

2020s – Hopefully, scientists will discover the missing particle for gravity in the standard model.

Understanding the Standard Model

It was thought that everything is made up of atoms. Then it was discovered that atoms themselves were made up of a nucleus containing protons and neutrons, and that electrons revolved around the nucleus. Later, it was found that protons and neutrons were made up of quarks and down quarks.

When particles were smashed in particle accelerators, a wide variety of new particles was discovered. The term "particle zoo" was used for these new particles. On analyzing these particles, it was found that many of them had the same or similar substratum. Based on this understanding, the standard model of particle physics was formulated in the 1970s. This standard model showed the elementary particles which make up everything in this universe. They are called elementary particles because it is believed that they cannot be divided further. Every living and nonliving being in the universe is made up of elementary particles included in the standard model.

The standard model also includes the different forces which hold the elementary particles together. These forces are also made up of particles. Matter is made of particles, and forces are also made of particles. Strange but true!

The standard model shown below is like the periodic table taught in a chemistry class. The periodic table is laid out in a systematic and logical way to include all the elements in the universe. In the same way, the standard model lays out the elementary particles in a logical manner.

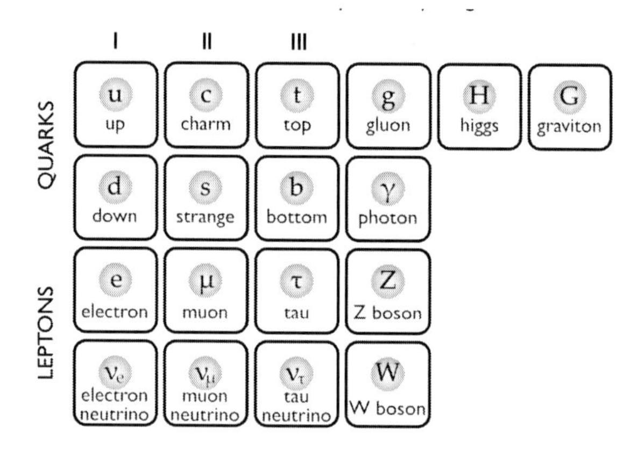

Standard Model of Elementary Particles and Gravity

The standard table can be divided into two parts. The first three columns are elementary particles which make up matter, and the remaining columns are particles which pertain to force. Understanding the details of the standard model is not critical for this essay, but let's briefly discuss it to set the scene. There are two parts to consider.

1. Elementary Particles for Matter

The first three columns pertain to elementary particles for matter. There are 12 elementary particles for matter. The first column is what we encounter in our daily lives. All the objects around us are made up of the elementary particles in the first column. The particles in the second and third columns are found in high-energy situations like the stars and the sun. The four cells in the first column can be described as follows:

Quarks: The quarks in the top two cells are the building blocks of protons and neutrons. Two up quarks and one down quark make up a proton. Two down quarks and one up quark make up a neutron. This applies to all the protons and neutrons in the universe. The cousins of quarks are shown in columns II and III.

Electrons: These are the electrons we know, which revolve around the nucleus. The cousins of electrons are shown in columns II and III.

Neutrinos: The neutrino is the most abundant particle in the universe, but it is largely unknown. The reason is that it does not interact with any matter. It is a silent operator. At this moment, millions of neutrinos are passing through your body. The neutrinos are generated because of radioactive decay. There are two varieties of neutrinos as shown in columns II and III.

2. Elementary Particles for Forces

There are four fundamental forces in the universe. These are shown in the fourth column of the standard model. There is a particle which generates these forces. Yes, it does seem strange, but there is a particle which creates force.

Electromagnetic Force: This is a force which repels particles with a similar charge and attracts those with an opposite charge. The force particle which mediates this repulsion and attraction is a photon. The way the photon force mediates between two similarly charged particles is simple and interesting. To compare, think of two people playing catch with a baseball. When they catch the ball, the force pushes the person backward. For the baseball, the force may be small, but with a heavier ball the force could be substantial. When that person returns the ball, the first person is pushed back. With this continuous back and forth, the two people are pushed further apart. This is what happens when the photon is shared between two similarly charged particles. The two similarly charged particles are pushed apart with a continuous up-and-down movement of the photon. The photon is the force which helps repel these particles.

Strong Force: This force operates only within the nucleus. Logically, the two positively charged protons should repel each other by electromagnetic force. However, there is a strong force which holds similarly charged protons together in the nucleus. The strong force is 100 times stronger than the electromagnetic force, and it overcomes the repulsive force. The gluon is the strong force particle which mediates within the nucleus.

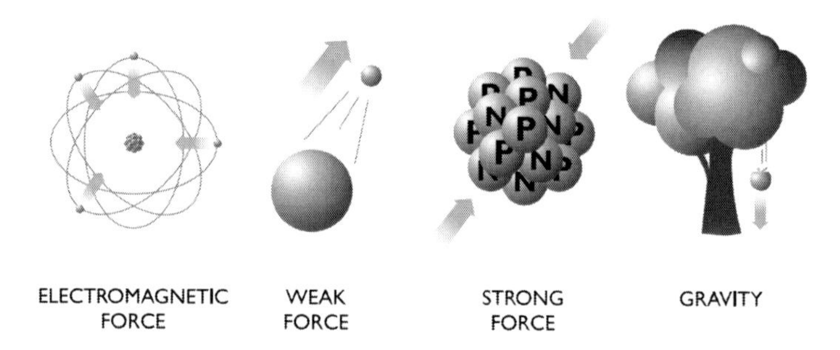

Weak Force: The weak force also operates within the nucleus of the atom. In atoms with many protons and neutrons, the nucleus can be unstable. The weak force facilitates the decay of the atom. Radioactive decay is the best example. W and Z are the two force particles which mediate the decay of the nucleus.

Gravity Force: Gravity is the most common force, which allows the attraction between any two objects. A lot is known about the effects of this force, but little is known about the cause. Physicists think that there is a force particle called graviton which mediates this force. The property of this force particle is known, but unfortunately this force particle is yet to be discovered. The search continues. As we have discussed in the essay "How Gravity Really Works," the only place graviton can be found is in the spacetime fabric.

Grand Unified Theory: At the time of the Big Bang, all the four forces were unified. The forces came from a single source. The search is on to find the single source of the four fundamental forces. As you increase the energy levels, you will be able to locate the single source. Science successfully unified the electromagnetic and the weak force and called it the electroweak force. Science knows that if you increase the energy levels, these fundamental forces can be unified. The problem is that it is impossible to experimentally prove it. Human beings cannot generate the amount of energy required for the unification.

Limitations of the Standard Model

The standard model is not the Theory of Everything. The Theory of Everything must have Singularity. You cannot have 12 elementary particles for matter and four elementary particles for force. There must be a single source which creates both the particles for matter and the particles for force. Both must come from the same source. This means that there is something deeper which is the cause of the standard model. Science agrees with this. Scientists are currently building much more powerful particle accelerators in the hope of discovering this Singularity. They plan to smash particles with much higher energy to discover the underlying reality.

String theory is another pursuit which seeks the substratum of everything. In string theory, it is believed that matter and force are made up of strings. These strings vibrate in 10 dimensions. These vibrations are supposed to be the source of the particles in the standard model. This knowledge is still theoretical with no experimental proof.

Even if the vibrating strings are the substratum of the standard model, you can still ask the question: what is the cause of the strings? Of what are they made? This will lead to another round of scientific investigation. If scientists do find the substratum of the vibrating strings, the same question can be asked: of what is that substratum made?

This can be a never-ending quest to find the ultimate substratum–the Theory of Everything. How do we solve this never-ending problem? The only solution is to find a new and different approach to the question of Singularity–the Theory of Everything.

Theory of Everything–A New Approach

This new approach and conclusion are the same as discussed in the essay "The Large Hadron Collider and the Truth."

The final goal of the Large Hadron Collider, built by CERN in Europe, is to find the Theory of Everything. They are smashing particles in the LHC to find the underlying reality of the matter–the substratum of everything. They are looking for the Singularity. Will they be successful? Till date, they have not been successful, and they will not be successful even in the future. The reasons for this we have explained in the above-mentioned essay. The problem is that they are looking at the wrong end of the object to discover this underlying reality.

What is the solution? The only solution is the proper understanding of Vedanta. Vedanta teaches that every object in the universe must have the following two components:

1. Form
2. Content

The form is superimposed on the content to complete the object. In the classic Vedanta pot-clay example, the pot form is superimposed on the clay. The content is always clay for all the pots, irrespective of the shape and size of the pots. In the same way, for everything in this universe the form comes from the five senses (eyes, ears, nose, tongue, and skin) and it is superimposed on the content to create an object. So, what is the content? If you have followed these essays, I am sure you have guessed it—that Awareness is the content of all the objects. Without Awareness you would not be aware of any objects. The object must be filled with Awareness, then only will you be aware of the different objects.

All the objects in the universe are made up of only Awareness. Awareness is the content of all objects. In our ignorance we do not see this. We focus on the different forms and not on the content. We live in a world which thinks that object forms are the only reality. With this deep-rooted ignorance, science is trying to find the Theory of Everything by studying the object forms. With all the investigation over the centuries, science has discovered the standard model, which is the building block of the object forms. It is still not the content of all objects.

Theory of Everything = Awareness

Awareness is the only content of all objects. It is impossible for science to discover the real content of objects by studying object forms. If science wants to climb the ultimate mountain of discovery, it needs to rethink its approach. Scientists need to realize that Awareness is the only content of objects. The current path is not going to take them to the destination.

How does one investigate Awareness? Luckily, you do not have to hunt for Awareness; it is hiding in plain sight. If you see an object, Awareness is already present in it. It is right in front of you. It is present in every object; it is present in every experience you have. If science wants to find the Theory of Everything, it must study Awareness. That is the only path forward.

Science must understand and appreciate the different powers of Awareness. Infinite energy, time, intelligence, power to become any object is all within Awareness. Scientists need to change focus from the form to the content. That is the only way to discover the Theory of Everything.

26 | Understanding Time

In classical physics, space and time were considered completely different and independent of each other. Newton considered space to have three dimensions and a separate single dimension for time. Einstein, with his Theory of Relativity, showed that space and time were interlinked, and he changed the terminology from "space and time" to "spacetime," and this spacetime had four dimensions. But it's hard to understand four dimensions; it's not intuitive. We can visualize the three dimensions "out there" in space. We are used to the three dimensions. Time is supposed to be the fourth dimension. Where is the fourth dimension? Where is it located? How does it function? Neither Einstein nor science has given a proper explanation for the fourth dimension. Once we have a better understanding of time, the fourth dimension will be self-explanatory. So, let us start our investigation of time.

Location of the Time Dimension

This is not an easy question to answer. Most people will answer that time must exist "out there." They see changes in objects "out there." The object was in location A, but now it is in location B. An object was three feet tall and now it is five feet tall. They see these changes in the objects and conclude that time is the cause of these changes, and therefore time is the inherent property of space "out there." They think that time is operating within the space "out there." Is this correct? It is true that time is the cause behind all the changes we see in the objects "out there," but it is incorrect to conclude that time is operating within space "out there." "Out there" is only the three dimensions; there is no place for the fourth dimension in space. Time must be located elsewhere, away from the three dimensions of space. But where?

To understand the location of time, we need to understand time better. If you look at time carefully, you can break it down into the following three components:

- Past
- Now or present
- Future

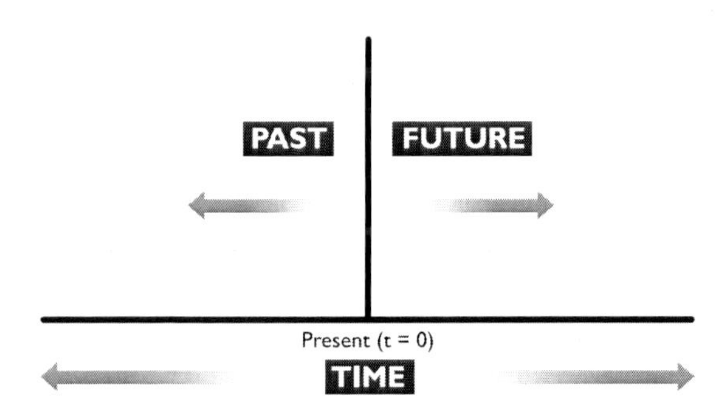

Time is made up of only these three components. A simple question: can you look at the past in space "out there"? Obviously not. The only thing you can see "out there" is the present. The past is something which is gone; it cannot come back. It must be understood that every passing event which we experience is stored in our memory. This memory is part of our mind. When the present becomes the past, that event is stored in the mind. In this way, all the past events are stored in the mind–though we may not remember all of them. When we remember something, we are bringing a past event from the mind. We can remember past events only in the mind and not "out there." This does mean that the time for the past event is available only in the mind.

As mentioned earlier, what is "out there" is only the present. This present is the "now" moment. It must be appreciated that what is "out there" is always the present. It can never be the past or the future. What is the duration of the present? According to the Planck constant, the smallest block of time is 10E-44 seconds. Once this tiny time duration passes, the current present becomes the past, and it is replaced by a new present. We know these past events are stored in the mind. When we compare the current present with the past event in the mind, we get a sense of time. This comparison of two events is the key for the generation of time.

Let us imagine that we did not have any memory; this would mean that no past events would be stored in the mind. If there were no past events, there would be no way of comparing the present "out there" with the past event stored in the mind. What does this mean? It means that we would only see the present "out there." We would always be in the present. Since we would always be in the present, time would be an unknown entity. There would be no time. We would never have the need to understand time. This reasoning does indicate that the mind is required for the generation or presence of time. The mind is the location and creator of time. Therefore, the location of the fourth dimension, which is time, is present only in the mind. Space has three dimensions, and the mind has the fourth dimension.

Vedanta has always been clear that time or "kaala" is present only in the mind. The source and location of time is the mind. Vedanta also teaches us that everything in the mind is subtle and is made of vrittis or waveforms. Since we have shown that time is generated only in the mind, it must be made of vrittis. It is quite difficult for us to understand or visualize the composition of these waveforms, but one thing is certain–that time is subtle and therefore it is a waveform and is present in everyone's mind, and it creates time.

Origin of Time

We now know that time is generated and is operational in the mind. So, the next question is: what is the origin of time and from where does this time come? The time waveform must come from somewhere; it cannot come from nothing.

Time comes from Self-Awareness or SatChitAnanda. In other essays, we have discussed that our inner core is Self-Awareness or SatChitAnanda. It is our inner bulb of Awareness. It is self-shining, full, and complete. This Self-Awareness is unborn, it is formless, and it is unchanging. In this essay, we will focus on the unchanging nature of Self-Awareness.

Unchanging: Awareness is unchanging. It always remains the same and it will never change. It is the same now, it was the same in the past, and it will remain the same in the future. Nothing in this physical universe fits this bill. Everything in the universe keeps changing. If you dig deeper into "unchanging," you can conclude that time is present in an unchanging environment, but it is static and unmoving. Time is an inherent quality within something which is not changing, but this time factor remains dormant. The entity is unchanging due to the sole reason that the time factor is not active. If, for whatever reason, this "unchanging" starts "changing," time will and must pop out from this unchanging entity. If something is changing, it means that what is now is no longer the same. Since the two events are not the same, the time factor comes into play to connect them. It is not incorrect to say that time drives the change between two events. Self-Awareness is unchanging, and the only reason it does not change is that the time factor is static or remains dormant.

How does unchanging Self-Awareness become the changing mind? The simple answer is: ignorance. We have seen in other essays that ignorance has the power to break up the non-dual Self-Awareness into duality with the object "out there" and the subject "in here." This ignorance also breaks up the "unchanging" Self-Awareness into a "changing" mind. When this unchanging Self-Awareness becomes the changing mind, the dormant time in the unchanging environment pops out and becomes available, and it is active in the mind. This time then becomes operational in the mind. This changing part of the time waveform is the driving force of the time we know and see.

Powers of Time

Time is powerful. It interacts in our daily life in many ways. Some are known and some are unknown. Let us discuss some of the powers of time to show the scope and width of its power.

- Time and Objects
- Time and Space
- Time and Spacetime
- Time and Energy
- Time and Gravity
- Time and Motion

Time and Objects: Time is a waveform in the mind, and all the objects in the world are also a waveform in the mind. Do they interact with each other? Of course, the time waveform interacts with every object waveform in the mind. When any Seed Body germinates (or is born) and becomes a waveform in the Subtle Body, the time waveform superimposes itself on the object waveform. In the essay "Life Is a Living Wave," we have discussed how there is a fully functional subtle universe made of waveforms. When a new object waveform is born, it is the t=0 or the birthday of the object waveform. Right from the t=0 moment, the time waveform is the driving force for the object waveform to modify itself, to grow itself to play out the blueprint of its life. If there was no time waveform, all the object waveforms would remain static and in the same state, with no growth. The time waveform is the underlying force which moves this universe and object waveforms forward.

Life Cycle of a Tree

The t=0 for each object is different. The t=0 for the universe was 13.7 billion years ago. The t=0 for the sun was about four billion years ago. In the same way, every object in the universe had its own t=0 when it came into existence. From t=0 to "now," each of the objects has gone through a history of events. From one moment to the next, each of the objects modifies itself. As time moves forward, the object waveform keeps changing, playing out the blueprint of its life cycle. It is like a small shoot coming out from the seed, and then over time it becomes a fully grown tree with branches and leaves, and finally it decays and dies. The tree waveform plays out its blueprint as time moves forward. This life cycle applies to everything in the universe. It must be noted that the time waveform does not change the object waveform; it only moves it forward. The change in the object waveform is due to many reasons, including the fulfillment of its pending karmas and interaction with other object waveforms.

Time and Space: Time and space are interconnected. They are two sides of the same coin. Einstein's Theory of Relativity confirms this. Time is subtle and space is gross. It is correct to conclude that time creates space. Time is the source of space. How do we understand this? Science tells us that the universe is 13.7 billion years old. If a photon must travel from the beginning of the universe, it will take the photon 13.7 billion light-years to reach us. One light-year is the distance that light travels in one year. The size of the universe will be the distance traveled by the photon from the Big Bang. This distance traveled by the photon is the outer limit of the universe, because there was no universe before the Big Bang. If you assume the universe is 13.7 billion years old "right now," then after one second, the age of the universe will be 13.7 billion years + one second. The photon now has to travel an additional 186,000 miles (speed of light) to

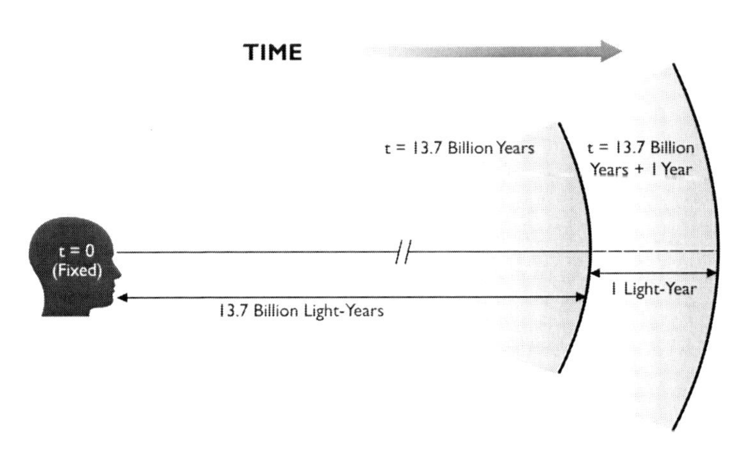

Universe Outer Edge Expanding at 1 Light-Year Every Year

reach us, which means the size of the universe has grown by 186,000 miles. After 10 seconds, the size of the universe would increase by 186,000 x 10 = 1,860,000 miles. One year from now, the size of the universe will increase by one light-year. By this reasoning, it is quite clear that time is creating the expansion of the universe. Every year, the universe expands by one light-year. As more time passes, the space of the universe keeps expanding. It is therefore only correct to conclude that time (which is subtle), creates space (which is gross).

From the above discussion, it is clear that time is the cause of the space "out there." Without time, there would be no space.

Time and Spacetime: Einstein's Theory of Relativity postulated the existence of the spacetime fabric. All objects rest on this fabric. A detailed analysis of this fabric is made in the essay "Understanding the Fabric of Space."

This spacetime fabric has no space, but it is made up of time. Yes, it is made up of time. Time is the source of the spacetime fabric. This fabric operates only in the mind. Since it is made up of time, it must have a starting point and an end point. The starting point of this fabric is the observer/mind within each one of us. This is the t=0 for spacetime. The end point of this fabric is the age of the universe, which is around 13.7 billion years. So, this time-based fabric stretches from the observer/mind to the current age of the universe. As time passes, this fabric keeps expanding.

All the objects in the universe are placed appropriately on this time-based fabric. The sun is placed eight minutes away on the fabric, the moon is three seconds away, the tree some milliseconds away. In this way, all the objects are placed on this fabric. This time-based fabric is then converted into space "out there."

Time is the underlying fabric of this universe. Without time, there would be no space and no universe.

Time and Energy: Einstein's Theory of General Relativity interlinks time and energy. This theory states that in the presence of energy, the spacetime fabric curves or bends and, in the process, time slows down. This bending of the spacetime fabric slows down time. This is a proven fact. The slowdown will depend on the mass of the object. The higher the mass, the higher the curvature, the slower the time.

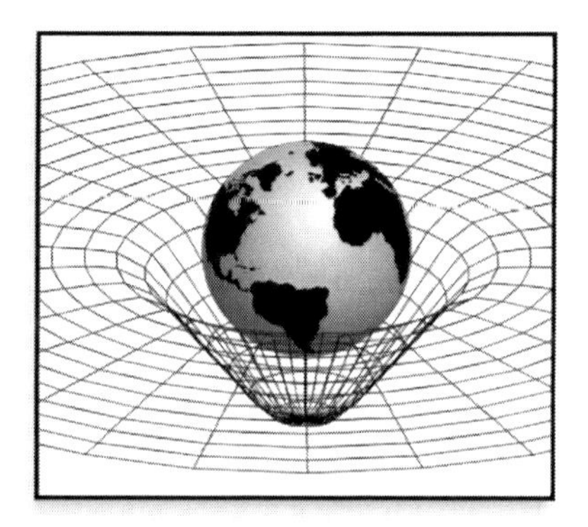

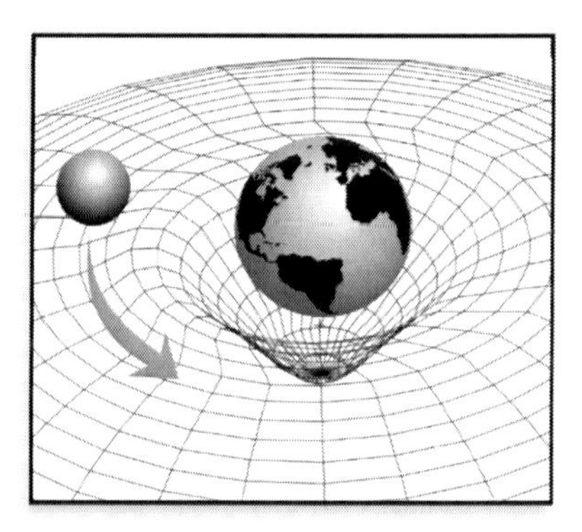

A question can be asked: does the mass of energy slow down time, or does the slowing down of time create the mass of energy? Which came first–time or energy? It is like the chicken and the egg–which came first? This question is not easy to answer. However, both time and energy are subtle; both are vrittis and function only in the mind.

Time and Gravity: As taught in school, gravity is a mutual pull between different objects. There was no proper understanding of gravity till Einstein's Theory of General Relativity. This theory clearly showed that time is the key factor for the creation of gravity. The bending of the spacetime fabric or the slowing of time is the cause of the pull of gravity between objects. Please read the essay "How Gravity Really Works" for a detailed analysis.

We have seen in the previous section that an object bends or curves the spacetime fabric around itself. Any object which is within the curvature of the fabric will tend to slide down the curve toward the other objects. This tendency of sliding down is the cause of the gravitational pull between objects. See the image shown. The only reason why the object may not slide down is that the horizontal velocity is large enough to avoid the downward slide of the object. The downward pull is always present between all objects. This is the gravitational pull between objects.

The spacetime fabric is made up of time, so the curvature of time is the cause of gravity. It is not easy to grasp, but time is the only factor which creates the gravitational pull. The deeper the time-based curvature, the stronger the gravitational pull. With a shallow curvature, the gravitational pull is weaker. Once again, time plays a key role, this time in the creation of gravity.

Time and Motion: We see so much motion in the universe. On planet Earth, we see people walking, we see cars, trains, planes moving around. If we look at our solar system, all the planets, including Earth, are moving around the sun. Then the sun and other stars are moving around the center of the Milky Way galaxy. The Milky Way is moving in relation to the other galaxies in the universe.

How is this motion generated? You will be surprised to learn that time is the cause of motion. Einstein's Theory of Special Relativity supports this. If you study this theory, you will understand that wherever there is motion, time slows down. The faster the motion, the slower the time clock. If you achieve the speed of light, time will completely stop. It must be pointed out that this theory gives the impression that there is motion, therefore time slows down. Motion is cause, and time is effect. This is incorrect. It is the other way around. Time slows down, and it creates a sense of motion of the object. Time creates motion. Please read the essay "Understanding Motion" for a more detailed analysis of this connection between time and motion.

Time is highly active in the mind. It drives every object to play out its life-cycle blueprint. Time is the source of the creation of space. Time is interconnected with energy. Time creates gravity. Finally, time is the source of object motion.

Time has awesome powers. Nothing works without time.

27 | Classical Physics vs. Quantum Physics

Physics, in the Western tradition, can be divided into two distinct divisions or phases:

- Classical Physics
- Quantum Physics

Classical physics has a long history. Since the beginning of civilization, continuous attempts have been made to understand the universe and objects "out there." Great discoveries were made, and different laws were formulated. These laws are relevant even today. The focus was always on the objects "out there"–mainly macro-objects. Based on these laws, science believed that the universe was a giant machine, where one could easily predict the motion of the planets and the objects therein. In this way, they knew exactly what was happening in this universe and, in some way, could even predict all the future movements of celestial bodies. Physicists thought they knew everything in the universe and that there was nothing new to discover.

In the early 20th century, things took a dramatic turn. As physicists started moving from macro-objects to micro-objects like atoms, etc., they found that none of the classical laws were applicable to micro-objects. Classical physics did not apply at the atomic and subatomic levels. To understand and explain the happenings in the realm of the subatomic, quantum physics was born.

Things at the subatomic level behave in unpredictable ways. Quantum physics is trying its best to provide a proper explanation which is rooted in science and supported by experiments. Sometimes, an object is a "wave," and, at other times, it is a "particle." This discovery marked the starting point of quantum physics with many unanswered questions.

We know that the particle resides in the world "out there" (we see it everywhere). All the laws of classical physics apply to the particle part of the object. What about the wave part? Where does the wave reside? Of what is the wave made? What is the connection between the wave part and the particle part of matter?

Schrodinger's Wave Function

Like Newton's Laws of Motion are at the heart of classical physics, Schrodinger's wave function is at the heart of quantum physics. To understand the wave part, Schrodinger formulated a complex equation for the wave function. Schrodinger's equation represents a physical system, and this physical system always consists of:

- Observed system - the observed system is a wave function, and this wave function is the wave component of the wave/particle duality.
- Observing system - when this observing system interacts with the observed system at any given time, the wave function of the observed system collapses to become a particle.

In other words, when the wave function enters the presence of the observing system, the wave function collapses and becomes a particle. It would seem that an observing system is necessary for the wave function to collapse to become a particle. Quantum physics never explains who and what the observing system is which has the power to collapse a wave function and create a particle.

Vedanta fills this gap. This connection between wave and particle is at the heart of Vedanta. Vedanta teaches us that there are three types of universes:

1. Seed Universe
2. Subtle Universe, made up of mental waveforms or vrittis
3. Gross Universe, which is the world we see "out there"

Every object in the universe needs a "seed." For a plant or a tree to grow, there must be a seed. In the same way, this universe and all the objects therein must have a "seed." Under the right conditions, this seed germinates to become the subtle universe. This subtle universe is the cosmic mind. A subset of this universe functions within individual minds. The subtle universe is made up of mental waveforms or vrittis. Each object in this universe has a unique waveform.

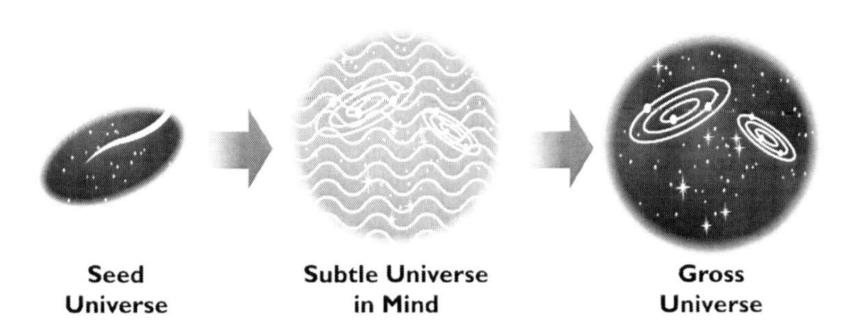

If you think about it, the mental waveform taught by Vedanta is the same wave function which is explained by Schrodinger. When this mental waveform comes in the presence of the observing system, which is our Atma or inner core, this waveform collapses to become the gross universe "out there." This is exactly like Schrodinger's wave function. The observing system in Schrodinger's wave function is nothing but Atma. Only Atma has the power and capacity to collapse any mental wave function. It is just impossible for matter "out there" to collapse any wave function.

In the essay "Quantum Physics and Vedanta," a detailed explanation is given to show that the wave function mentioned in quantum physics is the same as the mental waveform or vritti as taught by Vedanta.

Classical Physics vs. Quantum Physics

Science tells us that the laws which operate in the classical world do not work in the quantum world, and laws which operate in the quantum world do not work in the classical world. From this statement, it would seem that both function in different worlds. What is the difference between these two worlds? We have just seen that there is a fully functioning subtle universe and a fully functioning gross universe. The subtle universe is made of vrittis or waveforms which are operating within the individual mind and the cosmic mind. The gross universe is the universe which is made of objects "out there."

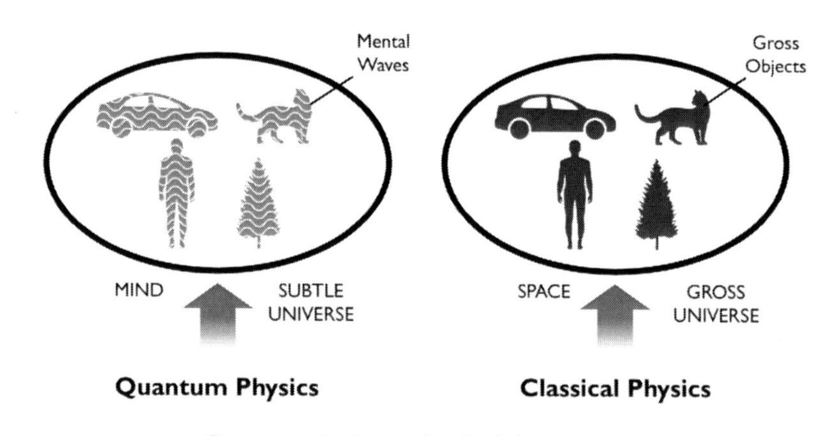

Quantum physics: study of subtle universe.
Classical physics: study of gross universe.

Since the focus of quantum physics is on understanding the wave part, this would mean that the focus of quantum physics is on the subtle universe, while the focus of classical physics is on the gross universe. We know that the gross world is made up of only gross objects, and the laws of classical physics apply to this realm. The subtle universe is made up of mental waveforms, and the laws of quantum physics apply to this realm. Therefore, the focus of quantum physics is on mental waveforms, while the focus of classical physics is on gross objects.

Mental waveforms and gross objects are quite different. There is no way classical physics can learn about mental waveforms by studying gross objects. It is for this reason that the laws of quantum physics do not apply to the gross/physical world; only the classical laws will work in the physical world. The same reasoning will apply to the subtle universe. The classical laws will not be suitable; only the quantum laws will work in the subtle universe.

To conclude, classical physics is concerned with the physical universe "out there," while quantum physics is concerned with the subtle universe which is functioning within our minds. They operate in two mutually exclusive realms.

28 | Mind Does Not Move. What Moves?

Truly, the mind never moves. It is the truth, but it seems so counterintuitive. We see people moving everywhere, and we know each one of us has a mind. If people are moving, then the mind must also move. Correct? No, this is incorrect.

In other essays we have discussed that the mind is outside the spacetime fabric. We know that the mind is at t=0 and it projects the spacetime fabric and the world "out there." This applies to every living being that has a mind. The t=0 is the "now" moment, and all the individual minds at this "now" moment are at the same place, just outside the spacetime fabric.

It is only logical that the movement takes place in the spacetime fabric. Movement needs space. Without space there can be no movement. The mind is outside the spacetime fabric; since there is no space outside the spacetime fabric, therefore the movement of the mind is impossible. It is therefore correct to conclude that the mind is fixed; it does not move. Okay, the mind is fixed and does not move; what about the body? The body is within the spacetime fabric. In fact, my body, your body, everyone's body is at the starting point of the spacetime fabric. If the mind is fixed, can the body move in the spacetime fabric?

This is a good question and needs some logical thinking. One point of which we are all sure is that, wherever we are, we always have our mind with us. We know we have a mind, and we know the mind is always with us. It is never separate from us. The body and mind are always together. None of us have an "out-of-body" experience, with the body in one place and the mind in another. If this is right, it is only correct to conclude that the body and mind are inseparable. If the mind is fixed outside the spacetime fabric, the body—even though it is within the spacetime fabric—must also be fixed. It cannot move.

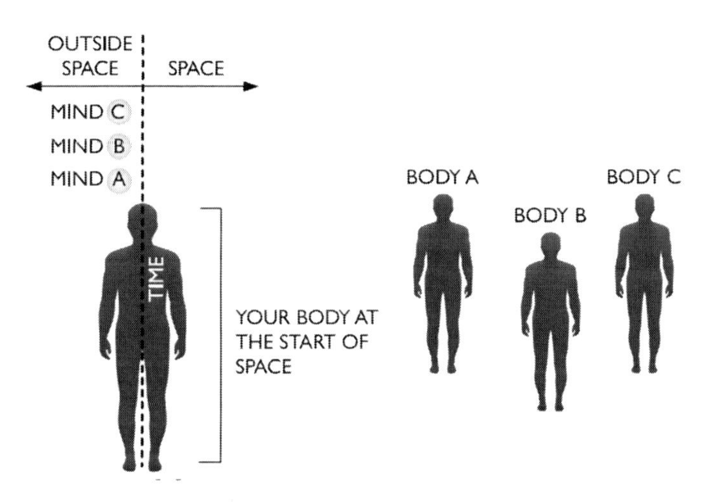

Mind outside Space. Body inside Space.

Wow! So, the body-mind complex does not move; it is fixed. My body-mind complex is fixed, your body-mind complex is fixed and, in the same way, the body-mind complex of all living beings is fixed. If this is correct, how to explain the movement we undertake? We are rarely static, and, in the waking state we move around quite a bit. A simple example will explain this. It is something we have seen many times in the movies. A movie scene shows a stationary car with a driver, and the outdoor scenery is passing by. We in the audience feel that the car is moving, and the passing scenery is stationary. This is an illusion which is created, and it seems very realistic. Is it possible that this illusion takes place in real life too? We have just seen that the body-mind complex is fixed and everything else is moving. This illusion is exactly like the stationary car and moving background that we see in the movies.

Is this possible? We do not feel it. We feel we are moving while external objects like trees, houses, lampposts are fixed. We need to understand this because we have discussed that the body-mind complex is fixed and does not move. So, how do we explain the trees, houses, and lampposts that are moving while the body-mind complex is fixed? To get a proper understanding of this, we need to apply the concepts of Einstein's Theory of Special Relativity and some basic concepts of Vedanta.

As we have discussed in other essays, the Theory of Special Relativity shows that motion and time are interconnected. When motion speed increases, then time slows down. It seems that motion comes first and then time slows down. Motion is the cause, and the slowdown of time is the effect. Is this the correct interpretation? I do not think so. Motion is gross; we see motion everywhere. In contrast, time is subtle–you cannot see it, touch it, or feel it. Time is present in the mind as a mental waveform. This waveform has the power to create time.

Vedanta teaches us those subtle mental waveforms come first, and that the subtle waveforms are the cause of the gross world around us. The subtle waveform projects the physical world "out there." If you apply this reasoning, time must come first, and the time waveform is the cause of motion. So, the correct way to interpret the connection between motion and time is that when time slows down, then motion is created. Not the other way around.

When time slows down, it is only logical to expect that the objects will be closer to the fixed observer. The physics equation $s = v^*t$ will support this. When time t is a smaller value, the distance s will be less, meaning it is closer to the fixed observer. This means there is motion of the object by slowing of time. Before the slowdown of time, the objects were at a certain distance. With the slowing down of time, the objects have moved closer to the fixed observer. The objects have moved, meaning there is motion.

This is exactly what is happening–the body-mind complex is fixed and, with the slowing down of time, the external objects move closer, giving a sense of motion. It is not easy to understand how a tree or a house or a lamppost uproots itself and moves closer. As explained in the essay

"Projection–The Only Truth," the physical world is a projection of the mind. If this is understood, it is easier to comprehend that external objects can move closer. The external objects are nothing but a projection of the mind.

It is like having a potentiometer for time in the mind. Move this potentiometer and slow down time, and this will bring the objects closer to the fixed body-mind complex, giving a sense of motion. Just like in the movies, we feel the car is moving in relation to the external objects. In the same way, we have the illusion that the body-mind complex is moving in relation to the external objects. Actually, the body-mind complex does not move.

So, time controls motion and not the other way around. Time is the cause of motion. Increase or decrease the time factor in the mind, and the resulting motion (or speed) of the objects will change in the physical world. Time is also the cause of the spacetime fabric expansion or contraction. Increase or decrease the time, and the spacetime fabric will also expand or contract. This corroborates Einstein's Theory of Special Relativity.

A good way to corelate this with our daily experience is with the navigation system we use in the car. We see the map and the car is moving in the map. What if the car is fixed and the map keeps moving to give a sense of motion? This is what is happening in real life. The body-mind complex is fixed and does not move. If the body-mind complex wants to move, it slows down time in the mind. When this is done, the map of the universe "out there" starts moving closer to the fixed body-mind complex, giving a sense of motion. Slow down the time potentiometer further, and the objects will come closer to the observer more quickly, giving a sense of increased speed of motion. Increasing or decreasing the time factor will increase or decrease the speed of motion. This is how motion and speed are managed in this world. Time is the boss of motion.

One may ask this question: if the body-mind complex is fixed, how come we see and perceive so many bodies (all living beings) moving around us?

This is a good question, but it must be understood that the bodies of the living beings we see “out there” are memory objects and not “now” objects. If you are standing in front of me, I see a memory object of you. It is not a “now” object but a memory object, which is a dated version of you. Why? Light takes some finite time to reach me, so it means that I see a dated version of you, which I call a memory object. In the same way, you will see a dated version of me standing in front of you. Everything in the world “out there” is made up of only memory objects. As we have discussed in the essay “Unity of Minds,” all the minds–your mind, my mind, and everyone’s mind–are at t=0, which is the “now” location. The memory objects are “out there,” but the mind is at t=0, which is within each one of us. In other words, there is no mind within the memory objects we see “out there”; the mind is within us at t=0. For me, I have my body-mind complex which does not move, but all the memory objects move around me. In the same way, your body-mind complex does not move but the memory objects will move. This logic will apply to all living beings.

The next time you go for a walk or for a drive in a car, imagine that you are not moving and the objects around you are moving closer. This is the only reality. The Theory of Special Relativity supports this by showing the connection between time and motion.

29 | Entanglement

Entanglement is a word used quite often in quantum physics. Entanglement means that subatomic particles remain connected even if they are far apart. They could be 10 meters away or half a universe apart, but these particles remain connected. If you change the property of one of them, the property of the other connected particle changes automatically and instantaneously. For example, the total spin of the connected particles is zero. If one of the particles has an up spin, the other will have a down spin. Now, if you change the spin from up to down, the spin of the other particle will change from down to up, maintaining a total spin of zero. How this connection works is one of the biggest mysteries of quantum physics. The communication between the entangled particles is instantaneous. Einstein, with his Theory of Relativity, made it clear that nothing in this universe can travel faster than light. If this is true, how do the entangled particles communicate even if they are light-years apart?

This is one of the biggest unsolved problems in quantum physics. The focus of this essay is to give a different perspective to resolve this issue. We will see that the entangled particles are never apart; what we see in space is the dated version of these entangled particles.

The issue of particle entanglement became popular when, in 1935, Albert Einstein along with his co-authors, Boris Podolsky and Nathan Rosen, wrote the paper *Can Quantum-Mechanical Description of Physical Reality be Considered Complete?* This paper became known as the Einstein-Podolsky-Rosen paradox (EPR paradox). Einstein was not a fan of some of the findings in quantum physics. He felt quantum physics was incomplete, and he had many objections. "God does not play dice with the universe" and "Spooky action at a distance" are two of the famous quotes regarding his views on quantum physics. Till his dying day, he felt that there were some hidden variables within the objects. These hidden variables predetermined the property of the objects, without actual communication between them. Unfortunately, neither Einstein nor any other scientist till date has found these hidden variables within the objects.

In 1951, David Bohm proposed a variant of the EPR paradox. The Bohm thought experiment can be explained by using electron-positron pairs, which are entangled. Suppose we have a source that emits electron-positron pairs, with the electron sent to Destination A and the positron sent to Destination B. If the observer at Destination A takes a measurement and finds that the spin of the electron is up, what about the spin for the positron at Destination B? With 100% certainty, the spin measurement will be down. If the spin of the electron is modified to point down at Destination A, the spin of the entangled particle at Destination B will be up. The distance between the entangled particles is not a factor; they seem to communicate and respond to each other instantaneously.

This understanding was theoretical; there was no practical experiment nor any direct observation. To help resolve this issue, in 1964, John Bell wrote a paper, *On the Einstein Podolsky Rosen Paradox*. Under the Bell theorem, he made certain predictions of how the entangled particles would behave when they were far apart. In 1972, his predictions were experimentally proven. Since then, his theorem has been repeatedly tested by many different scientists using different methods.

The actual experiment was done with entangled particles and by comparing the spin of these particles on the three axes–x, y, and z. The data collected was compared with the prediction made by the Bell theorem. They matched on every occasion.

To give a sense of this experiment, here is a simplified thought experiment. Imagine you are part of an experiment which involves two rooms. You are told by the hosts that the two rooms are completely isolated from each other. No communication is possible between the two rooms and between the two hosts. The first host prepares three boxes (A, B, and C) and places them on a table in one room. The second host prepares three other boxes (A1, B1, and C1) and sets them on a table in the other room. Each of the six boxes contains either a black or a white ball.

You can open one box from each room. First, you go into one of the rooms and open one of the three boxes there, and then you go into the other room and open one of the boxes there. The only restriction is that whatever box you choose to open in each room, you will not be allowed to find out what is in the other two boxes. Each time the boxes are prepared afresh and set back on the table. You can repeat the experiment as many times as you want.

After repeating this experiment many times, you notice that 100% of the time when you open A and A1, the color of the balls inside matches each other. The same is true for B and B1 and for C and C1. 100% means 100%. How can this happen? There is no communication between the two rooms, but still, 100% of the time the color of the balls is the same. Choose A and A1 or B and B1 or C and C1, the color of the balls will always be the same. It seems that boxes A-A1, B-B1, and C-C1 are entangled. There is some unknown communication which allows the color of the balls in the boxes to always be the same.

This is exactly what is happening with the entangled particles. This is a proven fact. They could be at the two ends of the universe, but they still communicate. How they communicate is one of the biggest mysteries!

Entanglement–A New Perspective

To give a new perspective to this issue, it is important to understand these entangled particles. A thought experiment: suppose two entangled particles move from the same starting point in opposite directions, and say they travel 186,000 miles (i.e., one second) before they hit a detector and a measurement is taken. At this separation, all the weirdness of entanglement will apply. If you change the spin of one particle, the spin of the other will change instantaneously. Let us understand these two particles from a different perspective. These particles are not "now" particles but dated or "memory" particles. Why? The answer is simple. These particles are 186,000 miles away, so the version of the particle "out there" is the "now minus one second" version of the particle. Light will take one second to reach us from this particle. It is not the "now" version of the particle.

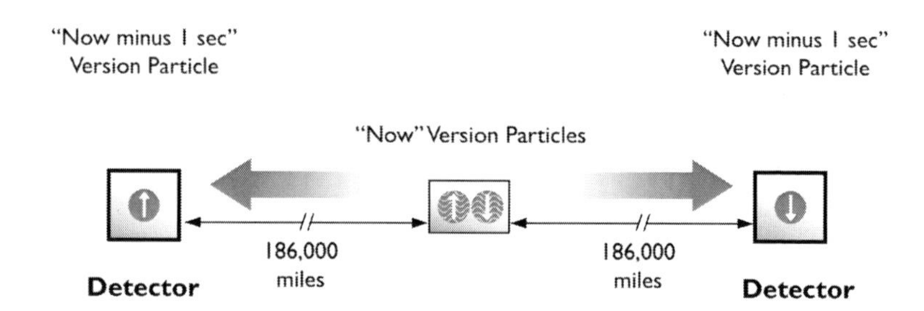

Movement of Entangled Particles

As we have discussed in many essays, every object in the universe is a dated version of the object. Light will take a finite amount of time to reach us from the different objects. Light takes eight minutes to reach us from the sun; the sun we see in the sky is a "now minus eight minutes" version of the sun. This reasoning and logic will apply to every object in the universe. This could be a micro-object like a subatomic particle or a macro-object like a living being, planet, or galaxy. There are only dated or memory objects "out there."

The next question to ask is, where is the "now" version of these objects? It cannot be in space because there you will find only memory objects. It must be outside space. As we have discussed in other essays, you will find the "now" objects in the mind, which is outside space and time. Mind is the t=0 location for the objects. All the "now" objects are in the cosmic/individual mind.

To reconfirm that the mind is the location of the "now" objects, let us play around with the two entangled particles which are 186,000 miles apart. At 186,000 miles, the particle is a "now minus one second" version of the particle. It is not a "now" version. Why? Light takes one second to reach us from the particle which is 186,000 miles away. If the particle is 93,000 miles away, you will see a "now minus 0.5 seconds" version of the particle. This is because light will take 0.5 seconds to reach us from this particle. If the particle is 46,500 miles away, you will see a "now minus 0.25 seconds" version of the particle. Light takes 0.25 seconds to reach us from this distance. If the particle is 30,000 feet away, you will see a "now minus 10E-3 seconds" version of the particle. If the particle is 10 feet away, you will see a "now minus 10E-9 seconds" version of the particle.

As the distance reduces, the particle comes closer to the "now" version. So where is the "now minus zero seconds" version of the particle? At this "now" location, light does not travel any distance to reach us. If you extrapolate the above data backward, the only location for the "now" version of the particle is the mind. Here light takes zero seconds to reach you. That is the location of the "now" object; it is the t=0 for the particle.

We saw earlier those two entangled particles were sent 186,000 miles in opposite directions. Where is the "now" version of the second particle? Logically, the "now" version of this particle will also be within the mind.

Can you see what is happening? The "now" version of both entangled particles is at the same place–the mind. The "now minus one second" version of the two entangled particles is 2 x 186,000 miles apart, but the "now" version of both particles is at the same location. Even if they are five light-years apart, the "now" version of these particles will still be in the mind. It does seem that the "now" version of the particle never moves; it is always present in the mind.

The biggest takeaway from this discussion is that there are two versions of the particle–the "now" version and the memory version. To solve the riddle of entanglement, it is important to understand the two versions of the particle.

Quantum physics teaches us that it is a fact that every object has a particle and wave duality. Is there a connection between the wave/particle duality and the memory/"now" object duality? Yes, there is. The physical world is made of only memory objects. These memory objects are the particle aspect of the duality. What about the "now" object? The "now" object can never be physical. It is outside the physical world. It is in the mind. The "now" universe cannot contain the particle aspect. So, what does the "now" object contain? Since the particle aspect is not possible, the only right answer is that the "now" object is made of the wave aspect of the duality. So, the correct conclusion is that "now" objects in the "now" universe are made of waves.

Science has been dealing with only the memory version of the particle. Scientists check the spin for one of these memory particles and find that the spin of the other entangled particle is exactly the opposite. These entangled particles could be nearby or at the two ends of the universe. Dealing with memory particles will never resolve the issue. Entanglement–how these far-apart particles can communicate–will continue to be a mystery. "Spooky action at a distance" will continue to mystify everyone.

It must be understood that everything happens first in the "now" universe and then in the memory universe. Everything happens in the wave version first, and then it happens in the particle version. Below we will give three different reasons that illustrate why this is the only correct conclusion.

1. Using Logic: Everything in the "now" universe is live stuff. Everything in the memory universe is dated or old stuff. A good comparison is the playback of recorded events. You can record a live event and play back that recorded event at your convenience. The recorded event is made of only memory objects; they are events from the past. So, the live event must happen first, which is then recorded and played back later. This is exactly what is happening with the "now" universe. Everything happens first in the "now" universe, and then it is projected or played back as memory objects "out there."

This simple reasoning shows that events must happen in the "now" universe first and then in the memory universe.

2. Using Quantum Physics: Quantum physics has confirmed the wave/particle duality for all the objects in the universe. Everything in the universe has a wave version and a particle version. Also, quantum physics teaches us that when the wave version comes in the presence of the observer, it collapses and becomes a particle. See the sequence–the wave version comes first, and this wave version becomes a particle version in the presence of an observer. We know that the wave version operates in the "now" universe and the particle version functions in the memory universe.

So, quantum physics confirms that the "now" universe comes first, and the memory universe comes afterwards.

3. Using Vedanta: Vedanta teaches us that there is a seed universe, a subtle universe, and a gross universe. The seed universe is like a seed of a tree. The potential of the tree is inbuilt; it lies within the seed. In the same way, the potential universe is within the Seed Body of the universe. When this Seed Body germinates, the subtle universe is created. The subtle universe is the "now" universe, which is made of vrittis or waveforms representing all the objects. In the presence of the observer, this subtle universe becomes the gross universe full of memory objects.

From this, we can see that Vedanta also confirms that the "now" universe comes first and then the universe is made of memory objects.

So, we have seen in different ways that everything happens first in the "now" universe. In fact, there is a fully functioning "now" universe. Please read the essay "Life Is a Living Wave," where we have given a detailed analysis of the "now" universe.

The key to understanding the entanglement issue is to deal with the "now" version of two entanglement particles. They are always at the "now" location. They are always connected and part of the same unit. They are part of the same wave function. They are never apart. If the spin of one entangled particle changes at the "now" location, the spin of the other will change instantaneously. There is no communication issue because they are at the "now" location; they are part of the same system, the same wave function.

If this is true, the entanglement issue resolves itself. Entanglement and communication happen only in the "now" version. The properties of the entangled particles are decided in the "now" version. When this "now" version becomes the memory version, the two memory particles travel in opposite directions in space for one second till they hit the detectors. The two detectors at the opposite ends record the spin of the two particles. They will find that the two particles are entangled. There is no spookiness, because the spin of both the particles is already determined in the "now" version. If the spin for one particle is changed, the change will take place in the "now" version first. The spin of the entangled particle will also change in the "now" version. The two memory versions of the particle will travel and carry forward the changed spin till a detector records the change. This simple explanation resolves the mystery behind the entanglement.

It seems that Einstein's intuition about entanglement was correct. He knew that it was impossible for particles that were far apart to communicate faster than the speed of light. Till his death he was criticized for his views on this subject. He always believed that the spin and other properties were predetermined. They were known at the start of the particle journey and they did not change till the detection at the end of the journey. Even if the property of one of the particles changed, the change in the other particle was predetermined at the start of the journey. He believed that this happened, but he could not give a proper explanation of why this happened. He said there was a hidden variable. If the hidden variable is found, this issue will be resolved. Till his dying day, Einstein tried to find this hidden variable.

The current approach taken by quantum physics regarding entanglement is not exactly accurate. Quantum physics believes that the entangled particles travel from the source in multiple states. Multiple states mean, for example, that the spin of the particle could be up, down, right, left, all at the same time. All the possible multiple states are present within the particle. When a measurement is taken, only then is one of the states confirmed by the detector. According to quantum physics, all this happens with the memory particle. This is the mistake being made. The correct answer is that this does happen but with the "now" particles in the "now" universe. It does not happen with the "memory" particles. The multiple states are present in the "now" particles. In the presence of the "now" version of the detector, the "now" particle collapses to one of the states. This state is transmitted by the memory particle.

We have seen that the entanglement issue gets resolved if you can understand the difference between the "now" particle and the memory particle. Everything happens first in the "now" universe and then it is reflected in the space "out there."

Entanglement and More

Our current understanding is that the entanglement of particles happens at a subatomic level. How and why this happens is not clear. One thing that is clear is that entanglement happens in the "now" universe. We have seen earlier that the "now" universe is made up of vrittis or waveforms. In fact, there is a single cosmic waveform which contains all the objects in the universe. Any scene you watch is a subset of the cosmic waveform. Right from subatomic particles to stars and galaxies–all are part of the cosmic waveform. There is nothing which is missing. Even living beings and nonliving objects in the universe are part of the cosmic waveform. You can only imagine how complex this waveform is.

Every subatomic particle has its own independent waveform. This applies to photons too. These photons are very tiny and are part of the building blocks for the complex waveforms. The photon waveforms combine to be part of the complex waveforms, but the photons still maintain their independence. These independent photon waveforms are not entangled. However, under certain circumstances, these photons can become entangled. When two photons become entangled, the waveforms are no longer independent, and a single waveform will represent these two waveforms.

In entanglement, a single waveform will represent the two photons. This type of entanglement occurs not only with photons but also with other subatomic particles like electrons, protons, etc. Physicists have found that entanglement takes place in elements with a dense atomic structure. In a high-density atomic structure, the interaction between the photons or the other subatomic particles is much greater, so the chances of entanglement between the waveforms of particles is much higher.

After entanglement, the particle waveforms behave as one unit–a single waveform. If entanglement is a known fact, can these particles untangle themselves later? Can the entangled photons untangle themselves? Can a single entangled waveform representing two particles become two independent waveforms with no entanglement? Also, how long will these particle entanglements last–10 minutes, 10 years, or 100 years? These are interesting questions. Unfortunately, there is no answer. No study has been made. If you want to make an educated guess, then the answer is that entanglement and un-entanglement are part of nature. The cosmic waveform is made of so many different waveforms that there is always a possibility of entanglement taking place somewhere.

We only know of entanglement taking place between subatomic particles. What about macro-objects? What about our ego with other objects? As we have discussed in other essays, ego is also a waveform which is part of the cosmic waveform. Is it possible for our ego to be entangled with other distant object waveforms? Maybe this is happening already. Telepathy is one example which comes to mind. It can be quite uncanny when two people think of the same thing at the same time, like calling each other on the phone. We have all experienced these coincidences. Maybe entanglement of the two waveforms is taking place, allowing this unspoken communication to occur irrespective of the distance.

If you have studied Patanjali's *Yoga Sutra*, there is mention of people acquiring siddhis (supernatural powers) by connecting with the physical and subtle worlds. Patanjali indicates that you can acquire these siddhis through years of practice in meditation and by gaining full control over the five senses and the mind. It does seem that acquiring these powers is nothing but the entanglement of the person with the other object waveforms. The person with a pure mind may have the ability to entangle with object waveforms. When this entanglement happens, the person can communicate with the object waveform. In the "now" universe, the person and the object waveform form a single composite waveform. In the physical world, this person and object may be far apart, but there is instantaneous communication between them. There is telepathy between them, just like the two entangled particles described earlier.

Vedanta indicates that one can acquire such power, but it cautions that this can be a great hindrance in the path of the final goal of attaining moksha or the state of Self-Awareness. Moksha is the only goal; trying to acquire siddhis will not help in this pursuit.

In conclusion, the mystery of entanglement can be resolved only when we accept the presence of a fully functioning "now" universe.

30 | How Gravity Really Works

We learned about gravity in school, and the famous legend of Isaac Newton sitting under a tree with the apple falling on his head. He wonders why the apple fell on his head. This incident started his investigation of gravity. He made great strides and eventually quantified this force with the following formula:

$F = G (m1 * m2/r^2)$

F = Gravitational force between two objects with mass m1 and m2

r = Distance between the two objects

G = Gravitational constant

Any two objects anywhere in the universe will have a gravitational pull between them.

- The larger the mass of the objects, the greater the gravitational force between them. We do notice the pull between larger objects like planets, etc. (we experience high and low tide because of the pull between the moon and Earth). Smaller objects also have a mutual attraction, but it is unnoticeable. The same equation is used for large or small objects.
- The greater the distance, the smaller the force. Even if the objects are far apart, the gravitational force is there, but it is negligible.
- If there are multiple objects, an object will have a gravitational interaction with each of the multiple objects. This can make the process complex.

This simple formula is still valid and is used to calculate the gravitational force between any objects. It was a great discovery, and it gave a deep insight into the functioning of the universe. Newton discovered the formula, but he did not understand how this force worked. Why would two objects which are apart, try to pull each other closer? What connects these objects? Is there an invisible string which connects these objects? Newton tried his best but was unable to answer these basic questions.

Since Newton, gravitational force or gravity continues to be a mystery. Existence of this force is a known fact, but how it operates is still a mystery. Over the years, physicists have discovered that the universe is made up of the following four fundamental forces.

Electromagnetic Force: This is a force which repels particles with a similar charge and attracts those with an opposite charge.

Strong Nuclear Force: This force operates only within the nucleus. Logically, two positively charged protons should repel each other because of the electromagnetic force. However, there is a strong nuclear force which holds these positively charged protons together in the nucleus. This nuclear force is 100 times stronger than the electromagnetic force, and it overcomes the repulsive force.

Weak Nuclear Force: The weak force also operates within the nucleus of the atom. In atoms which have many protons and neutrons, the nuclei can be unstable. This weak nuclear force facilitates the decay of the atom. Radioactive decay is the best example.

Gravity: Gravity is the most common force, which allows the attraction between any two objects.

Great strides have been made to understand the electromagnetic, strong, and weak forces. Unfortunately, our knowledge of gravitational force is still lacking. A lot is known about the effects of this force, but little is known about the cause. We see gravity everywhere, but little is known about how and why it functions. Physicists think that there is a force particle called graviton which mediates this force. The property of this force particle is known, but unfortunately this force particle is yet to be discovered. The search continues.

Spacetime and Gravity

A hint on how gravity functions is provided by Einstein's Theory of General Relativity. One of the outcomes of this theory was that it showed how gravity functioned. Einstein proposed the presence of the spacetime fabric. This fabric is like a stretched rubber sheet. If you place a heavy ball on this rubber sheet, the sheet will curve around the heavy ball. The heavier the ball, the deeper the curvature of the rubber sheet. Now if you place a smaller ball anywhere in this curvature, what will happen? The smaller ball will slide down the curvature toward the heavier ball. This sliding down is the cause of the gravitational pull between the two objects. If the smaller ball is further away, the gravitational pull will be less. If the smaller ball is placed outside the curvature of the heavier ball, the smaller ball will not slide down toward the heavier ball. There is gravitational pull, but it is negligible.

The same principle can be applied to the objects in the universe. Each object makes a curvature on the spacetime fabric. Let us analyze some scenarios to get a feel for the interaction of gravity.

- The sun is the heaviest object in our solar system. It has the largest curvature on the spacetime fabric. Earth and the other planets in our solar system are within the curvature of the spacetime fabric of the sun. All the planets in our solar system must slide down this curvature and meet their doom in the hot burning sun. Luckily, this is not happening. Why? Earth and the other planets have a horizontal velocity which is greater than the downward gravitational pull. This sustains the rotational path of the planets around the sun. It must be understood that each rotating planet is within the curvature of the spacetime fabric of the sun. Mercury is the closest planet and has the highest pull. Neptune is the furthest planet, and it has the least pull.

- For us, Earth is the biggest object. The curvature of the spacetime fabric of Earth is massive compared to other objects on Earth. This means that there is a constant gravitational pull for the objects to slide down the curvature toward Earth's center. If we drop anything, it must fall toward Earth's surface. This is the reason the apple fell on Newton's head. His head stopped the apple's journey toward Earth's surface.
- Every object, every living being on Earth will curve the spacetime fabric. The curvature of these objects is small. This means the gravitational pull between objects is negligible. It may be small, but it is not zero.

It does seem that the curvature of the spacetime fabric is the cause of the gravitational pull between objects. Comparing the spacetime fabric with the stretched rubber sheet gives a good visualization for the functioning of gravity. That may be correct but, unfortunately, this does not really solve the problem. The problem is that there is no fabric in the space "out there." No one has seen it or discovered a fabric for space. Einstein did mention the presence of the spacetime fabric, but in reality, there is no fabric in space. How do we understand this?

Understanding Spacetime: The term "spacetime" is the cause of the confusion. It must be understood that there is no space in spacetime. Spacetime is made of only time. Time is the building block of the spacetime fabric. Space is made of distance and spacetime is made of time. This difference must be understood. Before we move forward, it is important to have a good understanding of spacetime. We have discussed spacetime in many different essays, including "Understanding the Fabric of Space." Here, we will summarize some key aspects of the spacetime fabric:

1. The spacetime fabric is made of only time.
2. The starting point (t=0) of the fabric is the observer within you. This applies to every living being. The end point is the Big Bang moment, which is 13.7 billion years away. As time flows, the end point keeps expanding.
3. The spacetime fabric is subtle and will not be found in space. Einstein said that time is the fourth dimension. Where is the fourth dimension? Space has only three dimensions; there is no possibility of a fourth dimension in space. The only logical place for time to function is the mind. Please read the essay "Understanding Time" for details. Vedanta is clear that kaala (time) is part of the mind. This would mean that the spacetime fabric is also part of the mind.
4. The spacetime fabric is not continuous; it is like a grid. The separation between each nodal point is 10E-44 seconds. When each of the time-based nodal points interacts with energy, the full electromagnetic energy spectrum is present at each nodal point. This energy is the undercoating of the spacetime fabric. Science calls this the vacuum energy.
5. There is energy in the cosmic mind which stretches out time to create space. Yes, this special energy can stretch time. This energy is the missing dark energy. According to science, dark energy makes up about 80% of the total available energy. This dark energy stretches one second of the spacetime fabric to create 186,000 miles of space. Space is created by the stretching out of the spacetime fabric.

Interconnection–Motion, Time, and Space: One of the major conclusions of Einstein's Theory of Special Relativity is that motion, time, and space are interconnected. Put simply, wherever there is motion, time slows down and space contracts. If you are moving, then your clock will slow down and space around you will contract. The faster you go, the slower time becomes and the more the contraction in space. This connection between motion, time, and space is a proven fact.

According to the Theory of Relativity, motion comes first, and this motion slows down time and compresses space. Understanding this is not easy. Why should motion slow down time and contract space? What is the connection between them? Why should motion be the cause, and the effect take place in time and space? If you apply the teachings of Vedanta, the sequence of motion coming first is not correct. Why? We know time is subtle and that both space and motion are gross. There can be no dispute over this. We see space and motion in the universe "out there," therefore they must be gross. Time is not part of space; time is not gross; time is subtle. So, time is subtle, and space and motion are gross. The teachings of Vedanta make it clear that the subtle objects must come first and then the gross objects. The subtle objects are the cause, and the gross objects are the effect.

The conventional thinking is that motion is the cause of the slowing of time and compression of space. This is an incorrect approach. The correct approach is that slowing of time comes first for motion to take place. This can be shown logically with the following two-step process.

Step 1. Time and Space: A good starting point is understanding how the slowing of time influences the spacetime fabric. What is the change in the spacetime fabric? Slowing down of time means that the spacetime fabric is more compressed. The time nodes in the fabric are closer; they are tighter. The higher the speed, the closer the time nodes in the fabric. We have seen that dark energy stretches one second of the spacetime fabric to 186,000 miles of space. When the spacetime fabric is more compressed, one second of the fabric is still stretched to 186,000 miles of space. However, to an outsider, the size of space will be smaller than the earlier version with no spacetime compression. This means that whenever time slows down, the spacetime fabric is more compressed and there is contraction in space. There is a direct connection between time and space.

Step 2. Space and Motion: When space contracts, what about all the objects in space? It is logical to expect the objects to also move inward along with the contraction of space. Let us understand this with a practical example. If you have a rug with different objects on it, and you hold the rug and pull it toward you–what happens? The objects on the rug will also move closer to you. This is what is happening to the objects in space. When space contraction takes place, the different objects in space also move closer. Did you notice the movement in the objects on the rug? Similarly, with the contraction, the objects move from their initial location to the new location. This movement is the source of object motion. There is motion of the object. If there is continuous contraction in space, there will be continuous object motion. This may seem strange and counterintuitive, but this is how motion happens. Contraction of space is the source of motion. Please read the essay "Understanding Motion" for a detailed explanation.

From the above discussion we can summarize that slowing down of time contracts space. With the contraction of space, object motion happens. From this we can also conclude that the slowing down of time generates motion. This is the same as Einstein's Theory of Relativity, but in the reverse order.

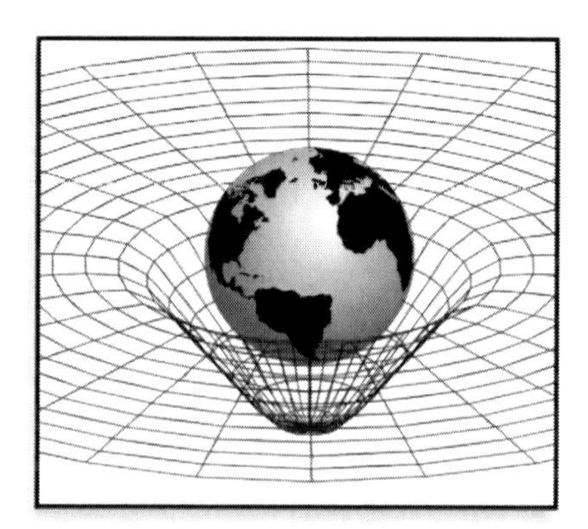

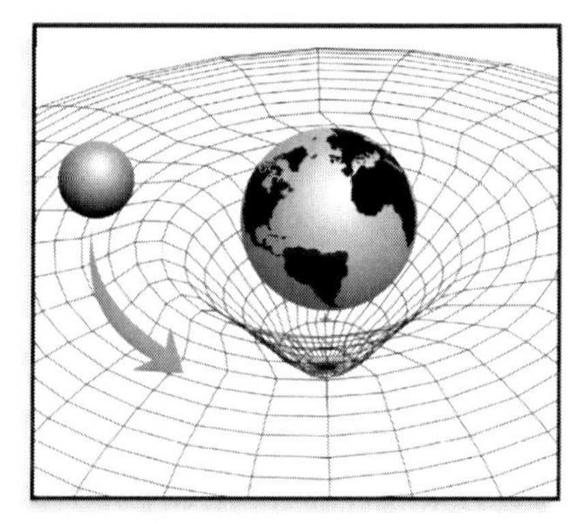

Gravity and Spacetime Curvature

Let us apply the connection between time, space, and motion to the spacetime curvature. The placement of the planet (or any other object) on the spacetime fabric will curve the spacetime fabric. Around the curvature, there are horizontal and vertical timelines. It is important to understand these timelines.

Vertical Timelines: The vertical timelines in the curvature are the source of the rotational or orbital motion. The speed of objects depends on how close or far apart the vertical timelines are in the spacetime fabric. The more compressed the vertical timelines, the higher the object speed. When the timelines are more compressed, this means that time has slowed down and the motion speed has increased. It seems that the motion of any object is due to the compression and decompression of time in the spacetime fabric.

If you study the curvature around any massive object, the vertical timelines will be further apart at the top and more compressed at the bottom of the curvature. What does this mean? This means that wherever the vertical timelines are more compressed, the orbital speed of objects will be higher. Therefore, the orbital speed of objects near the bottom of the curvature will be higher than the orbital speed of objects at the top of the curvature.

This is what physicists predict with their calculations. In our solar system, Mercury (closest to the sun) rotates faster than Earth, and Earth rotates faster than all the other planets, except Venus, in the solar system. Neptune, which is furthest away, is the slowest. The planets in our solar system do show that the rotation speed of the planets is directly proportional to the compression of the vertical lines. More compression of the vertical timelines means higher speed. Less compression of the vertical timelines means lower rotational speed. Mercury has the highest timeline compression and therefore rotates the fastest, while Neptune has the lowest timeline compression and rotates the slowest.

Horizontal Timelines: The curvature of the spacetime fabric is mainly due to the horizontal timelines. This curvature is the source of the gravitational pull between objects. The horizontal timelines in the image shown on page 273 do not faithfully represent the exact format. They should follow a squared function graph. The top horizontal timelines should be more spaced out and, as we move down the curvature, the timelines should be more compressed. This curvature should follow the t^2 function. Why? Gravity is a function of t^2. The horizontal timelines in the curvature should reflect this.

Gravity at Work: Einstein was famous for his thought experiments, especially with people jumping from tall buildings. Let us undertake a similar thought experiment. Let us imagine a person standing at the top of a tall building and planning to jump. From his position, let us assume that he can "see" the horizontal timelines in Earth's curvature. Our experience tells us that this person will fall downward till he hits Earth's surface. Motion speed keeps doubling as the object falls downward. We call this the force of gravity, which is pushing the object downward. This is our normal experience. This is our normal understanding of gravity. But this is not what is happening.

Let us understand correctly how gravity works. As we have mentioned earlier, the spacetime fabric always starts with the observer. The t=0 for the spacetime fabric is this person. Even after the jump, t=0 is still the observer. This person will always be the starting point of the spacetime fabric. This starting point will not change. What will this person "see" with the horizontal timelines? With the horizontal timelines, this person will see time slowing down following the squared function t, t/2, t/4, t/16, t/256 ...

As the person encounters the slowdown of time, what happens to space? From the perspective of this person, space will also start contracting at the same ratio. This shrinking space will continue till the spacetime curvature comes to an end and the space between this person and Earth's surface is zero. Did you notice that the person did not really move? This person is always at t=0, the start of the spacetime fabric. The space shrank rapidly but the person did not move. Strange but true. It is like the rug with the objects moving closer to the person pulling the rug. The person has not moved, the rug space has reduced, and the objects have come closer. This is exactly what is happening. Space is shrinking and Earth's surface is being pulled closer to the person. The person does not move, but Earth's surface comes closer to the person with ever increasing speed.

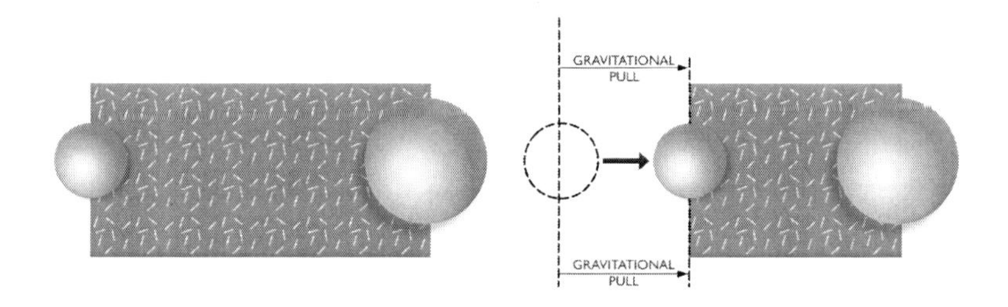

Shrinking of Space Causes Gravitational Pull

This is how gravity works. The gravitational pull or force is the shrinking of space which brings the two objects closer to each other. Pulling the rug is the force which brings the object on the rug closer to you. The objects move along with the rug and not by themselves. In the same way, the force which shrinks space to bring the two objects in space closer to each other is gravity. The power which shrinks space is nothing but gravitational force.

Gravity is not a force acting on the objects but the shrinking of space, which causes the movement of objects. Shrinking of space is the source of the gravitational force between objects. The force which shrinks space is gravity. This is the only correct way to understand gravity.

Gravity and More

Now that we have understood how gravity really works, let us apply this to Newton's Law of Gravity and the other issues which have been raised in this essay.

Newton's Law of Gravity: Based on Newton's law, all objects in the universe have a mutual gravitational force connecting them. They may be close or far away, but these objects have a mutual attraction. How do we understand this with the correct functioning of gravity? Imagine two objects in space. These two objects will curve the spacetime fabric. The size of the curvature will depend on the energy. Each of the objects "sees" the other objects' horizontal timelines or slowdown of time. This slowdown of time will create space which is shrinking. This shrinking of space creates gravitational force. This gravitational force may or may not move the objects. If the force is large, the objects will pull each other like Earth and the objects nearby. If the force is small, gravitational force is present, but there is no movement between the objects. For example, while pulling the rug, the pull force is very small–the objects on the rug will not move, but they will feel the force pulling them inward. In the same way, gravitational force is present between two small objects or faraway objects, but it is very weak.

Hunting for Graviton: Graviton is the missing force particle for gravity. Physicists believe that this missing particle is the source of gravitational pull. They are searching for this particle but with little luck. The problem is that physicists are looking for these particles within matter. They believe that gravitational force acts upon objects, and therefore they are hunting for the missing graviton within these objects. Unfortunately, this is the wrong place to look for these particles. We have just seen that gravitational pull does not act upon the objects. It is the shrinking of space around the objects which creates the gravitational pull between objects.

Space is everywhere, but the effect of gravity is in space, around the objects. The effect is not on the objects but in the space around the objects. Wherever space is shrinking, graviton particles will be found. To take a step back, space shrinks because time slows down. Time slows down because the spacetime fabric is more compressed. The real source of the graviton is in the spacetime fabric. How does the spacetime fabric compress? The graviton is the particle which compresses the spacetime fabric. The slowdown of time is caused by the graviton particle. I am guessing that the force particle graviton can be found in the spacetime and space around the objects. This is the place where physicists need to focus if they want to find the missing graviton particle. The graviton particle will not be found within matter but within space, especially where space is shrinking around the objects.

Unification of Fundamental Forces: As we have discussed earlier, there are four fundamental forces: electromagnetic force, strong force, weak force, and gravity force. If you study the forces carefully, you will realize that the electromagnetic, strong, and weak forces operate within the atom. The domain of their activity is within matter, within objects. Energy is the common source of all the three forces. Physicists have confirmed that the unification of these three forces is possible with lots of energy. So, we can conclude that these three forces are born out of energy.

Gravity is the missing force. It is not possible to unify gravity using energy as the source. Why? The simple answer is that gravity works in the domain of time. Unlike the other three forces, it does not work in the domain of energy. This is the main difference. The cause of gravitational force is the curvature of the spacetime fabric due to time slowing down. Gravitational force is born out of time.

So, electromagnetic force, strong force, and weak force work in the domain of energy and gravity works in the domain of time. Does that mean that unification of the four forces is not possible? Vedanta teaches us that there is only One Reality. That Reality is Self-Awareness. The source of everything in this universe is Awareness. Both energy and time come from Awareness. If you read the essays "Awareness–The Infinite Source" and "Understanding Time," you will see that both energy and time come from Awareness. Awareness is the substratum of everything in the universe. Energy, time, and the four forces are part of Awareness. In this way, gravity and the three forces unify within Awareness.

Cosmos

There is a good deal of confusion about space. What is the structure of space? How and why does it expand? Do multiverses really exist? Dark energy and dark matter continue to be a mystery. These questions and other related issues are tackled in this section.

31 | Hubble Constant–A Mathematical Proof

What Is the Hubble Constant?

Does the universe expand? Science tells us the universe is expanding. Why is the universe expanding? How fast is the universe expanding? Science is not very sure about the answers. Using powerful telescopes, scientists have watched the movement of different planets and galaxies and noticed that the expansion is uneven. At some places the expansion is faster and at others it is slower. There is no explanation for this uneven expansion. Looking at some faraway planets and their rate of expansion, scientists have come up with the Hubble constant.

The Hubble constant states that the rate of expansion is about 72 kilometers per second per megaparsec. A megaparsec is a million parsecs, or about 3.3 million light-years. It means that objects which are 3.3 million light-years away are expanding at 72 kilometers per second. This is based solely on observation. There is no mathematical proof of the Hubble constant. If you correctly understand the fundamentals of the expansion of the universe, it is possible to calculate and prove the Hubble constant. We will be calculating the Hubble constant in this essay and proving that what has been observed through telescopes is indeed correct.

Fundamentals of the Spacetime Framework

So, what are the fundamentals of this expansion? Understanding the spacetime framework is the key to understanding this expansion. So, how is the spacetime framework structured? This is where the confusion begins. Science teaches us that the spacetime framework started with the

Big Bang about 13.7 billon years ago. Thus, the starting point of the spacetime framework is the Big Bang. Is this correct? Yes, the start of the spacetime framework is the Big Bang, but that event was 13.7 billion years ago. Where is the start of the spacetime framework right "now"?

It is not the Big Bang; the Big Bang is the outer edge of the universe. It is the other end. It is therefore NOT the start of the spacetime framework. No one has seen the edge of the universe, so how can it be called the start of the spacetime framework? This incorrect understanding about the start of the spacetime framework is the underlying cause of the confusion about space. This misunderstanding leads to the lack of proper knowledge about the construction of space, how fast it is expanding, and why there is an uneven expansion all over the universe.

So, what is the starting point of the spacetime framework right "now"? Since we have discussed this in different essays, you may have guessed the correct answer. The correct answer is that *you* are the starting point of the spacetime framework. The observer within you, the observer within me, the observer within every living being is the starting point of the spacetime framework. You can call this starting point t=0 for the spacetime framework. The observer is the start of the spacetime framework; it is therefore the t=0 for the framework. This is because light takes a finite time to reach us from different objects. The farther the objects, the more time light takes to reach us. Light takes less time to reach us if the objects are closer to us. So, a question can be asked: at which point will light take zero seconds to reach us? Think about it. The observer within us is the only location from which light will take zero seconds to reach us. This observer is therefore the starting point of the spacetime framework or the t=0 of the spacetime framework. This is logical and the only correct interpretation.

Now that we have seen that the individual person or the observer is the starting point of the spacetime framework, let us try and estimate the size and the expansion rate of the universe.

Size and Expansion of the Universe

What is the maximum size of the spacetime framework? Science tells us that the age of the universe is 13.7 billion years. This is the Big Bang moment. Light reaching us (or the observer) from the Big Bang moment would be the outer edge of the spacetime fabric. Light will take 13.7 billion light-years to reach us from this Big Bang moment. This is the outer edge because there was no universe before the Big Bang. So, the size of the universe is 13.7 billion light-years or 12.9 x 10E+25 meters. One light-year is the amount of distance light travels in one year, which is equal to 9.46 x 10E+15 meters.

Is this spacetime expanding? Yes. How much? Let us try and understand this. If you assume the universe is 13.7 billion years old "right now," then after one second, the age of the universe will be 13.7 billion years + one second. Light must now travel an additional 186,000 miles to reach the observer, which means the size of the universe has grown by 186,000 miles. After 10 seconds, the size of the universe will increase by 186,000 x 10 = 1,860,000 miles. After one year, the size of the universe will increase by one light-year. One light-year is the distance light travels in one year.

From the above, we can conclude that the rate of expansion of the outer edge of the universe = one light-year per year.

Calculation of the Hubble Constant

Imagine the spacetime fabric as an elastic rubber sheet, beginning from the starting point t=0 (which means you) and stretching to the outer edge of the universe. The end at the observer's side is fixed. It is always t=0; it does not change. The other end, which is the outer edge of the universe, is being pulled outward. The outer edge of the elastic spacetime fabric is expanding by 186,000 miles every second. It is expanding at the speed of light every second, which is one light-year every year. As time flows, the expansion of the spacetime fabric will continue at the speed of light.

It must be understood that only the outer edge of the universe is expanding at the speed of light; anything in between will not expand at the same speed, it will be proportional to the distance from the observer. Using the rubber sheet example, if you pull the outer edge by a certain distance, the inner part will not be stretched by the same amount. The stretching will be more at the outer edges and it will be much less as you move inward to the other side, which is fixed. This idea can also be applied to the spacetime framework. This means that the rate of outward

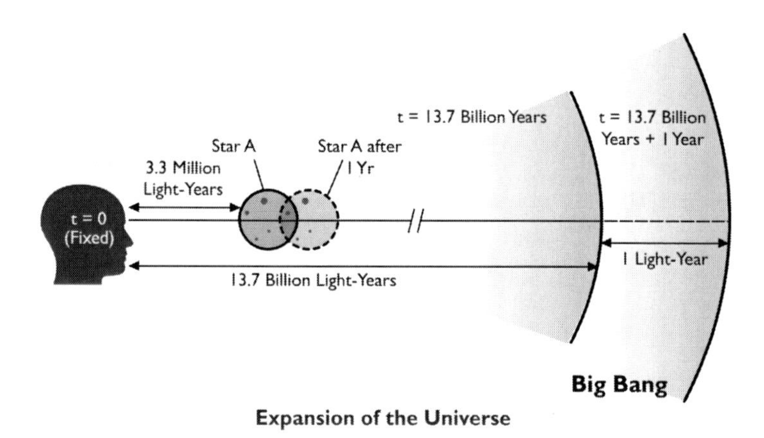

Expansion of the Universe

expansion of galaxies, stars, and so on would really depend on how far these galaxies are from the observer. The observer is t=0. Stars close by will expand more slowly compared to stars which are further away. This is because the spacetime for the stars nearby will stretch less compared to the stars which are further away.

Based on this understanding of the stretching of the spacetime fabric, let us try and calculate the Hubble constant for objects which are 3.3 million light-years away from us.

- The size of the universe is 13.7 billion light-years, and the outer edge expands by one light-year every year
- An object which is 3.3 million light-years away from us will expand proportionally by 3.3 x 10E+6/13.7 x 10E+9 = 0.240 x 10E-3 light-year per year
- One light-year = 9.46 x 10E+12 km
- Therefore, 0.240 x 10E-3 light-year per year = 2.27 x 10E+9 km per year
- One year = 3.15 x 10E+7 sec
- 2.27 x 10E+9 km per year = 72 km/sec

The above calculation shows that the Hubble constant is indeed 72 km/second. We have just calculated and proven mathematically what has been observed by science.

Spacetime and the Sun

In the same way, let us calculate the expansion of the sun, which is the closest star for us.

- The size of the universe is 13.7 billion light-years, and it expands by one light-year every year.
- The sun is 1.58 x 10E-5 light-years away from us; it will expand by 1.58 x 10E-5/1.37 x 10E+10 = 1.15 x 10E-15 light-year per year.
- One light-year = 9.46 x 10E+15 meters.
- Therefore, 1.15 x 10E-15 light-year per year = 10.8 meters per year.

The outer edge of the universe is expanding at the speed of light, but the spacetime fabric around the sun is expanding by only 10.8 meters per year. I am not sure if observation has already been made of this expansion. If it has been made, I am confident the expansion rate will be what we have calculated here. In fact, this model can be used to calculate the expansion rate for other stars and galaxies in the universe. I am positive that this expansion model will be proved to be correct.

Since the calculation of the Hubble constant is accurate, it only shows that the expansion model explained in this essay is correct, accurate, and the only truth. This proves that the spacetime fabric starts with the observer within each person. Also, each person creates their own spacetime framework. This is indeed a revolutionary and novel idea, and since it proves the Hubble constant, it must be correct. This does shake the current foundation of our understanding of space and the universe around us. In any case, the current foundation is shaky and full of doubts, confusion, and unanswered questions. It is time for science to accept this new way to look at the universe "out there." It will help solve many of the unanswered questions.

32 | Multiverses?

Multiverses or multiple universes is a topic which is often debated by scientists. Multiverses are also called parallel or alternative universes. If quantum physics is properly understood, it does indicate the existence of multiple universes. Is this even possible? We have hypotheses, but there is little understanding of how and where the multiple universes exist.

It all began with the famous Schrodinger's cat. This was a thought experiment created by Nobel Prize-winning physicist Erwin Schrodinger. A cat is enclosed in a box which contains a vial of poison attached to an atomic trigger. The atomic trigger can randomly trigger or not trigger the poison vial. If it triggers the vial, the poison will kill the cat. If it does not, the cat will be alive. One is never sure if the cat is dead or alive at any given time. Both possibilities exist. Only upon opening the box can one confirm if the cat is dead or alive. Observation is a must. Both a dead cat and a live one have the same probability.

If you find the cat is alive, some scientists suggest that the other

Schrodinger's cat experiment—cat, dead or alive?

possibility of the cat being dead is equally possible. Schrodinger's wave function indicates this possibility. This means that the scenario of the dead cat will happen in an alternative universe. If the cat is found dead in this universe, then in a parallel universe the cat will be alive. The idea of multiverses became popular with this interpretation of Schrodinger's cat.

Frankly, it is an incorrect interpretation of Schrodinger's wave function. Even Schrodinger himself was not trying to show this possibility of alternative universes with the thought experiment of the cat. He was trying to show how the wave functions of the different objects superimposed on each other. For a proper interpretation, it is important to understand Schrodinger's wave function correctly. We will do this without being too technical.

A proper diagnosis of the wave function will show that we do live in a multiverse, that too right in front of our eyes.

Understanding Schrodinger's Wave Function

We have discussed Schrodinger's wave function in other essays. It is worthwhile repeating some key findings, because the proper interpretation of this wave function can lead to the correct understating of multiverses.

Quantum physics took off in the early 20th century, when scientists found that light had both a wave property and a particle property. Sometimes it behaves like a wave and sometimes like a particle. If this subject of quantum physics is new to you, you must watch a YouTube video which shows the famous double-slit experiment. It highlights the strangeness of light being both a wave and particle.

In this double-slit experiment, light behaves like a wave, but whenever a measuring device is added, light starts behaving like a particle. Strange but true.

In 1923, French PhD student Louis de Broglie went further and confirmed that not only light or subatomic particles, but ALL matter has wave and particle properties. You, me, a molecule, a tree, planets, stars, galaxies–everything in this universe has a wave property and a particle property.

The wave and particle are two sides of the same coin. Everything can be a wave or a particle.

In 1925, Schrodinger formulated a complex equation to understand the wave part of the wave/particle duality. Schrodinger's wave equation is a generic equation which can represent all the possible wave functions in the universe.

Schrodinger's wave equation represents a physical system consisting of the following two parts:

1. Observed system
2. Observing system

Observed System: The observed system is the wave function of objects which are being observed. In the double-slit experiment, the observed system is the waveform of light which passes through the two slits. If you think about it, the wave function is much broader and not limited to light. De Broglie confirmed that all objects in the universe have a wave property. This would mean that the double-slit plate also has a wave property, and so do the measuring device and photographic plate. Everything in this universe has a wave property.

Schrodinger, in his thought experiment about the cat, was trying to highlight this wider impact of the wave function. In the cat experiment, the box has a wave function, the vial of poison has a wave function, the atomic trigger has a wave function and so also the cat. All these wave functions in this thought experiment "entangle" with each other to form a single wave function representing the full system.

Entangle means they are part of one system, and they interact with each other. This interaction means that the combined wave function has many different possibilities. The technical term for the different possibilities is "superpositions." Superposition means that the system wave function has many possibilities. The wave function could become any one of these possibilities. However, whenever any observation or measurement is made, only one of the possibilities will take effect.

In Schrodinger's cat experiment there are many possibilities. The atomic trigger may activate or may not. The box may collapse and the cat may escape. The cat may be dead or alive. All these possibilities are inherent in this combined wave function. We have given just one example of how different individual waveforms entangle to create a system wave function. If you look outside your window, the waveforms of all the objects will combine to form a single system wave function of that view. If you now look elsewhere, the waveform of those objects will combine into one system. The system wave function could be complex, but it will follow Schrodinger's wave equation.

Observing System: The observing system is the observer or a measuring device. The observer observes the observed system or the wave function. In the double-slit experiment, the measuring device or camera is the observing system. In the cat experiment, the person opening the box is the observing system. When the observing system interacts with the system wave function, only one of the possibilities will happen. The wave function collapses and a single possibility from all the possibilities will take place. In the cat experiment, either the cat is dead, or it is alive.

There is always some confusion around what an observing system is. Who is the actual observer? Can a measuring device have the capacity to collapse a wave function? Very unlikely. What is the inherent power within a measuring device to collapse a wave function? If you think about it, the measuring device is also a wave function. It is also made up of subatomic particles. What is happening is that the wave function of the measuring device gets entangled with the system wave function of the observed system.

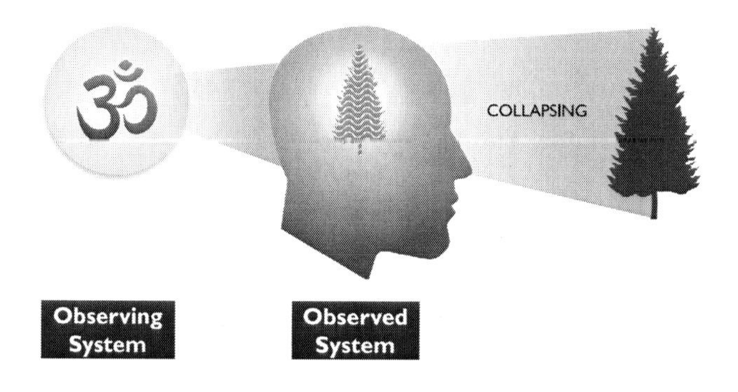

Wave in Mind Collapsing in the Presence of Self-Awareness

In this way, they interact with each other. Even the person opening the box in Schrodinger's cat experiment is not the ultimate observer. This person is also a wave function. Okay, a person is a wave function, but what about his brain? Even a brain is made up of cells and is a wave function. Where does this chain of linkages end to find the real observer of any event?

The only logical place to find the observer is within you. This observer within you is the witness to everything happening around you. This observer is not a wave function; it is the witness to the wave function. The system wave function has many possibilities. It will collapse in the presence of the observer to one of the options to become particles.

Still, the unanswered question remains–what and who is this observer within us? Science has never attempted to answer this critical question. It must be answered because the observer is a component of Schrodinger's wave function. Since science is unable to answer, it is best to look elsewhere.

Fortunately, the teachings of Vedanta have a clear and precise answer to this question. Vedanta teaches us that the nature of the Observer within us is like a bulb of Awareness. This bulb keeps shining Awareness. If you want to learn about Awareness, please read the essay "Understanding Self-Awareness." When the system wave function comes into the presence of Awareness, the system wave function collapses to become a particle or object of which you are aware. Awareness collapses the wave function and the witness within you observes it.

Composition of the System Wave Function

The system wave function is much more complicated than we have discussed so far. We will see that ultimately there is a single system wave function representing every possible object in this universe–right from a single atom to a living being to stars and to complex galaxies. There is a single system wave function for the universe. We can call this the cosmic wave function. This cosmic wave function represents every object in the universe.

1. Schrodinger's wave function represents the energy profile of an object at any given moment. As time passes, the energy profile will also change. A new energy wave function is created with every passing moment. No energy wave function is lost. All the past wave functions are still available within the object wave function. All the past wave functions,

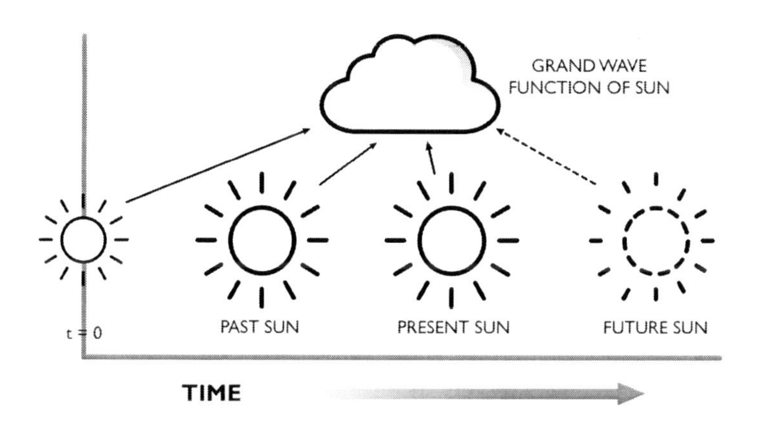

Sun—Historical Timeline

right from the birth of the object to this current moment, combine to create a single wave function for the object. The object wave function is the total of all the wave functions for the object, right from its inception to the present time.

The energy profile of an object is the total of all the profiles since the birth of the object. For example, the sun is over 4.5 billion years old. The energy profile of the sun will include all the profiles for every passing moment. Every moment in time is part of the wave function for the sun. All these individual wave functions combine to create a "grand" wave function for the sun. As time passes, new wave functions are added to the cumulative profile of the sun. In the sun's cumulative wave function, the profile for each moment of the sun since inception is available.

This cumulative wave function has the possibility to become any of the suns in the historical timeline. All the possibilities of the sun are available in the sun's wave function. How do we understand this? Let us take an example. You are on Earth, your friend is on Mars, and your alien friend lives on a planet five million light-years away. What happens if each one of them looks at the sun at this "now" moment?

Light takes eight minutes to reach Earth from the sun; it takes 13 minutes to reach Mars and five million light-years to reach the remote planet. The total wave function of the sun is available to every observer. This wave function has all the possibilities in the sun's historical timeline. Every moment is present in the sun's wave function. When this wave function collapses in the presence of the observer, you on Earth will see the sun which is "now minus eight minutes" old. This is because light takes eight minutes to reach you; you will only see an older version of the sun–the "now minus eight minutes" version–not the "now" version. This "now minus eight minutes" version of the wave function is present within the sun's cumulative wave function.

For your friend on Mars, the wave function which is "now minus 13 minutes" will collapse so that he can see the sun which is "now minus 13 minutes" old. Your alien friend will see a very ancient sun. He will see a "now minus five million years" version of the sun. Each one of us will see a different version of the sun. All these different versions of the sun are available in the cumulative wave function. Even if millions of people are looking at the sun right "now," each one of them will collapse one of the versions of the sun.

We have just seen the example of the sun with all the historical wave functions. This will apply to all the objects in the universe. Every object in the universe is a cumulative wave function of every moment in time. Your wave function will be a total of all the wave functions since your birth. The trees, cars, planets, galaxies–each one of them will have a time-wise total wave function.

2. To add to the complexity of the wave functions, all objects in the universe with their own cumulative wave functions will combine to create one big wave function for the universe. We can call this the cosmic wave function. This cosmic wave function includes everything which is contained in the universe. Nothing is left out.

3. A single cosmic function which contains every object in the universe since the start of time, which is the Big Bang–it is not easy to grasp this. How can a single waveform represent everything? How does each object's wave function keep its own identity within the cosmic wave function? It is not an easy question to answer. A good analogy to answer this question is Google Maps. We use Google Maps often, and it has the road map of almost the entire world. The central server stores the software content for Google Maps. This one single server has the information of all the required

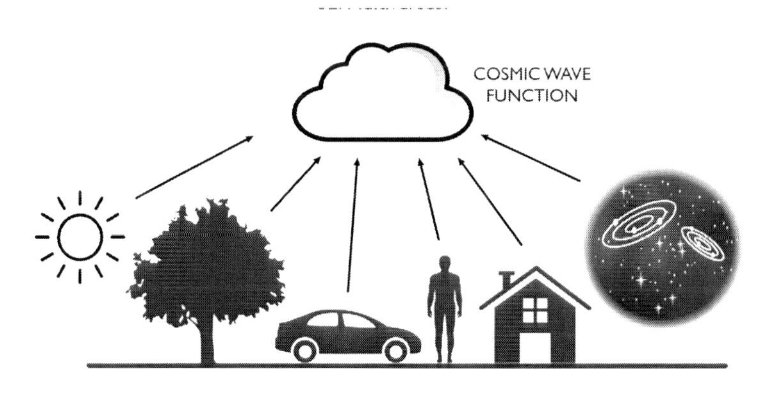

Grand Wave Function of Different Objects

content. If you are in New York, you will see the maps of that city; if you are in New Delhi, you will see the maps of that area.

In many ways, this centralized software code is like the cosmic wave function. Both are one big bundle of information. The cosmic wave function is much more complicated and extensive. It contains the entire universe and keeps the historical information of all the objects.

4. Vedanta teaches us that there are mental waveforms or vrittis in the mind. These mental waveforms represent different objects. It is important to understand that these mental waveforms or vrittis are made of knowledge. Yes, knowledge or intelligence. This intelligent wave function knows what object it represents. Please think and reflect upon this. Knowledge or Intelligence is the substance of the wave function. This is a great insight because it will help understand the object wave functions we

have been discussing. Even if all the object wave functions combine to form a single cosmic wave function, knowledge of each object is maintained. It is not wrong to say that the cosmic wave function or mental waveform is the total knowledge repository of the universe. Total knowledge or intelligence of the universe is present in the cosmic wave function. The knowledge or wave function of an object can be found within the cosmic wave function. Just as Google Maps has the coding to keep track of all the roads in the world, the cosmic wave function has the coding to keep the knowledge of all the objects in the universe.

5. Another important conclusion which can be drawn is that the cosmic wave function operates only within the mind. Quantum physics has shown that matter has both wave and particle properties. We see and know that the particle is the universe we see "out there." But quantum physics rarely discusses the wave part. Where does it reside? The wave part of the wave/particle duality is largely unknown. If you are a student of Vedanta, you will learn that the only place where the wave part of objects can reside is the mind. It is the same as the mental waveforms or vrittis indicated by Vedanta. And these object wave functions are made of knowledge or intelligence. Please read the essay "Quantum Physics and Vedanta," where it is shown that the wave part of the object and the mental waveform or vritti as taught by Vedanta are the same.

Multiverses

We have just seen that the cosmic wave function is one big wave function. It is a combination of all the objects in the universe. In this cosmic wave function, there are a great number of possibilities.

The possibilities could be a combination of any number of objects. It does not matter if it is a large or small combination of objects. For example, if you look out of your window, you will see one possibility which is a combination of many objects. You look away from the window, and this is another possibility where you will see a different combination of objects. In this way, the cosmic wave function can be "sliced" into many different parts. Each slice which you see is a possibility.

Within each object, there are many possibilities–the historical wave functions for that object since its inception to this moment. Each one of these historical wave functions is a possibility. The sun's wave function has 4.5 billion years of possibilities. For each moment, the sun has a unique wave function. We saw earlier how three people saw three different possibilities of the sun from different locations.

Combine these two points and you will have an unlimited number of possibilities in the cosmic wave function. Each of these unlimited possibilities can be sliced out from the cosmic wave function. We will now show that each of these possibilities within the cosmic wave function is a universe by itself. Since there are unlimited possibilities, there could be an unlimited number of universes.

We have seen earlier that, in the presence of an observer, the wave function must collapse to take up only one of the possibilities. Only one possibility can take root from the unlimited possibilities. Before understanding which possibility, do you think there is only one observer? Is there only one observer in this universe? I am sure you will agree that the answer is *No*. Each one of us is an observer (ego). You are an observer, I am an observer, every human being is an observer. Besides the eight billion human beings, there is a huge population of animals and insects. Many of them also have eyes, so they must be observers. These are the observers on Earth. If you believe there are living beings on other planets, then you will need to add those observers to the total number of observers. The conclusion is: there is a gigantic number of observers!

We have seen earlier that the cosmic wave function operates only within the mind–in fact, in the cosmic mind. The cosmic mind is the total of all the minds. Add up all the minds and you will get the cosmic mind. Within every individual mind there is an observer. From the total cosmic wave function, each mind will choose a subsection or part of the cosmic wave function. Every mind will choose a different subsection.

1. Let us take an example of a single mind. This mind will choose one possibility, which is a subsection within the cosmic wave function. This subsection is a combination of different object wave functions. We have seen earlier that these wave functions are made up of self-knowledge. The wave function knows what objects it represents. In the presence of the observer in the mind, this knowledge in the wave function takes root to become the various objects. Quantum physics will call this the collapsing of the wave function to a single possibility.

One of the possibilities within the cosmic wave function has collapsed to become the universe this mind sees. This universe is created by the observing mind. It will not be wrong to say that this universe belongs to this mind. We will shortly see that this universe is not shared with other minds. Each mind has its own unique universe. As time passes, there is a constant change in the universe. New and different subsections of the wave function will keep collapsing in this mind, and the mind will witness a changing universe outside. This changing universe is unique to this single mind.

2. In the same way, all the available minds will choose a different possibility from the cosmic wave function. Each mind will have a different and unique subsection of the cosmic wave function. The objects are never the same in two subsections. Each possibility or subsection within the cosmic wave function is unique. A good comparison to understand this is cutting slices of a cake. All the cake slices will be unique and different. The same slice cannot be repeated. In the same way, each subsection of the cosmic wave function is unique. If one subsection is being used by one mind, another mind cannot use the same possibility or subsection. Thus, each mind has a unique subsection of the cosmic wave function.

The observer in each mind will collapse a unique subsection. When this wave function collapses, the mind will witness the objects contained in the wave function. Since the subsection is unique and not repeated, each mind will create a different and unique universe. From the point of view of Schrodinger's wave function, each mind collapses a different possibility. Each mind creates a different universe. No two universes are the same. There is a gigantic number of minds, each mind creating its own unique universe. Multiverses are being created by each mind.

3. It is easy to argue that we are looking at the same objects in the universe. How can each mind look at a different set of objects? If you and your friend are looking at a clump of trees, you will both say that we are looking at the same objects; how can they be different? Let us analyze this further to show that you and your friend are looking at different versions of the same objects. The objects may look the same, but you are looking at different versions of them.

- **Different object distances:** If your friend is standing 10 feet ahead of you, light will take less time from the trees to reach him and a bit longer to reach you. Since light takes a bit longer to reach you, you will see an older version of the tree, while your friend will see a more current version of the tree. The two versions are not the same. The different is so minute that the human mind cannot see the difference, but they are different. Even if you are a few millimeters apart, the version of the objects will be different. As we have discussed earlier, the object wave function keeps a history of all the wave functions since inception. Your friend's subsection wave function will have a more current version of the trees. Your subsection wave function will have an older version of the tree. In this way, your wave function is different from your friend's wave function.

- **Same object distances:** You could argue that you and your friend are standing at the same distance from the trees. The question then is: are you still looking at the same trees? The distance may be the same, but you are at different spots. This means that the angular view of the trees will be different. You and your friend will see a different view of the trees. The difference may be small, but still there is a difference. You will see the same view only if you and your friend occupy the same spot. This is impossible. You cannot occupy the same spot in space. There must be a difference. This not only applies to trees and other objects around us, but also to distant objects like the sun or stars. The angular view of these faraway objects will never be the same unless and until you occupy the same space as your friend. This is not possible. So, we see that the subsection wave function for each person would be different.

Thus, two minds can never have the same subsection wave function. When these subsection wave functions collapse in the presence of the observer, each person will see a different set of objects or different versions of the same objects. They can never be the same. In this way, each person creates and sees their own universe. No two universes will be the same. This does make sense; we can only see what we see. We have no clue what other people perceive or see.

So, multiverses are a reality. This fits in very well with Schrodinger's wave function, which states that a wave function has multiple possibilities and that, in the presence of the observer or measuring device, it collapses and only one of the possibilities takes root. The other possibilities could also take root, but this must happen in a parallel or alternative universe. This sounds mysterious, but after reading this essay it should make perfect sense!

To sum up, in our discussion we have seen that there are multiple observers–each living being is an observer. There is a gigantic number of observers. Each observer collapses one of the possibilities from the cosmic wave function. Each possibility is a subsection of the cosmic wave function. Each possibility is unique and different; it cannot be the same. Each possibility or each observer creates a different universe. All these different or parallel universes are present right here. As long as there are multiple observers, there will be multiple universes. It is not as mysterious as it sounds.

33 | Unlocking Dark Energy and Dark Matter

Both dark energy (DE) and dark matter (DM) are an unsolved mystery. Because they are undiscoverable, they are called "dark." Scientists know that dark energy and dark matter exist because, without them, the universe cannot sustain itself or function in its current form.

Scientists have been watching the universe with powerful telescopes, and they have discovered a lot. They have a good idea of the number of galaxies and of the number of stars and planetary systems within each galaxy. Watching the expansion of the universe and movement of these galaxies, they have estimated the energy composition of the universe to be:

- Dark energy (DE): 79%
- Dark matter (DM): 26%
- Visible matter: 5%

The visible galaxies and the stars and planets within them make up 5% of the energy. The balance 95% energy is unknown, and scientists believe it is made up of DE and DM. Why? They believe that DE and DM are necessary for the universe to function. Here is a current understanding of dark energy and dark matter.

Dark Energy: Cosmologists know there is a gravitational pull between galaxies, which means that the galaxies are pulled closer to each other. So, the space between the galaxies should contract as they come closer to each other. Observation has shown that this is not happening. Instead, what is seen is that space is expanding and the galaxies are moving apart. The only way this can happen is if there is some force which is pushing all the galaxies apart. We can deduce that this force is greater than gravitational pull and is the reason for the expansion of space. This expansionary force requires energy–lots of energy. This energy is the mysterious dark energy, which is responsible for the expansion of the universe.

Scientists estimate that dark energy makes up 79% of the total energy requirement of this universe. Dark energy is unknown. They have no clue about its composition. It is not like visible energy. It is not gamma rays, x-rays, or any other electromagnetic waves which make up the spectrum of visible energy. Researchers are looking for DE, but it continues to elude them.

Dark Matter: If you follow science, you will know that each galaxy rotates around its center. The center is usually a massive black hole. All the stars and planets within a galaxy rotate around its black hole. This also applies to our Milky Way. Earth, part of the solar system, rotates around the sun. Our solar system, including the sun, rotates around the center of the Milky Way. Fun fact: it takes 228 million years for our solar system to make one complete round of the Milky Way. Just imagine–there were dinosaurs on Earth when our solar system was last at its current location.

When scientists look at the rotation of these galaxies, they find something strange and inexplicable. The orbital speeds of galaxies do not follow the physical laws found in other orbital systems such as stars, planets, and moons. Stars and planetary systems revolve around their galaxy's center at equal or increasing speeds over a large range of distances. In contrast, the orbital speed of planets within their planetary systems declines with distance.

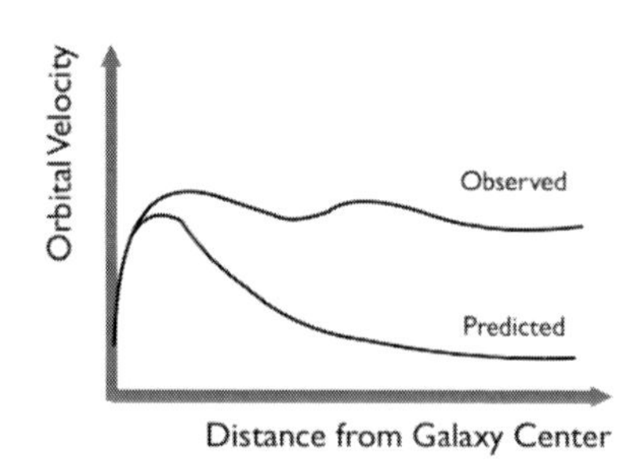

Rotational Speed of Galaxies

For example, in our solar system, the orbital speed of Neptune is much lower compared to other planets in the system. This decrease in orbital speed as distance increases is proven by calculations. This logic does not apply to stars and planetary systems in galaxies. As the graph shows in the previous page, as the distance from the center of the galaxy increases, the orbital speed of observed objects in the galaxy is much higher than predicted by scientific calculations.

This increased orbital speed of objects in a galaxy has many implications. The high rotational speed of objects at the outer edge would mean that they should not and cannot rotate around the galaxy but should escape or fly out. They are rotating so fast that they should escape their orbits. But this is not what is observed. Why this contradiction in physical laws? No one has yet been able to figure this out. It is a mystery. Scientists have postulated that there is additional matter around these stars. The increased matter in the galaxy means that there is an increased gravitational pull to the center. This allows the stars of the outer edge to maintain their rotation in their mother galaxy. Scientists do not know what this additional matter is, and so it's called dark matter. Scientists estimate that DM makes up 26% of the total available energy in the universe.

There is an increasing effort in scientific circles to find dark matter. Scientists think that dark matter must be made of particles. Initially, they thought it was like visible matter, made of protons, neutrons, electrons, and an array of subatomic particles. Atomic particles interact with light and other electromagnetic waves. After a series of experiments, scientists are finding that dark matter does not interact with light and other electromagnetic waves. There is no absorption or reflection of light. So, the conclusion is that dark matter is not the same as visible matter. It is something different; it is something unknown. To continue the search, a wide range of unique experiments are being conducted in various parts of the world to discover the particles which make up dark matter. In one high-profile experiment, a tunnel has been dug one mile underground to make sure no known particles can pass through. Scientists are hoping that a dark matter particle will show up in this tunnel so that they can then study its properties.

Will they be successful? I believe it to be unlikely. They are not going to find dark energy and dark matter in space "out there." They have already tried and failed to find DM and DE within visible matter. The time has come to look elsewhere.

Going back to Einstein's Theory of Relativity, we get a clue. In this theory, Einstein made a connection between space and time. He stated that space and time are two sides of the same coin, and he called this spacetime. He also stated that spacetime is like a fabric made up of time and that the entire universe rests on this spacetime fabric.

Since we have seen that scientists are unable to find dark matter and dark energy in space, I believe that to understand them, we need to properly understand this time-based spacetime fabric. If scientists shift their focus and attention to the spacetime fabric, they will find answers to dark energy and dark matter.

In this essay, we are going to focus on spacetime and show how a better understanding of spacetime can lead to unlocking the mystery of dark energy and dark matter. Before we move forward, it is important to repeat the following key issues once again:

- Spacetime vs. Space
- Framework of the Time Fabric
- Einstein's Theory of Relativity

Spacetime vs. Space

In other essays we have clarified the difference between spacetime and space. Since this is important for this essay, we are restating the difference. Einstein coined the term "spacetime." This term causes confusion. There is space and there is spacetime. What is the difference? Space is what we see when we look out, and everything in space is measured in distances. The tree is 200 feet away; the plane is flying at 30,000 feet. Space is visible and operates in the three dimensions.

Spacetime looks at the same thing in terms of time. This term is confusing because there is no space in spacetime; there is only time. In spacetime, the measurement is in units of time alone; no distances are measured. For example, light takes eight minutes to reach us from the sun; the distant star is 500 million light-years away. Everything in spacetime is measured only in time. There are NO distances, only time. The following images will help in understanding the spacetime fabric, but they wrongly convey the impression that the spacetime fabric operates in space. This is wrong because spacetime operates on a different plane. As Einstein stated, spacetime operates in the fourth dimension. Where is the fourth dimension? One thing is clear: the fourth dimension cannot function in the three dimensions, otherwise we would have to say that space has four dimensions.

Henceforth in this essay we will refer to spacetime as time fabric to avoid the confusion created by the term spacetime. This is more accurate and conveys the meaning that time alone is the variable in spacetime.

Spacetime Fabric = Time Fabric

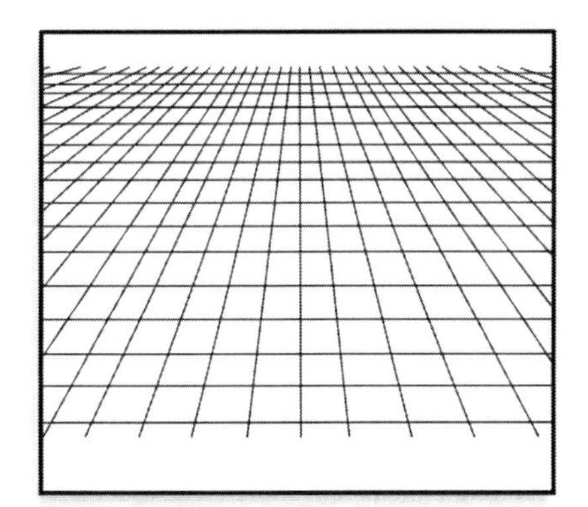

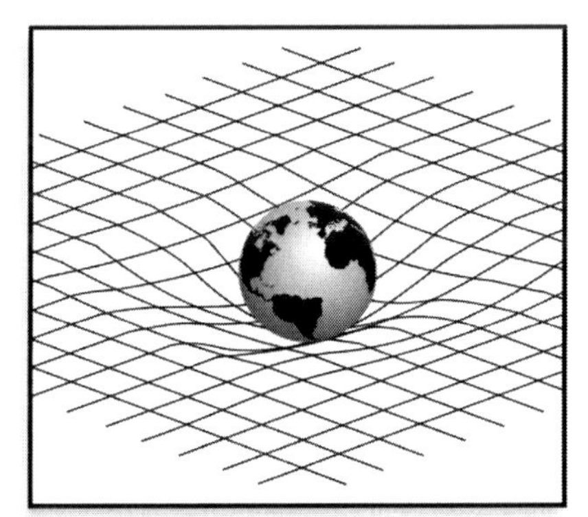

Nobody knows where the fourth dimension is. We could speculate, but the location of the fourth dimension is not the focus of this essay. We will show later that energy interacts with the time fabric to create space. The time fabric is discussed in many other essays. Some of the points are repeated here because understanding this fabric properly is the key to unlocking the mystery of dark energy and dark matter.

Framework of the Time Fabric

If you look at space, it is impossible to find a starting point or even the edge of space. Space is everywhere. But for the time fabric, there must be a start and end point. Why? Because time fabric is made of time. Time must have a beginning and an end.

Where is the starting point of the time fabric? The starting point of the time fabric must be t=0. To understand the t=0 point for the time fabric, let us visualize space in terms of time. As we have discussed in many different essays including the essay "Time (t)=0 Is Pure Awareness," the time fabric starts with the observer within us. This observer is the t=0 for the time fabric. The end point of the fabric is the Big Bang, which is 13.7 billion years away on the time fabric.

Construction of the Time Fabric: Based on the Planck constant, it is proven that time is made of discrete elements. The shortest separation between two discrete elements is 10E-44 seconds. These discrete time elements make up the time fabric. The start of the time fabric is t=0, which is the observer within you. The first node will be at 10E-44 seconds away from the observer. The second node will be at 2 x 10E-44 seconds away; the third node will be 3 x 10E-44 seconds away. The entire time fabric is built up with these small increments of time nodes.

Einstein's Theory of Relativity

To connect space and the time fabric properly, it is important to summarize the findings of Einstein's Theory of Relativity. In 1905, he postulated the Theory of Special Relativity and, in 1915, he introduced the Theory of General Relativity.

Theory of Special Relativity: One of the major conclusions of this theory is that time and motion are interconnected. Wherever there is motion, time slows down. This connection between motion and time is a proven fact.

If you think about it, motion operates in space (in the three dimensions) and time with the time fabric (in the fourth dimension). So what is the connection between motion and the time fabric? According to science, motion is the cause, and the effect of that motion is the change in the time fabric. What is the change in the time fabric? Slowing down of time means that the time fabric is more compressed. The time nodes in the fabric are closer and more compressed. The higher the speed, the closer the time nodes in the fabric. At the speed of light there is no time, there is no time fabric.

Motion happens in the three dimensions, and the time change happens in the time fabric (the fourth dimension). Is this the correct way to interpret the Theory of Special Relativity? Another way to look at this interconnection is the reverse–time slows down first, and this causes motion. Compress the time fabric and motion happens in space. This is contrary to conventional thinking. Which is correct? We are so used to conventional thinking that it is difficult to accept that compression of the time fabric causes motion.

We will see later that to decode dark energy and dark matter, it is important to study the time fabric. We will see that dark energy and dark matter operate within the time fabric. The cause of dark energy and dark matter is in the time fabric and the effect is seen in space. Everything happens first in the time fabric and not in space. Even the motion of planets and stars is only due to the compression and decompression of time in the time fabric. Understanding this will help solve the mystery behind dark energy and dark matter.

Theory of General Relativity: Einstein introduced the Theory of General Relativity in 1915. The major outcome of this theory is that in the presence of matter, time slows down. The slowing down of time is

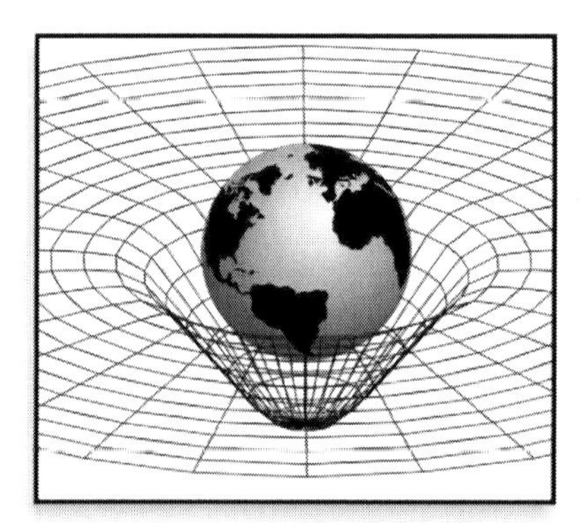

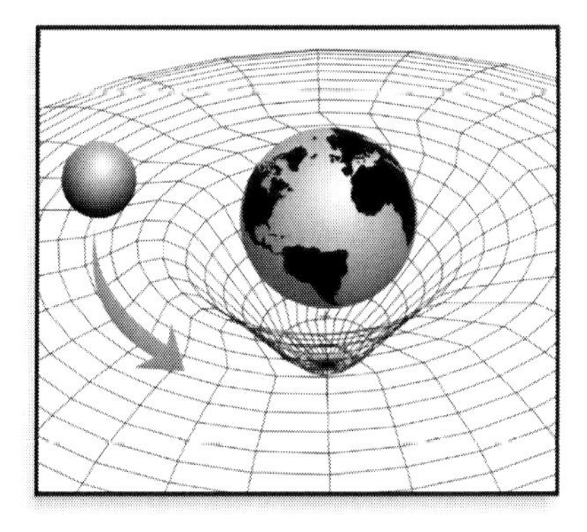

represented by the time fabric bending or curving around an object. The heavier the mass, the greater the curvature. Not only planets and stars, but matter with any mass will slow down time and curve the time fabric. For objects with a very small mass, the curve will not be noticeable.

As we can see in the images shown in the previous page, placing a planet (or any other object) on the time fabric is a good way to understand the curving of the time fabric. However, are the images accurate? No, they are not. A planet is matter and functions in the three dimensions of space. The time fabric is in the fourth dimension. There is no place for matter in the fourth dimension. Matter cannot exist in the fourth dimension. So, what is the alternative? We know that energy and matter are connected by the famous equation $E=mc^2$. So, it is the energy profile of objects which is available in the time fabric and not matter. So, in images like the ones on page 305, where an object is shown dipping down into the curve, it must be understood that this is the energy profile of the object and not the physical object itself. This applies to every small and every large object in the universe.

Around the curvature, there are horizontal and vertical timelines. It is important to understand these timelines.

Vertical Timelines: The vertical timelines in the curvature are the source of the rotational or orbital motion. How can we say this? In the earlier section we showed that the time fabric and motion are connected. The speed of rotation depends on how close or apart the vertical timelines are in the time fabric. The more compressed the vertical timelines, the higher the orbital speed. Vertical timelines are the cause of planetary orbital motion.

If you study the curvature around any massive object, the vertical timelines will be further apart at the top and more compressed at the bottom of the curvature. What does this mean? This means that wherever the vertical timelines are more compressed, the orbital speed of objects will be higher. Therefore, the orbital speed of objects near the bottom of the curvature will be higher than the orbital speed of objects at the top of the curvature.

This is what physicists predict with their calculations. In our solar system, Mercury (closest to the sun) rotates faster than Earth, and Earth rotates faster than all the other planets, except Venus, in the solar system. Neptune, which is furthest away, is the slowest. We see that the compression of the vertical timelines complies with observed facts and calculations regarding the solar system.

Horizontal Timelines: The curvature of the time fabric is mainly due to the horizontal timelines. These timelines are the source of gravitational pull. The horizontal timelines in the images on page 305 do not faithfully represent the exact format. They should follow a squared function graph. The top horizontal timelines should be more spaced out and, as we move down the curvature, the timelines should be more compressed. This curvature should follow the t^2 function. Why? Gravity is a function of t^2. As time increases, the speed of objects increases in a squared manner. The horizontal timelines in the curvature should reflect this.

Let us imagine that an object rolls down the time fabric. From the earlier discussion we have seen that the time fabric is the cause of the motion of objects. At the top, the separation of the horizontal timelines will determine the initial speed of the object. As the object moves further down the slope of the curvature, the timelines are more compressed following the t^2 function. This means that the object will gather speed following the rules of gravity. With the curvature, the time fabric provides the framework for the gravitational pull in space.

Before we continue, let us review some key aspects of the time fabric:

1. The time fabric is made of time and functions in the fourth dimension.
2. The starting point or t=0 of the time fabric is the observer within you. The end point is the Big Bang.
3. As time flows, the time fabric keeps expanding.
4. The compression and expansion of the time fabric is the source of motion and gravity/acceleration.
5. With this understanding, let us see if we can decode the mystery behind dark energy and dark matter.

Understanding Dark Energy

The time fabric (the fourth dimension) creates the space which you see all around. How? To create space from the time fabric, there must be an energy source. Unfortunately, little is known about energy. How is it created; where is it created? We have answered this question in the essay "Awareness–The Infinite Energy Source." Awareness is the source of energy.

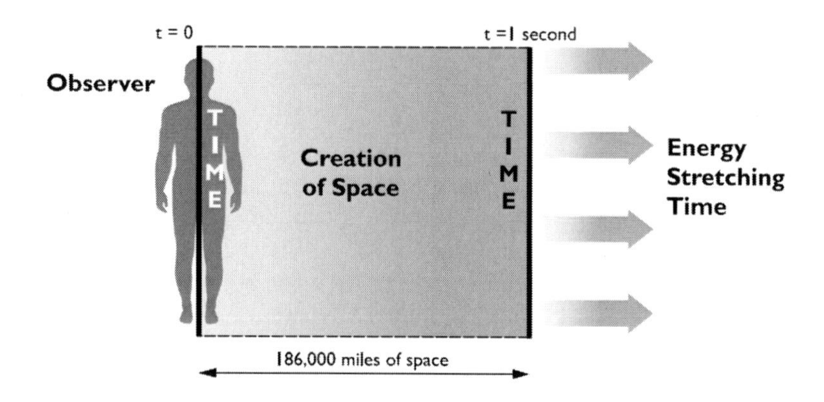

It would seem that this energy plays different roles. Visible matter is created by this energy source. Let us see what happens when a part of this energy interacts with the time fabric. This energy stretches out the time fabric, so that every second of the fabric is equal to 186,000 miles (speed of light). Just like a rubber band can be stretched outward, in the same way, the time fabric is stretched outward by this energy. With this stretching of the time fabric, space is created. One second of the time fabric becomes 186,000 miles of space. This is the space we see. Therefore, we see that space is created when energy stretches out the time fabric. From the Big Bang to today, there are 13.7 billion years of the time fabric. The entire time fabric is stretched out by dark energy to create space for the visible universe "out there." A great deal of energy is required to stretch out the entire time fabric. This energy requirement for stretching the time fabric is nothing but dark energy. Scientists have estimated that dark energy is about 79% of the total energy requirement of this universe.

So, this energy which can stretch the time fabric is dark energy. It is not your ordinary energy, which is part of the visible universe. Dark energy is not part of the electromagnetic spectrum. Electromagnetic energy is good for visible matter, but it cannot stretch the time fabric to create space. To discover dark energy, more investigation must be done to understand the time fabric.

1. Does the compression of the time fabric change the size of space we see outside? No. There may be no compression, little compression, moderate compression, or extreme time fabric compression. In all these conditions, dark energy will continue to expand one second of the time fabric to make 186,000 miles in space. The size of space will always be 186,000 miles per second irrespective of the level of time fabric compression. Compression or no compression, dark energy will always stretch one second of the time fabric to 186,000 miles. We know that light travels at 186,000 miles per second. Light travels at this speed because one second of the time fabric is stretched to 186,000 miles. So, the speed of light will always remain constant, irrespective of how slow or fast time moves. This is the major finding of Einstein's Theory of Special Relativity.

2. We have seen earlier that as time flows, the time fabric keeps expanding. This means that dark energy stretches the time fabric to create an ever-expanding space "out there." As long as time flows, space will continue to expand. More and more dark energy is being used to continue the expansion of space.

Understanding Dark Matter

We have seen earlier that scientists believe in the existence of dark matter because the orbital speed of stars/planets in the galaxy is much higher than predicted. Because of this high speed, scientists believe there is dark matter around these stars/planets which holds these planetary objects in their respective orbits. Without this dark matter, the planets/stars would escape the orbit of the galaxy.

So, what is this dark matter? Let us go back to the time fabric. We have seen that when the energy profile of an object is placed on the time fabric, it curves the time fabric. As we discussed earlier, the vertical timelines in the time fabric provide the orbital speed to the objects, and the horizontal timelines provide the gravitational pull of the object to the bottom of the time curvature. Physics has a standard way of calculating orbital speed depending on how far the object is from the center of the orbit.

Looking at these planets/stars in the galaxy, scientists have discovered that the orbital speed of the objects is much higher than it logically should be. Why is the speed of these objects higher than it should be? Nobody really knows. A good guess would be that this orbital speed is required to maintain the structure of the galaxy. Without the higher orbital speeds, the galaxy cannot hold itself together. It will fall apart. Everything is precise in nature, so this increased orbital speed is required to maintain the galaxy as one unit.

Based on standard calculations, the orbital speed of objects must have a certain value, depending on how far the object is from the center. However, we see that the speed is much higher. How does the object increase its speed? The object cannot increase its speed on its own. The only way to increase speed is to compress the time fabric around the object. Compressing the time fabric means that time slows down. We know from the Theory of Special Relativity that when time slows down,

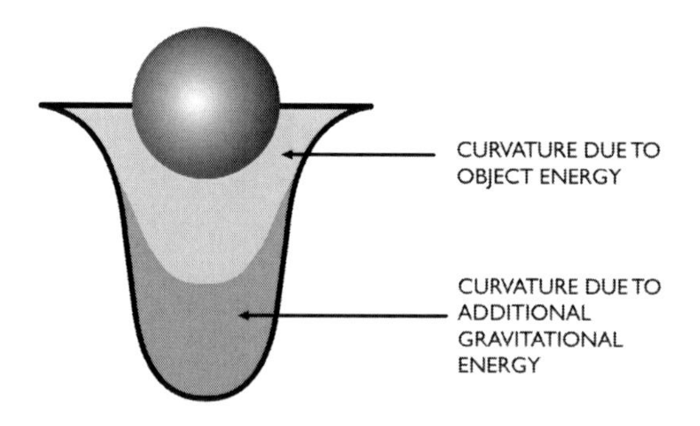

Dark matter = Additional gravitational energy

the speed of the object increases. You may ask the question, who compresses the time fabric to increase the speed of the object? This is not an easy question to answer. Like so many other things, Nature has the intelligence to compress the time fabric to slow down time. This slowing down of time increases the orbital speed of the object.

The slowing down of time in the vertical timelines also affects the horizontal timelines. Time slows down in the horizontal timelines too, and they become more compressed, just like the vertical timelines; but, in this case, it is the acceleration which increases. This happens because the horizontal timelines follow the t^2 function. This increase in acceleration and, therefore, in orbital speed, means that the gravitational pull is much stronger on the orbiting object.

Another effect of the slowing of time and increase in gravitational pull is that the slope of the curvature of the time fabric will also change. This change in the slope means that the curvature of the time fabric will be much deeper than it should be. This is a key point to understand and remember.

The energy profile of the object, or object energy, will bend the time fabric and create a certain curvature. The slowing of time and increase in the speed of the object creates a much deeper curvature. The object's energy does not fill up the deeper curvature of the time fabric. This area in the time fabric cannot be left empty. The gravitational energy which interacts with the time fabric fills up the balance of the curvature. So, the deeper curvature of the time fabric that is created contains both the object's energy and gravitational energy.

Time Fabric Curvature Energy = Object Energy + Additional Gravitational Energy

When dark energy stretches the time fabric to create space, the object's energy is converted to visible matter and the additional gravitational energy is converted to dark matter. So, dark matter is the direct result of the additional gravitational energy which is required to maintain the enhanced rotational speed of the object.

Dark matter is available in all parts of the universe where the orbital speed of planetary objects is higher than physical calculations will show.

Scientists have estimated that dark matter makes up 26% of the energy requirement of this universe.

If you want to find and understand dark matter, it is important to study the horizontal timelines in the curvature of the time fabric. The change in slope of the horizontal timelines in the time fabric directly results in the creation of gravitational energy. This gravitational energy is the source of dark matter.

So, in conclusion, we can say that the mystery of dark energy and dark matter can be solved if a better understanding of the time fabric is gained. Science should focus its attention on the study of the time fabric, which operates in the fourth dimension.

34 | Where Is the Center of the Universe?

Where is the center of the universe? Where is the x=0, y=0, z=0, and t=0 for the universe? Before Galileo, people in the West thought Earth was the center of the universe and that everything revolved around it. Galileo peered into the stars using his telescope; he found that Earth and all the other planets moved around the sun. He realized that the sun was the center of the solar system we live in. Using more powerful telescopes, people found that there are billions of stars like the sun in the Milky Way; our solar system is part of this galaxy. All the stars in this galaxy rotate around the center of the Milky Way. Cosmologists have now discovered that there are millions of such galaxies in the universe, and all these galaxies are moving in relation to each other. There is continuous movement in this vast universe. This continuous movement makes it difficult to find the center of the universe. So, how do we locate the 0,0,0,0 coordinate for the entire universe? If you think logically, this point should always be stationary or fixed compared to the continuously moving universe. The 0,0,0,0 coordinate must be non-moving and fixed.

It is impossible to find these three coordinates–x=0, y=0, and z=0–in space. We see space everywhere. This space is expanding. It is continuously moving. This makes it impossible to locate the center of the universe. However hard you try; this location is not available in space. There is no non-moving point in space.

What about t=0, the fourth coordinate? t=0 deals with time; it deals with the spacetime fabric. Science states that the Big Bang is the t=0 or the start of the spacetime fabric for the universe. As we have stated in other essays, this t=0 may have been correct at the time of the Big Bang, but right now the Big Bang is 13.7 billion years old or t= -13.7 billion years.

The Big Bang moment is the other end of the fabric. It is not t=0. So, the quest is to find the location where it is always t=0. Once the "now" or t=0 location is found, the coordinate x=0, y=0, and z=0 will also be at the same location.

Everything in space is moving, so finding the non-moving point in space is impossible. This non-moving point must be just outside space, or at the beginning point of space. We have seen in multiple essays that the observer within us is the t=0 location. Light takes zero seconds to travel to this observer. At all other points in space, light takes a finite amount of time to reach the observer within us. This is the t=0 for the universe. The observer within us is the t=0 location.

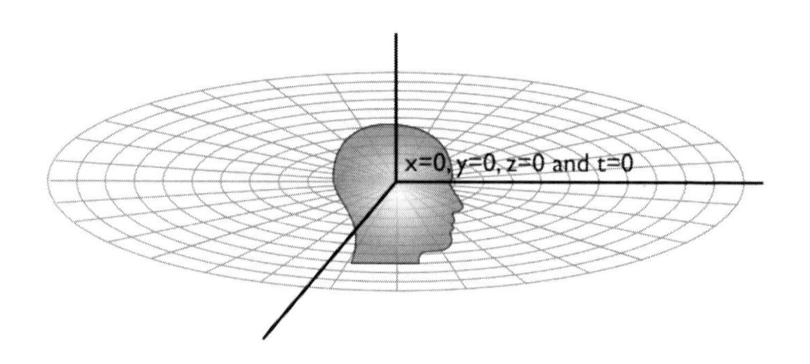

Who is the observer? Based on the teachings of Vedanta, Atma (your underlying reality) is the observer. The Atma observes all the events within the mind. It is the Atma within you where t becomes 0. This t=0 is always "now." Atma is beyond the spacetime framework, so it does not move; it is always fixed at t=0. This non-moving Atma is the center of the universe.

If Atma is t=0, then Atma is also the x=0, y=0, z=0 coordinate for the universe. So, Atma is the x=0, y=0, z=0, and t=0 coordinate for the universe.

Since the observer is the t=0, does that mean that there are multiple centers for the universe, one for each person? Does it mean there are multiple Atmas? No, there is a single Atma. This Atma is common to each observer. How do we understand this? Atma creates the illusion of being a different observer within every living being. To explain this, the classic example given by Vedanta is that of buckets filled with water.

Picture the sun shining over an unlimited number of buckets filled with water. What will you see? The sun reflected in each bucket. You will not see a partial image of the sun but the complete image of the sun in each bucket. There is one sun, but multiple reflected suns. Now imagine that the bucket represents our body, and the water in the bucket is our mind. There are an unlimited number of living beings with a mind in this universe. The shining sun is the Atma. There is one Atma which is reflected in the mind of every living being. So, you can see how the Atma/Observer within each one of us is t=0.

Earth, the sun, the center of the Milky Way are not the center of the universe. The center of the universe is your Atma/Observer and is right within you.

35 | Understanding the Fabric of Space

Note: *While reading the different essays, you may have noticed that understanding the fabric of space is an important subject. We have discussed aspects of the fabric in different essays. I believe it is a good idea to put all its aspects in one essay. That is the goal here. By doing so, some of the subject matter has been repeated.*

Is there a fabric of space? Is there an underlying fabric on which the entire universe rests? Looking at space in all its vast eternity, we do not see any fabric. Space looks empty and only the distant stars and planets are visible; no fabric can be seen. However, if you are a student of science and follow the latest happenings, you will already have seen the following images:

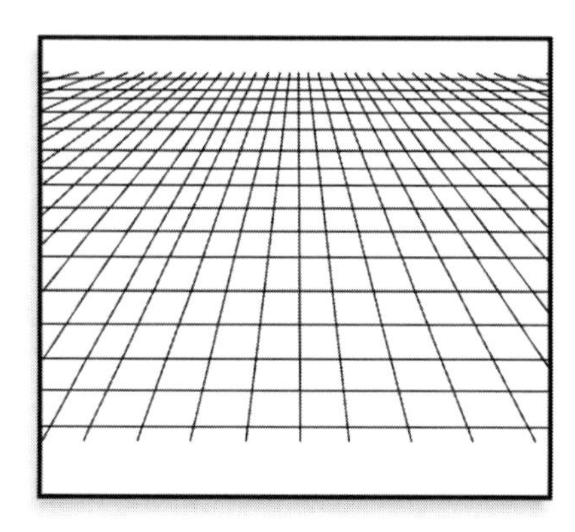

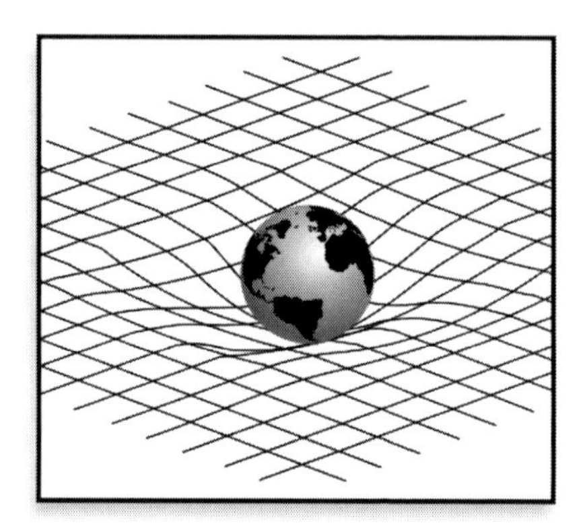

The above images represent the fabric of space. It may not be visible in the universe "out there," but Einstein, through the discovery of the Theory of Relativity, confirmed the presence of the fabric of space. This fabric is not your typical fabric; this fabric is made up of time. Yes, it is made up of time. A concept not easy to grasp. Einstein showed that space and time were interlinked, and he changed the terminology from “space and time” to “spacetime.” This spacetime has four specific dimensions, of which three dimensions are for space and the fourth is for time.

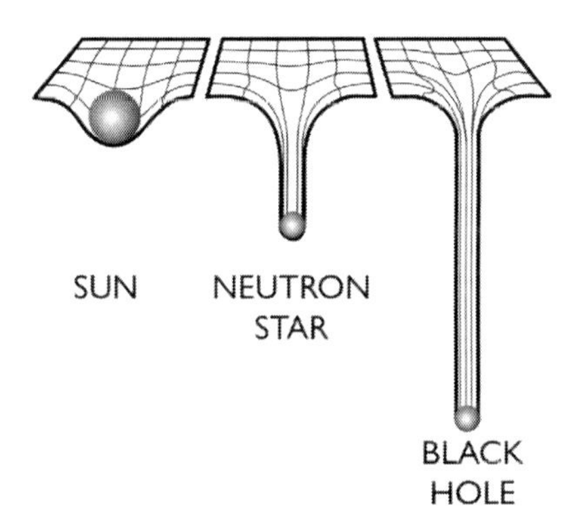

One of the objectives of the Theory of Relativity was to show that in the presence of energy, time slows down. The slowing down of time is represented by the spacetime fabric bending or curving around an object. This bending or curvature is like placing a heavy ball on a stretched-out rubber sheet. The weight of the ball will curve the rubber sheet around itself. The spacetime fabric operates in a similar manner. Place a heavy ball on the spacetime fabric, and the spacetime fabric curves around the object. It is to be noted here that the heavier the mass, the greater is the curvature. A black hole as shown above has a much deeper curvature as the mass of the black hole is much greater.

The images on the previous page do show the spacetime fabric, but there are many unanswered questions that follow:

1. Let us say, for instance, that the fabric is made up of time and that it operates in the fourth dimension. A good question arises–where exactly is the fourth dimension? We know that space has only three dimensions. It is impossible for time to function in the three dimensions of space “out there.” So, where do time and the fourth-dimension function?

2. If the fabric is made up of time, then there must be a t=0 for the fabric. There must be a starting point for the spacetime fabric. Where is the t=0 for the fabric?

3. Time is never static; it is always moving forward. So, what is the implication of this forward-moving time on the spacetime fabric?

4. Did you notice that the spacetime fabric is not continuous, that it is represented by a grid? Why a grid and why not a continuous fabric?

5. Spacetime and Einstein's Theory of Relativity are interconnected. What impact do these theories have on time and on the spacetime fabric?

So, we can see that there are many unanswered questions regarding the fabric of space. We will try and answer these questions in this essay.

The unanswered questions can be summarized as follows:

1. Location of the Spacetime Fabric
2. Starting Point of the Spacetime Fabric
3. Construction of the Spacetime Fabric
4. Creation of Space
5. Expansion of Spacetime Fabric
6. Spacetime Fabric and Special Relativity
7. Energy and Spacetime Fabric

Location of the Spacetime Fabric

Where is the time-based spacetime fabric located? It should be at the same place where time is located. We have seen earlier that time is supposed to be the fourth dimension. In that case, then, the spacetime fabric is also operating in the fourth dimension. Where is the fourth dimension? To find the fourth dimension, let us understand the functioning of time.

Most people would try and locate time in the space "out there." In other words, they would try and locate the fourth dimension within the three dimensions of space. This is an impossible task. For time to be effective, it must operate in three zones–past, present ("now") and future.

Are these three time zones available in the space "out there"? The answer is a definite NO. Why? Try and focus on the space "out there." At any given moment, what you will always see in space is the present or "now" moment. You can never see the past or the future. There is no past or future in space, there is only the present or "now" moment. Just try it. At this moment, you will see only the present. What is the duration of the present? According to the Planck constant, the smallest block of time is 10E-44 seconds. Once this extremely tiny time duration passes, the current present becomes the past, and it is replaced by a new present. It is always the present or "now" in the space "out there." There is no chance or possibility of having the past or the future in the space "out there."

As mentioned, for time to function properly, it must have the ability to operate in the past, present, and future. This is not possible in space, because space only has the present moment–no past and future. Therefore, we need to look elsewhere for the fourth dimension for time and the spacetime fabric.

The only possible location is the mind. Please read the essay "Understanding Time" for more details. Vedanta has always been clear that time or "kaala" is present only in the mind. The source and location of time is the mind alone. Since time operates and functions within the mind, the spacetime fabric also functions only within the mind.

Starting Point of the Spacetime Fabric

It is not easy to grasp but the spacetime fabric, which is made up of time, is only in the mind. The space with all the objects is "out there," but the fabric is only within the mind. As far as accepting or seeing and visualizing the concrete form of this spacetime fabric is concerned, it is not possible to locate it. You can only imagine or visualize the spacetime fabric. We are going to use this imagination to try and locate the starting point of the spacetime fabric.

It is important to know the starting point of the spacetime fabric. It will answer many unanswered questions. There must be a t=0 for the fabric.

Since the fabric is made up of time, it must have a starting point; it must have a t=0 location. The question is, where is this starting point for spacetime?

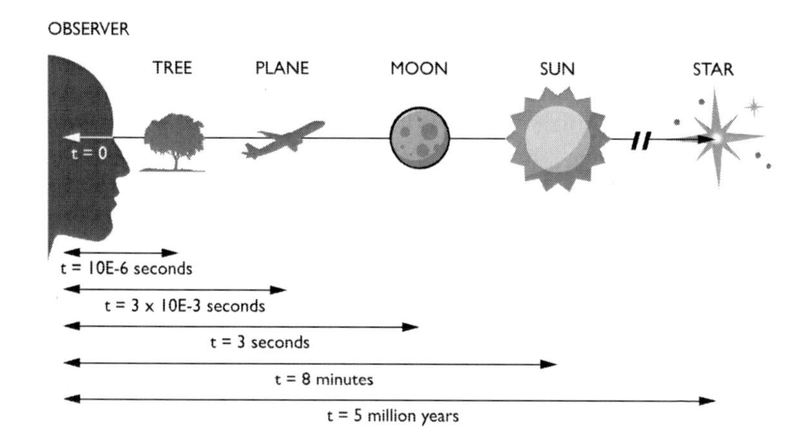

As we have discussed in other essays, if you study external objects by studying the amount of time light takes to reach us from different objects, you will conclude that the starting point for the fabric is the observer within you. The objects which are further away will take more time to reach us than objects which are closer to us. For example, light from the sun takes eight minutes to reach us while light from the tree outside the window will take about 10 microseconds (10E-6) to reach us. As the distance reduces, the time taken for light to reach us also reduces. If you extrapolate this backward, the only logical place for t to be equal to 0 is the observer, who is watching all these objects. This means that the observer within you is the starting point of the spacetime fabric. This is the t=0 of the spacetime fabric. This means that the spacetime fabric starts with the observer within you.

Thus, an important conclusion is that the t=0 for the spacetime fabric is always the observer within you.

Construction of the Spacetime Fabric

Logically, you would expect the spacetime fabric to be continuous. In the images shown earlier, the fabric is not continuous but constitutes a grid with discrete nodal points. Why? This is because time is not continuous. Time does feel continuous, but it is not continuous. Based on the Planck constant, it is proven that time is made of discrete elements. The shortest separation between two discrete elements is 10E-44 seconds. These discrete time elements make up the spacetime fabric. The start of the spacetime fabric is the t=0, which is the observer within you. The first node will be at 10E-44 seconds away from the observer. The second node will be at 2 x 10E-44 seconds away, the third node will be 3 x 10E-44 seconds away. The entire spacetime fabric is built up with these small increments of time nodes. 10E-44 seconds is a small value. The human mind cannot even comprehend this. Can you imagine the number of time nodes in the fabric to reach the sun, which is eight minutes away, or to a faraway star which is five million light-years away?

Do you see the entire spacetime fabric at any given time? No. If you are sitting in your house, the spacetime fabric will end at the four walls of the house. If you move out, during the daytime the spacetime fabric will end with the sun. The limit of the spacetime fabric really depends on what you are watching.

Creation of Space

The time-based spacetime fabric within the mind creates the space "out there." How? If you read the essay "Awareness–The Infinite Energy Source," you will find out that there is infinite energy available in the cosmic mind. The energy which is available in the mind is pure energy.

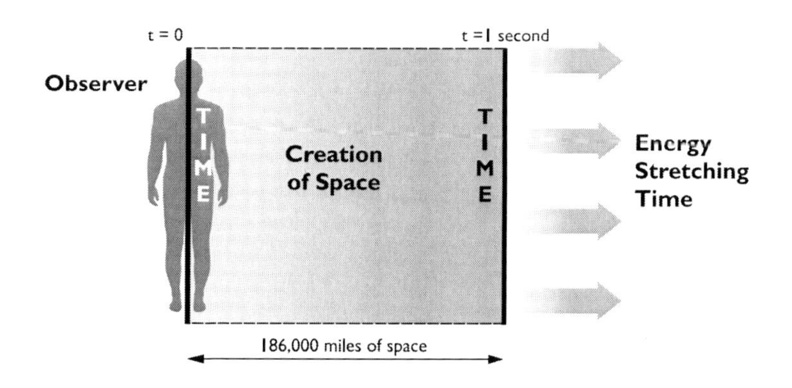

This energy plays different roles within the mind. It must be understood that this energy is raw or pure energy which is available in the mind.

Let us see what happens when a part of this energy interacts with the spacetime fabric in the individual mind. This energy stretches out the fabric, so that every second in time is equal to 186,000 miles (speed of light). Just like a rubber band can be stretched outward, in the same way, spacetime can be stretched outward by this pure energy. With this stretching of spacetime, space is created. One second of the fabric becomes 186,000 miles of space. This is the space we see "out there." So, space is created when this pure energy stretches out spacetime, which is part of our mind.

Expansion of Spacetime Fabric

Does the universe expand? Science tells us that the universe is expanding. Why is the universe expanding? How fast is the universe expanding? Science is not very sure about these questions. Using powerful telescopes, they have watched the movement of different planets and galaxies and noticed that the expansion is uneven. In some places the expansion is faster, and in other places the expansion is slower. There is no proper explanation of this uneven expansion. There is immense confusion around this subject.

To remove this confusion and gain a proper understanding of the expansion, you need to know the starting point or t=0 of the spacetime fabric, and you need to know the endpoint of the spacetime fabric. We have already seen that the t=0 of space is the observer within you. The observer within each one of us will always be the starting point of the spacetime fabric.

Science tells us that the age of the universe is 13.7 billion years. Light reaching us (or the observer) from the Big Bang moment constitutes the outer edge of the spacetime fabric. Light takes 13.7 billion light-years to reach us from this Big Bang moment. So, right "now," the size of the fabric is 13.7 billion years. Is this spacetime expanding? The simple answer is yes. As long as time keeps flowing forward, spacetime will keep expanding. How much? Let us try and understand this. If you assume the universe is 13.7 billion years old "right now" then, after one second, the size of the fabric will be 13.7 billion years + one second. After 10 seconds, the size of the spacetime fabric will be 13.7 billion years + 10 seconds. One year from now, the size of the fabric will increase by one year.

In the earlier section we have seen that the spacetime fabric is the source for creating space. The energy stretches out spacetime to create 186,000 miles of space every second. If spacetime is expanding by one year every year, it means an additional one light-year of space is created every year. One light-year is the distance light travels in one year. From the above, we can conclude that the rate of expansion of the outer edge of the universe = one light-year per year.

Spacetime Fabric and Special Relativity

Einstein's Theory of Special Relativity had and still has a great impact on science. It has given a new perspective to many aspects of science. Not only science–this theory also affects our daily life.

One of the major conclusions of this theory is that time and motion are interconnected. Wherever there is motion, time slows down. Yes, time does slow down with motion. Your clock will slow down. The faster you go, the slower time becomes. This connection between motion and time is a proven fact. Okay, motion and time are interconnected. So, what happens to motion and the spacetime fabric? We know the fabric is made up of

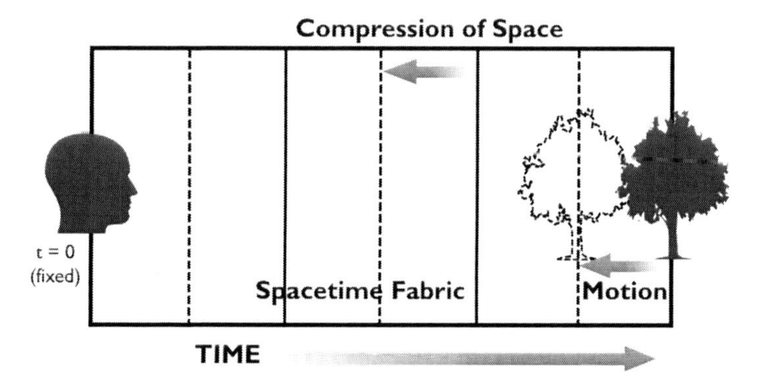

Motion Due to Compression of Space

time. Motion and the spacetime fabric must be interconnected. What happens?

The starting point of the spacetime fabric is always the observer, which is the t=0 location. This never changes; it always remains the starting point. When motion occurs (time slows down), the observer at t=0 does not move, but time nodes on the fabric get closer to the observer and the spacing between the time nodes gets closer. Overall, the fabric is more compressed compared to the fabric before the motion happens. If the speed of motion increases (time slows down further), the observer is still fixed at t=0 and the spacetime fabric gets further pulled toward the observer. Now, if you reach the speed of light, the fabric is so compressed that there is no spacetime fabric. The fabric will then merge into the observer at t=0. If you now slow down and come to a complete rest, the spacetime fabric will pop out from the observer, and you will reach the initial state before we started this exercise.

As you increase speed, the fabric starts getting compressed, and as you decrease speed, the fabric starts expanding. The interesting question to ask here is, what happens to the objects sitting on top of the spacetime fabric? These are the objects we see "out there" in the universe. With the increase in motion speed, the fabric will compress to bring the objects on the fabric closer to the observer, who does not move at t=0.

It must be understood–the observer does not move; it is fixed at t=0. So, the motion is not happening to the observer (who is you); instead, the objects on the spacetime fabric are moving closer to the fixed observer. Can you see the illusion which is taking place? We always feel that we, as the observer, are moving and the objects "out there" (like trees, houses, etc.) are fixed. This is our daily experience. We are being fooled. This is exactly like sitting in a stationary train and watching a moving train on the next track. We have the illusion that the train is moving, and the other train is stationary. This is exactly what happens with motion and the spacetime fabric.

Please read the essay "Understanding Motion" for a more detailed explanation of the connection between motion and time.

Energy and Spacetime Fabric

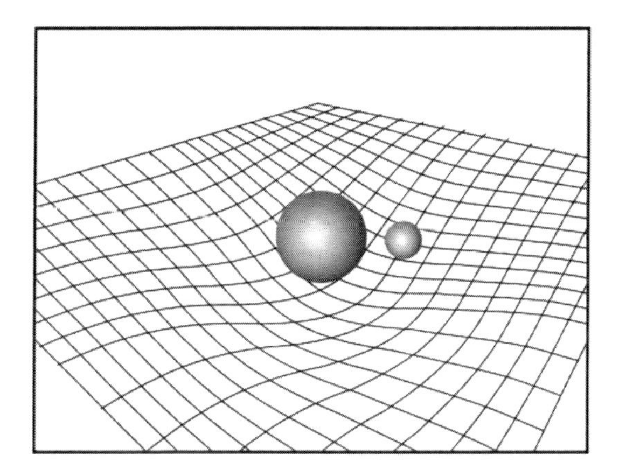

Is this image an accurate representation of the spacetime fabric? It does convey the idea of the fabric quite well, but it is not accurate. Why? The fabric is made of time and the Earth shown in the image is a physical form and is present in the space "out there." There is no spacetime fabric "out there"–it is only in the mind. So, logically, it is incorrect for the physical Earth to be shown on the time-based fabric.

Just like space and time are connected–space is physical, and time is subtle and is present in the mind–in the same way, mass and energy are also connected. Einstein's famous equation shows this connection: $E=mc^2$. Mass is the physical form and energy is the subtle form. Vedanta teaches us that everything subtle is and must be present only in the mind. Energy is subtle and must be part of the mind alone. As mentioned earlier, there is infinite energy available in the cosmic mind. A part of this energy is used to represent different objects in the universe. Every object has its own unique energy wave function, and this wave function is present in the mind. Even quantum physics confirms that every object in this universe has the particle and wave duality.

This energy wave function of the objects is placed on the spacetime fabric. In the image above, the energy wave function of Earth–not the physical Earth–is placed on the spacetime fabric. In the same way, the energy wave function of every object is placed appropriately on the spacetime fabric.

Based on Einstein's Theory of General Relativity, this energy wave function curves the spacetime fabric. It should be clear that every object with the energy wave function will curve the spacetime fabric. An ant, a stone, a human being, trees, planets, suns, galaxies, black holes–every object will curve the spacetime fabric. The only difference is that objects with greater energy will curve the spacetime fabric much more. The black hole has the greatest curvature because it packs in the largest amount of energy.

How do we understand the curvature of the time-based spacetime fabric? How is time affected by the curvature of the fabric? We have seen in the earlier section that the observer is the starting point (t=0) of the fabric, and the end point is the Big Bang, which is 13.7 billion years away. Also, this outer edge is expanding one year every year. The size of the spacetime fabric is fixed based on the amount of time which has elapsed. When the spacetime curves or wraps around the object, the size of the time-based fabric does not increase; it remains the same. Then what happens? The time around the objects gets curved, and that part stretches out. Let us take an example:

- Diameter of the sun is 1.5 x 10E+6 km
- Speed of light is 3 x 10E+5 km/second
- Time taken by light to cover the diameter = 1.5 x 10E+6 km/3 x 10E+5 km/second = 5 seconds

On the spacetime fabric, the sun will occupy five seconds of space. These five seconds of space on the fabric will curve and wrap around the energy waveform of the sun. Since the curvature is being stretched, time will slow down around the sun. If you are in that zone, your clock will tick slower compared to someone outside the curvature. The same principle will apply to every object, from an ant to a black hole. Yes, it is complex, but that is how energy and spacetime interact.

36 | Big Bang Every Moment

Science tells us that the Big Bang took place 13.7 billion years ago. Using powerful telescopes, scientists found that galaxies were expanding on a continuous basis. Working backward, they concluded that this expansion started from a single point, which they called a Singularity. This Singularity was an unimaginably hot and dense point, and it exploded to create the universe we see around us. Extensive research is being done by both cosmologists and physicists to understand the universe. And much has undoubtedly been achieved. Telescopes are looking deeper into space, and we have a much better understanding of how galaxies, stars, and planets are formed. Yet, there are still many unanswered questions.

One of the foremost questions is: what was there before the Big Bang? Obviously, such a huge universe cannot come out of nothing. There must have been something before the Big Bang. So, what was there before the Big Bang? This is a question which is going to be difficult for science to answer. Space and time only started with the Big Bang, and the focus of science has been within the confines of space and time. Science can observe and investigate the entire goings-on within the space and time framework. In a way, science only started with the Big Bang. There definitely was something before the Big Bang because, according to science, something cannot come out of nothing, especially such a huge universe.

So, what was there before the Big Bang? What was there at t=0? The solution can be found in the teachings of Vedanta. As we have discussed in the other essays, Self-Awareness or Atma or SatChitAnanda or Brahman is always present–it is unborn, uncreated, and unchanging. Based on this discussion, we can say that Self-Aware Atma was present at t=0; in fact, Atma is t=0. It is, therefore, logical to conclude that the Big Bang was born out of this Self-Aware Atma. All the matter and energy, all space was born out of this Atma.

Fast forward to "now," 13.7 billion years after the Big Bang. There is also a t=0 "now." We have seen in other essays that there is a t=0 within each of one of us. The t=0, which is Atma, is always present within each one of us. The universe emerged out of this Atma 13.7 billion years ago. In the same way, right "now" too, the universe is born out of t=0, which is within each one of us. In other words, each one of us has our own Big Bang. We all create our own personalized universe. 13.7 billion years ago the Big Bang created a baby universe, but right "now" the Big Bang will create a more mature universe which is 13.7 billion years old. Your universe is very different from mine. I am color-blind, so I am sure that what I see as the universe is different from how your universe looks. Each one of us has our own personalized universe.

The Big Bang takes place whenever we want to perceive the universe. The Big Bang is not a one-off event which took place 13.7 billion years ago; it takes place every time the Observer has a desire to perceive. Whenever the Observer has a desire to perceive, the Observer creates the universe anew.

How does the Observer create this universe? Vedanta teaches us that it is a three-step process:

1. Creation of the Cosmic Seed Body
2. Creation of the Cosmic Subtle Body
3. Creation of the Gross/Physical Body

As we have discussed in other essays, due to ignorance, Atma becomes the Seed Body. The Seed Body creates the Subtle Body. The Subtle Body

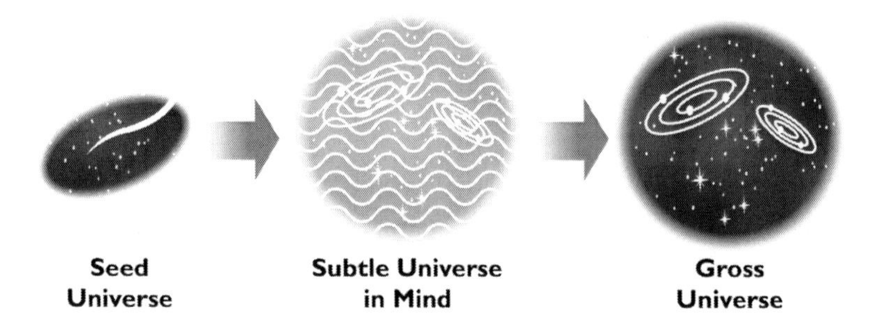

creates the Gross Body, which includes the universe "out there." This process of creation is the source of the universe. Let us discuss each one of them in a little more detail.

1. Cosmic Seed Body

We are all familiar with seeds for flowers, plants, and many other things. It is always mysterious how a plant comes out of such a tiny seed. It does seem that a potential plant or the blueprint of that plant is stored within this seed. When the seed germinates, all aspects of the plant come out. If the seed is for a rose plant, only roses will grow and nothing else. This is what the blueprint will tell the seed–a rose plant from a rose seed. If this is true for plants and other similar things, then why not for all living beings? This is only logical. This is what Vedanta teaches us. Every living being in the universe has a seed body. You have a seed body, I have a seed body, and so does every living being. The seed body is also called a causal body–because it is the cause or starting point for the living being.

What about the universe? Yes, the universe also has a cosmic seed body. All the individual seed bodies will be part of the cosmic seed body. The cosmic seed body will be a cumulation of all the individual seed bodies. The cosmic seed body has the blueprint of the universe. This cosmic seed body germinated 13.7 billion years ago, and ever since the universe has been growing out of this seed body. The Big Bang exploded from this cosmic seed body 13.7 billion years ago.

This cosmic causal body or seed body germinates and grows into the subtle body and gross body to play out the blueprint that is contained within. The seed body is the driving force and is the cause of the creation of the subtle body and the gross body.

2. Cosmic Subtle Body

For living beings, the mind is the subtle body. The mind is made up of waveforms called vrittis (which means "whirlpool"), just like the waves in a pond. All the thoughts, feelings, and perceptions coming from various sources like the senses, emotions, and memories are in the mind.

Just like there is a subtle body for living beings, there is also a cosmic subtle body for the universe. In Vedanta, the term for the cosmic subtle body is Hiranyagarbha. In Sanskrit, this means "golden egg." The cosmic subtle body is made up of vrittis representing all the objects in the universe. The vrittis representing individual objects are present within the cosmic subtle body. Nothing is missed out. You can only imagine the complexity of the waveforms or vrittis within the cosmic subtle body.

These vrittis are made of intelligence. The substratum of these vrittis is knowledge. These vrittis or mental waveforms know what they represent. The DNA and required knowledge are built into the complex vrittis. It could be a simple object vritti or a complex vritti for multiple objects–in each case, these vrittis know what they represent.

When the complex vrittis come in the presence of the light of Awareness, these vrittis are filled with Awareness to become conscious objects. With this step, the observer is now fully aware of the conscious objects in the mind.

3. Cosmic Gross Body

The next step is the projection of the subtle objects like a hologram or a painting. This projection is done by the power of Awareness. The power of Awareness is the creative power of the Atma. As we have discussed in other essays, the power of Awareness has the following powers:

Power of Awareness = Power of Knower + Power of Known + Power of Knowing

What you see outside in the universe is the projection of your mind and the objects therein. The power of Awareness has the capacity to do this. The projection of the content from the mind follows these four steps:

Step 1: You need space–the canvas

Step 2: Harden the canvas with energy

Step 3: Create the subtle image of the painting

Step 4: Add awareness to finish the projection

Please read the essay "Projection–The Only Truth," where a detailed analysis has been done of how a projection is made.

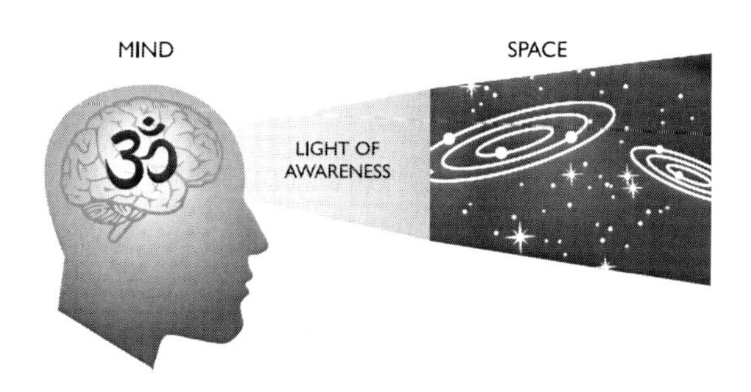

Projection by Mind

This projection is like the Big Bang. The universe is projected out from Atma, which is within each one of us. This projection started 13.7 billion years ago with an event called the Big Bang. Since then, the Big Bang is happening at every moment. Every moment is being projected as the Big Bang. Each moment is like a frame being projected. We know a movie is made up of about 25 still frames per second. The rate of 25 frames per second gives a sense of continuity.

In the same way, every moment or every frame is a projection of the mind. Every frame is a Big Bang moment. So, how many frames are projected every second? There is no scientific way to calculate this. You can only make a logical guess. Let us first define what is meant by "moment." A moment is related to time–it means "now"; it means the present. A moment is not the past nor the future; it is the present moment. From our experience, we know that every moment becomes the past. But then a new moment takes hold. Time is always flowing, so every moment must become the past, and be replaced by another moment.

Each moment is like a frame in the film of a movie. There are 25 frames per second. The duration of each frame is 1/25 second. What is the duration of each frame in the projection of the universe? What is the duration when the present becomes the past? What is the smallest time slot? Based on the Planck constant, the smallest time slot is 10E-44 seconds. This is the duration of each frame. A new frame is projected every 10E-44 seconds. So, 10 followed by 44 zeros is the number of frames which is projected by the mind every second. Wow, this number is incomprehensible. But that is the power of Atma. So, the Big Bang happens 10-followed-by-44-zeros times every second.

To add to the complexity, each mind projects its own personalized universe. Each mind has its own Big Bang projection. Each mind projects 10-followed-by-44-zeros frames every second. If you add the number of minds and the number of frames being projected, the number is countless.

This is the power of Atma or Brahman. This power is beautifully summed up in Brihadaranyaka Upanishad verse 5.1.1.

om. pūrṇam adaḥ, pūrṇam idaṃ, pūrṇāt pūrṇam udacyate.
pūrṇasya pūrṇam ādāya pūrṇam evāvaśiṣyate.

Om. That (Brahman) is infinite, and this (universe) is infinite. The infinite proceeds from the infinite. (Then) taking the infinitude of the infinite (universe), it remains as the infinite (Brahman) alone.

To summarize, the Big Bang did happen 13.7 billion years ago, but the Big Bang of projecting the universe is also happening every moment and will continue till the end of time.

37 | Is There a Cosmic Map?

Over the past decade, Google Maps has become part of our daily life. We use it while driving and for many other activities. The practical implication, simply put, is that though you may be in any part of the world, the map will show you the roads and other important landmarks. These incredible maps could be on your smartphone or on a dedicated GPS device. These devices have both software and hardware components. The software drives the maps, and the hardware displays what the software says. The ingenuity and the heart of the GPS lie in designing and writing the software code. This software could be in the cloud and/or installed in the hardware device itself.

Do you think there is an equivalent cosmic map? This cosmic map will have the details of everything which is present in the universe "out there." Every nook and corner are covered in this cosmic map. *A cosmic map? Seriously? Is that even possible?* Yes, there is a cosmic map. The software is presently functioning within every individual mind. The hardware is the world we see "out there."

To believe in the existence of the cosmic map, it is crucial that you are convinced that we are projecting the world "out there." You must be convinced that each one of us is projecting our own universe. To help in the process by which you get a firm conviction that we do indeed project our individual "universes," in the essay "Projection–The Only Truth" there are five different explanations which support the fact that we indeed project the external world with all its components.

1. Using science
2. Using logic
3. Using math
4. Using quantum physics
5. Using neuroscience

All these explanations are based on science and logic. You must read this essay to be fully convinced.

For this projection to work successfully, there must be a software code for the cosmic map. This software code operates within the cosmic mind, and a subset of this map operates within individual minds. This software code of the cosmic map is projected by the individual mind as the universe "out there." The focus of this essay is to understand the software code of the cosmic map.

In many ways, the cosmic map is like Google Maps, but it is more extensive, complex, smarter, and dynamic.

- The cosmic map covers the entire universe. It is extremely detailed and covers every inch of the universe. The cosmic map is ever active, and it encompasses every minute component of Earth and the universe. Every tree, every mountain, every planet, and every galaxy is covered by the cosmic map.
- Every perspective and view is covered in the cosmic map. If you are flying at 30,000 feet, that view from the window is covered. If you are underwater and look upward, that view is covered. If you are moving on a train, that view is covered. If you go into space, that view is covered. If you are underground inside a cave, that view is covered. There is nothing that is missing in this cosmic map. It is full and complete.
- The cosmic map is not static. It is dynamic. Everything in this universe ages. Every living and nonliving being in this universe ages. As time flows, every object in the universe grows and changes. Further, every object ages differently and for a different duration. The cosmic map reflects this for every object in this ever-changing universe.
- The cosmic map is always up to date. If you cut a branch or move a stone or if anyone makes any change to any aspect anywhere in the universe, the cosmic map will reflect those changes instantaneously. The cosmic map is never outdated. It is updated continuously and immediately.

We have just given a good overview of the cosmic map. The cosmic map is multi-dimensional, and it has varied implications. To understand this, we will look at the cosmic map in the following different ways:

1. Fabric of the cosmic map
2. Construction of the cosmic map
3. Design of the cosmic map
4. Functioning of the cosmic map
5. Evolution of the cosmic map
6. Updating of the cosmic map

1. Fabric of the Cosmic Map

The fabric of the cosmic map is time-based pixels. What are time-based pixels? Pixels = Picture Elements. We know that the chip in a camera is made up of millions of pixels. In the same way, the cosmic map is made up of time pixels (for lack of a better word). Each pixel in the cosmic map is a source of time. It is the generator of time. These time pixels have the special power and capacity to generate time.

Different objects are placed on this time-based fabric. Objects which are nearby–i.e., with a shorter time span–will be placed closer to us on the fabric. Objects at a distance will be placed further away on this time-based fabric.

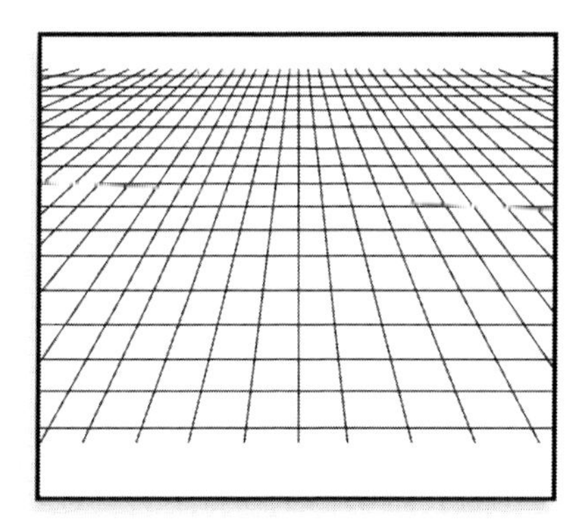

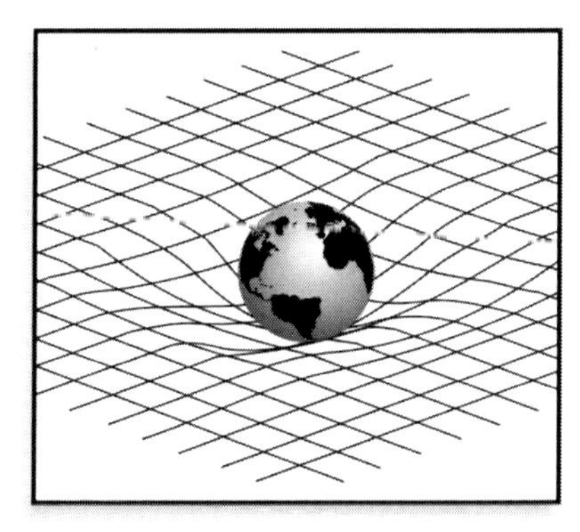

The shortest separation between two discrete elements is 10E-44 seconds. These discrete time elements are the time pixels we mentioned earlier. Therefore, the time-based fabric is not continuous but is made of time pixels, and each pixel is separated by 10E-44 seconds.

It is now clear that the fabric of the cosmic map is made of time pixels. If you read the essay "Awareness–The Infinite Energy Source," you will find out that there is infinite energy available in the cosmic mind. A portion of this infinite energy combines with each time pixel to create electromagnetic (EM) waves. Each time pixel in the fabric oscillates in such a manner that it is a combination of all the possible frequencies in the EM spectrum. This EM energy provides a coating for the cosmic fabric. Scientists too have reached the same conclusion. They call this the vacuum energy. They have discovered that this vacuum energy is just below the surface. It is present in every part of the universe.

2. Construction of the Cosmic Map

We have just seen that the fabric of the cosmic map is made of time pixels and that each pixel is separated by 10E-44 seconds of time. Also, each time pixel combines with energy and becomes the source of the full spectrum of energy. Time and energy are the basic ingredients which make up the fabric of the cosmic map. Objects are placed appropriately on this fabric to build the cosmic map. In this section, we will try and understand what these objects are and of what they are made.

The universe "out there" is made up of an unlimited number of objects. Right from atoms (small) to planets and stars (large), there is a wide range and variety of objects. What we see "out there" in space are physical objects. We did mention earlier that all physical objects are like hardware. This means that there must be a software version of all objects. The software code of the objects must be available. What is this software version of the physical objects?

Vedanta explains that every object has a gross version and a subtle version. The gross version is the objects we see "out there" in space. The subtle version of the objects is present in the mind as vrittis. Vrittis are mental waveforms, and each object has its own unique waveform. These waveforms are made of intelligence. Since these vrittis are made of intelligence, they know what they represent. They can be termed "self-knowing mental waveforms."

These intelligent mental waveforms of different objects are the software code which is placed appropriately on the fabric of the cosmic map.

3. Design of the Cosmic Map

If you are in Delhi and your friend is in New York, objects on the cosmic map would be quite different. This is exactly like Google Maps. If you open Google Maps in Delhi, you will see all the streets and buildings around you. In the same way, if you open Google Maps in New York, you will see the streets only of New York.

The cosmic map covers the entire universe. It is extremely detailed and covers every inch of the universe. There is no place which is left out. It cannot be more complete. Every tree, every mountain, every planet, and every galaxy is covered by the cosmic map. Every perspective and view is covered in the cosmic map. If you are flying at 30,000 feet, that view from the window is covered. If you are underwater and look upward, that view is covered. If you are moving in a train, that view is covered. If you go into space, that view is covered. If you are underground inside a cave, that view is covered. There is nothing which is missing in this cosmic map. It is full and complete.

Objects and the Cosmic Map: The placement of the objects on the time pixels of the cosmic map will depend on how much time light takes to travel from the object to you. We all know that light takes eight minutes to travel from the sun. Therefore, when you look at the sun, the software code of the sun will be placed eight minutes away on the time-based fabric of the cosmic map. Using this logic, all the objects you are going to see are placed appropriately on this fabric. The moon is placed three seconds away on the fabric, the tree outside the window is placed 10E-6 seconds away, the computer in front of you is placed 10E-9 seconds away on the cosmic fabric. All the objects are placed on the fabric in this way. When you project, these objects are placed appropriately in space so that light takes three seconds, 10E-6 seconds, and 10E-9 seconds respectively to reach you from these objects. The software code of the entire universe is written in this way on the fabric of the cosmic map. It must be understood that there is nothing in this universe which is not part of this cosmic map. If it is not part of the cosmic map, it means that it does not exist.

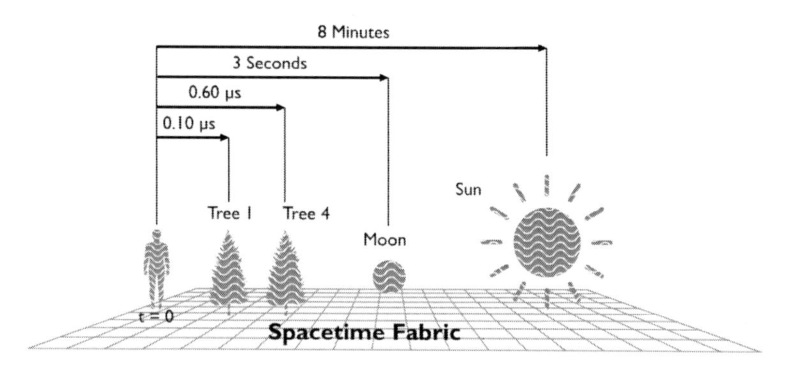

Placement of Subtle Objects on Spacetime Fabric

Depending on your location in the universe, the appropriate subset of the cosmic map will be available in your mind. It is this subset of the cosmic map which is projected by you, and this is the universe you will experience "out there." In the same way, my location on the cosmic map will be different and the appropriate subset of the map will be in my mind. I will project that part of the cosmic map. This is the explanation of how every living being projects their own portion of the cosmic map.

There is one single cosmic map covering the entire universe. Each living being will use a subset of this cosmic map depending on their location, and this subset is projected by each living being.

4. Functioning of the Cosmic Map

When you drive using Google Maps, you can see your current location on the map. As the car moves, the map keeps changing to provide the new surroundings. Do you think the cosmic map will also function in the same fashion? If you walk, run, drive, or fly in a plane, will the cosmic map keep changing as you move forward in your journey? It does seem logical and reasonable that the cosmic map will function in the same manner as Google Maps.

Unfortunately, no, the cosmic map does not function in the same way as Google Maps. Why? To explain this, let us see how a projector and cinema screen work. There is a projector with the software code for the movie; this projector then projects the movie on the screen. A question–is the projector a part of the movie? Does it show up on the screen? Of course, the projector is never seen on the movie screen. It is outside the movie and not part of the screen. Since we project the world "out there," the projection of space and hardware objects "out there" is like the example of the projector and screen. In this case, the individual mind is the projector, and this mind projects the software code of the cosmic map, which is present in the mind. If this is the case, the mind can never be part of the cosmic map. It must be outside the cosmic map. So, the mind is not part of the cosmic map.

Like the projector, the mind being outside the cosmic map is understandable. What about the body of the living being? What about your body, my body, etc.? The body must be part of the cosmic map. We can see our own body; therefore, it must be part of the cosmic map. The issue which arises is that our mind is within our body. We know this for a fact. The body and mind are always together; they are never separated.

See the contradiction–the mind is outside the cosmic map, but the body which contains the mind is always within the cosmic map. In fact, the body is all over the cosmic map. Today it is here, tomorrow it is flying to India, going to a restaurant, always moving within the cosmic map. How should we understand this issue? If the mind is outside the cosmic map, then the only logical way to understand this issue is that the body is always at the starting point of the cosmic map. The start of the cosmic map is always your body. This must be true because you are projecting the universe. Since you are doing the projecting, the body is always the (0,0) coordinate of the cosmic map. The first object you project is your body, and then follow all other objects you see "out there."

If this logic and reasoning is understood, it becomes clear that the body and mind complex is always fixed at the starting point of the cosmic map. Isn't this interesting? You think you are moving around in space "out there," but you are always fixed at the starting point of the cosmic map. You cannot enter and move around within the confines of the cosmic map because you are always fixed at the starting point.

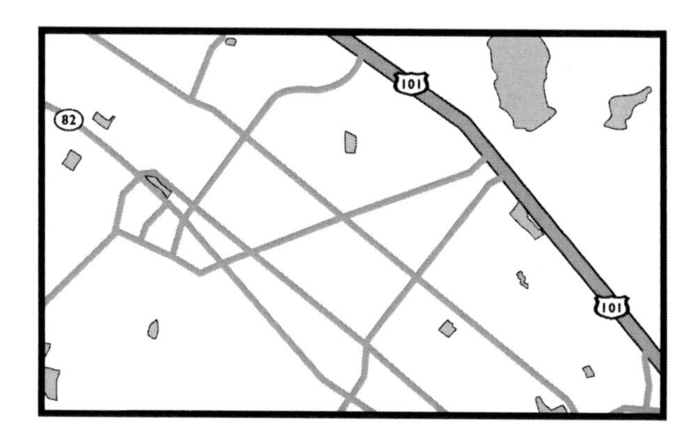

If we are fixed at the starting point of the cosmic map, how do we move around within the cosmic map? In the essay "Mind Does Not Move. What Moves?" we have given a detailed explanation about how objects move while the mind remains fixed. We have the illusion that the body-mind is moving while the objects around are fixed, but the body-mind is fixed while the objects are coming closer or further apart. Amazing but true.

You will be able to relate to this if we compare with Google Maps. Usually, the surroundings on the map are fixed and we see the car moving within the confines of the map. Let us now imagine the car is fixed on Google Maps and does not move. Instead, all the objects on the map are moving to give the illusion that the car is moving to reach its destination on the map. This is exactly how the cosmic map functions in the mind. The body-mind is fixed, and the objects around are moving. But we feel that the objects are fixed and we are moving around. I think this is one of the greatest illusions created by Nature.

5. Evolution of the Cosmic Map

The cosmic map is not static; it is always evolving. The cosmic map is made up of an unlimited number of objects. Each of these objects is evolving. We see these evolving objects everywhere. Each one of us was born, and since then we have evolved from baby to child to our current age. There is nothing in this universe which is not changing. Even this universe has a birthday, and it has been changing and evolving for the past 13.7 billion years. In fact, there is nothing static in this universe. Everything keeps on changing.

Time and Objects: How should we understand this change and evolution in terms of the cosmic map? We have seen earlier that every object in the universe has a subtle form or a unique waveform. This waveform is woven on the fabric of the cosmic map. We have seen that the fabric of the cosmic map is made of time pixels. So, what happens? When any object in the universe germinates (or is born), the object waveform combines with the time pixels. The time pixels superimpose themselves on the object waveform. When a new object waveform is born, it is the t=0 or the birthday of the object waveform. Right from the t=0 moment, the time wave is the driving force for the object waveform to modify itself, to grow itself to play out the blueprint of its life. If there was no time wave, all the object waveforms would remain static and in the same state and would evince no significant growth. The time wave is the underlying force which moves this universe and object waveforms forward.

The t=0 of each object is different. The t=0 of the universe was 13.7 billion years ago. The t=0 of the sun was about four billion years ago. In the same way, every object in the universe had its own t=0 when it came into existence. From t=0 to "now," each of the objects has gone through a history of events. From one moment to the next, each of the objects modifies itself. As time moves forward, the object waveform keeps changing, playing out the blueprint of its life cycle. It is like a small shoot coming out of a seed, and then over time it becomes a fully grown tree with branches and leaves, and finally it decays and dies. The tree waveform plays out its blueprint as time moves forward. This life cycle applies to everything in the universe.

6. Updating of the Cosmic Map

If a new road or new landmark is added to Google Maps, some programmers will have to add these changes to the software code. Any changes or updates to the map will need an external programmer. How does it work for the cosmic map? Is there an external programmer who updates the changes to the software code of the cosmic map? Interesting question. The only logical entity who could be the programmer is God. Is God looking at the universe and looking for changes and sitting and updating code for these changes? This does sound ridiculous.

The only logical answer is that the software code for the cosmic map is self-updating, self-changing, and self-evolving. The software code has all the intelligence to make the required changes and updates as and when required. It is self-sufficient to make all the required updates.

1. If you open the door of your car, it is logical to expect that the software code for the car has changed. Who is updating this code on the cosmic map? It must be understood that the act of opening the car door is first happening within the software code and not in the physical world "out there."

Let us study this example of opening the car door in more detail. You see this action in the physical world. But the action has already happened in the world of the software code. How does this work? There is a software code for the car. By itself, the car software code cannot do anything. We have seen in earlier essays that the ego and the body are also made up of a software code. The car software code has all the functions and features of the car. One of the features is that the car door can be opened. This feature is part of the software code for the car. The (ego + body) software code interacts with the car software code, specifically the car door software code. In this interaction, the (ego + mind) modifies the software code of the car. In this process of modification, the software code of the car is with the door open. In the software code, there is no actual opening of the car door, but the modification of the software code reflects the change.

With this modification, the software code of the car has been updated. When this car software code is projected in the physical world, any viewer will see the door of the car open. There is no delay; any change made to the software code by anyone is updated, and the updated code is available instantly to any individual mind. In the same way, the software code is updated after every action anywhere in the universe. With every action, the individual is responsible for the updating of the software code. Imagine the number of interactions taking place in the universe; with each interaction the software code of the universe is being continuously updated.

2. Many changes are made by Nature and not by living beings. Leaves falling during autumn and coming back during spring–this change is a function of Nature and not caused by any individual living being. How should we understand this? We have mentioned in the earlier section that time interacts with each object. With the passing of time, each object plays out the blueprint of its role. This blueprint is within the seed body of the object. The role of the tree is to shed its leaves in autumn and grow a new set of leaves in spring. In the same way, each one of us has a role in this universe and we are playing out that role in this universe. In the process of playing this role, the software code of the universe is being updated and changed on a continuous basis. This changing software is then projected "out there" as the universe we experience.

The size and complexity of this cosmic software code is unimaginable. Also, the latest version of the software code is always ready and available.

So, it is not incorrect to say that Nature is the chief programmer of the software code. Nature has assigned a role to each one of us, both living and nonliving beings, to keep updating the software code. So, each living being is therefore responsible for contributing to the updating of the software code of the cosmic map.

So, to conclude, there is a fully functioning cosmic map. A part of this cosmic map functions within each individual mind.

Made in United States
North Haven, CT
20 July 2023

39263934R00187